G000075335

PENGUIN
A MATTER

Nilanjana S. Roy is a columnist f
Telegraph, and reviews books for a host of publications.

A MATTER OF TASTE

The Penguin Book of Indian Writing on Food

EDITED BY

NILANJANA S. ROY

PENGUIN BOOKS

PENGUIN BOOKS

Published by the Penguin Group

Penguin Books India Pvt Ltd, 11 Community Centre, Panchsheel Park, New Delhi 110 017, India

Penguin Group (USA) Inc., 375 Hudson Street, New York, NY 10014, USA

Penguin Group (Canada), 10 Alcorn Avenue, Toronto, Ontario, Canada M4V 3B2 (a division of Pearson Penguin Canada Inc.)

Penguin Books Ltd, 80 Strand, London WC2R 0RL, England

Penguin Ireland, 25 St Stephen's Green, Dublin 2, Ireland (a division of Penguin Books Ltd)

Penguin Group (Australia), 250 Camberwell Road, Camberwell, Victoria 3124, Australia (a division of Pearson Australia Group Pty Ltd)

Penguin Group (NZ), cnr Airborne and Rosedale Roads, Albany, Auckland 1310, New Zealand (a division of Pearson New Zealand Ltd)

Penguin Group (South Africa) (Pty) Ltd, 24 Sturdee Avenue, Rosebank, Johannesburg 2196, South Africa

Penguin Books Ltd, Registered Offices: 80 Strand, London WC2R 0RL, England

First published by Penguin Books India 2004

This anthology copyright © Penguin Books India 2004

Introduction copyright © Nilanjana S. Roy 2004

The copyright for the individual pieces vests with the contributors or their estates

Pages 360–63 are extensions of the copyright page

All rights reserved

10 9 8 7 6 5 4 3 2 1

For sale in the Indian Subcontinent, UK and Commonwealth only

Typeset in Sabon by InoSoft Systems, Noida

Printed by Baba Barkhanath Printers, New Delhi

CONTENTS

HISTORY ON A PLATTER

FOOD AND THE SENSES

LINE OF CONTROL

MASALA MIX

DEPRIVATION

ACKNOWLEDGEMENTS

Other anthologists have editors; I had a miracle-worker in Diya Kar Hazra. She and David Davidar, former CEO of Penguin India, germinated the idea of a food anthology and then let me run with the ball. Diya saw the original concept change and grow through several versions and allowed me to make it a homage to good reading as much as to good food. Her patience, intelligence and determination saw this project through; her ability to combine feeding me excellent mangsho-bhaat while reminding me that I'd overshot yet another deadline saw me through. Like all good editors, she provided a firm hand on the tiller and told me what to exclude as well as pointed me in the direction of authors I'd never heard of; like all great editors, she shaped this book without taking it over.

Poulomi Chatterjee's energy and enthusiasm never waned; without her, we would never have survived the permissions process. Her gentle advice on structure and content made this a much better book than it would have been otherwise. She and Diya survived the constant updates, the endless revisions. They treated the frantic appeals to include 'just one more' with mercy while refusing to let the book bloat beyond all norms of decency. Without their dedication, their sense of what made a good piece of writing, and their kindness, *A Matter of Taste* would never have got off the ground.

I'll miss 'Auto Ravi', who patiently ferried masses of material back and forth between editor and editorial team, and who put up with my eccentric hours. This was definitely a team effort; if omissions and errors have crept in, that's my fault not theirs.

Two books in particular lit the way for me. K.T. Achaya's magisterial *A Historical Companion to Indian Food* tells you everything this doesn't, and is required reading for anyone who's interested in the rituals of food. Mark Kurlansky's *Choice Cuts: A Miscellany of Food Writing* told me what I should aim for: 'There is simply no better way for a writer to approach the fundamental subjects of the human condition than to talk about the food we choose to ingest.' It remains my benchmark, even if one that's impossible to live up to.

Many of the writers included here and the editors, publishers and agents we approached for permission rights were hugely encouraging and made significant concessions for us. We needed all the support we could get—our heartfelt thanks.

My Didima and my late Thakurma introduced me to the pleasures of eating and the rigours of cooking, while my mother's recipes led me out of a tangle of early failures in the kitchen. Together they introduced me to a world of women that's linked, but not circumscribed, by the kitchen.

To Tini, Baba, Ruchir, Kamini and Devangshu who fed me when I was too busy with this book to cook, a special note of thanks: for the doi-potol and the meat curry, for the haldi-laced Bloody Marys and the hummus, for the takeaway Punjabi Chinese and the home-made khichuri, and for everything else.

INTRODUCTION

Setting the Table

Even an anthology has to begin somewhere, and this one eventually found its moorings in memory. Fictional ones, drawn from books we've read, loved and been challenged by; and more personal ones, the kind we all carry, of meals eaten and new tastes, of times of deprivation and moments of sharp, new pleasures.

When Penguin suggested an anthology built around the idea of food, Diya and I speculated about the shape that such a compilation would take: did we want an anthology of Indians writing about food? An anthology of writing about Indian food? They are two very different beasts and, as we talked, other monsters loomed hungrily in the distance. The possibilities were endless.

Uncharted continents began opening up before our dazzled eyes, great landscapes where I. Allan Sealy's Smarmite shared the same table as Kesavan's all-inclusive, nationalist feast from *Looking through Glass*, and Daniel and Ramdoss made a mango pilgrimage of India (and, in the literary magazine *Biblio*, a controversy broke out over whether 'Blue Mangoes' was really a slang term in Tamil for certain unmentionable parts of the human anatomy). Frank Simoes expanded on the virtues of fresh fish in conjunction with Goan feni; but read Rohinton Mistry if you want to learn, in mellow comic fashion, about the perils of placing too great a premium on the freshness of your chicken. The famine of 1905 found several echoes down the ages, in mutated form, as Apu endured hunger in the middle of plenty, as a bull died from starvation in Sarat Chandra's 'Mahesh'. . .

Feasting, whether at a nationalist's banquet or in the presence of royalty, was always accompanied by its counterpart. The guide fasts twice, first as parody and then with genuine fervour in R.K. Narayan's masterpiece; in America, Anand discovers the strangeness of those who mortify their flesh in the middle of plenty as he explores the polarities of fasting/feasting; Manjula Padmanabhan's protagonist undergoes the thoroughly modern ritual austerities of The Diet. There were resonances, if you only cared to look for them. The caste norms that applied to Mulk Raj Anand's eponymous untouchable in the bad old pre-Independence days are refurbished for the times. And food is the ultimate religious divide. If an earlier generation rode the rails to the cries from vendors of 'Hindu pani, Musulmaan pani', Abdul Bismillah's guest in 'Guest is God' discovers that hospitality stops short of the dinner plate.

Compiling an anthology is a very, very demanding task. It requires the editor to spend most of her time lounging around in comfortable chairs, reading old favourites and devouring new titles to the detriment of anything resembling real work. Occasionally, in a Herculean display of astonishing effort, she sends a passage to the photostat man in the market. (He runs a small chaat centre alongside, where the pungencies of chutney and chaat masala are overlaid by the fumes of printer's ink—not an effect Vir Sanghvi recorded in his investigation into the origins of the ultimate snack, bhelpuri, but interesting all the same.) It is a task that requires, most of all, the strength of mind to ignore the anguished yelps from the good souls at Penguin as yet another deadline whooshes by.

But as the months rolled by, something happened. Overlapping with the insistent voices of authors—some newly minted, some flashing the stamp of Globalized World-Famous Author on their passports, some obscure—was the voice of memory, insisting that I take another look at the stuff we routinely bury in our bodies.

Initially, I had thought I wanted an anthology that provided a banquet, a feast for the senses. I wanted passages as evocative as the dismissive list of Indian dishes ('chooey-booey brown sauce') compiled by E.M. Forster, as wickedly contemporary as Busybee's evisceration of hotel offerings in 'My First Buffet Lunch', as directly sensual and funny as the passage from *The Last Jet-Engine Laugh* where Ruchir Joshi's characters discover truly alternative uses for shrikhand.

With honourable exceptions, including the three offered above, these were the most boring passages to read. Writing about food degenerates swiftly into a version of what a bad newspaper food critic—for a mercifully brief while I was one of the breed; I know whereof I speak—will serve up. With the exceptions of Vir Sanghvi and the late Busybee (both included here), and a handful of contemporary writers—Marryam Reshii and Geeta Doctor among them—most of India's 'food columnists' offer little more than warmed-over restaurant reviews or recipes, neither of which tempt the palate.

Nor did I want an anthology filled with learned essays on when exactly the potato came to India, or endless categories of food recommended by the Shashtras, or pieces quibbling over the shopping habits of the Mughal cooks. This is perverse on my part, given that I would gladly read such an anthology. But I wanted nothing to do with the compiling of it. What the stack of books before me promised, and what I was looking for, had to do with a certain kind of writing about food and its place in our lives. Some of the examples that follow are drawn from my store of personal memories: every reader will have his or her own, naturally.

The first section, 'Individual Portions', offers an overview of Indian food, quirky rather than comprehensive, thought-provoking rather than magisterially opinionated. Salman Rushdie explores nostalgia for naan and leavened bread even as he discovers the joys of brioche and foccacia abroad; an old woman in Githa Hariharan's 'The Remains of the Feast' discovers the pleasures of forbidden food on her deathbed. They're both reminding us that food is also about what's withheld, unavailable, banned.

And there's the nature of what we eat to take into consideration. Behind the story of the chicken bought and nurtured and finally slaughtered with so much care by Gustad Noble in Mistry's *Such a Long Journey*, I glimpsed the minor childhood trauma I experienced as a guest in a relative's house in Bokaro. Someone pointed out the direct connection between the absence of one or another of my feathered playmates and the presence of chicken curry on the table. Until then I had never given much thought to the difference between animal and vegetable and the violence inherent in many of the normal rituals of eating. Living is about killing; what we choose to bury in our bodies and what we choose to exclude says a great deal about us.

For some, the idea of eating meat raises Plato's chant in their heads: 'you are placing parts of a corpse in your mouth'. Some version of that chant is what Gandhi must have heard when he briefly took up meat-eating only to repudiate it thoroughly. (Non-violence in a nutshell, as generations of weary textbook writers have reminded us. They always skim over the other possible metaphor, the one that might remind us that perhaps the body politic could do with one of Gandhi's prescribed enemas on a regular basis.) For others, like Sudha Koul, the dilemmas are different: the perfect meat dishes produced by Koul's Kashmiri cook are a metaphor, not for the taking of life but for the loss of the past. The remembered odours from her Kashmiri kitchen are constant reminders of a time of innocence, now irrecoverable.

'History on a Platter' sets off on a brief exploration of the twentieth century through our palates—treat this as an indicative rough guide rather than a detailed map. If you look at the history of contemporary India through the palates of its people, you navigate with an alien but illuminating set of charts. Mukul Kesavan's short exposition on the truly nationalist feast brings together the best of Indian cuisine in an unusual menu. The taste of Independence must have been a curious blend, an uncertain mix, everything, no matter how fresh, tainted by the iron scent and flavour of the blood spilled over Partition. One of Manto's short shorts, 'Jelly', sums it up: there's the foreign object of desire, imported or newly indigenized jelly, more tempting than our syrupy, heavy sweets because of its wobbling blandness, but it's the ingredients that make it stand out.

Within the folds of the Raj, a soap opera unfolded in many episodes, eloquent first of the unbridgeable divide between 'native' cuisine and 'British' cuisine, then the birth of mulligatawny soup, until finally in the 1980s chicken tikka masala wreaked revenge on the descendants of the Raj by displacing fish and chips. Other once-familiar objects metamorphosed, too. As Amitav Ghosh discovered when humble momos, student food at the local 'Tib-Dhabs' in Delhi, were stuffed with salmon and asparagus to re-emerge as trendy emblems of a protest movement gone designer.

Some tastes and smells are deliberately missing, best left to the imagination. The taste of pre-Independence India is famine interspersed with abundance. Calcutta stank of dead bodies; famine smelled of a mixture of fleshly corruption, the unmistakeable odour of starvation and the starchy scent of rice gruel. The smell travelled all over India, and appears to have taken up semi-permanent residence in places like Kalahandi, where ground mango kernel flour replaces the rice gruel. For others, the pre-Partition days were times of unalloyed plenty, when oysters were sold by the bucket in Cochin and households consumed ghee by the seer; when family orchards supplied mangoes and lychees; when no one would be fool enough to sell coconuts because there were so many, so abundantly available.

Just as a thought-experiment, it's interesting to try and imagine the flavour of history on the tongue. The chapattis that announced the rumblings of rebellion in 1857 must have had a travel-stained flavour and a dry, crumbling texture. Years later, when Delhi went up in flames after the assassination of Indira Gandhi, and members of the Sikh community were butchered wholesale, my family watched from the dubious safety of a colony that had been scoured, but not targeted, by mobs. Because the sudden onset of rioting had left most families with no time to shop, the predominant tastes we remember are potato curry and dal. It didn't matter. Everything in Delhi during that time of officially sponsored butchery smelled and tasted of burning rubber—from the cars, trucks, taxis and buses that were being set ablaze and the car tyres set on fire before they were used to 'necklace' someone whose only fault was that his headgear matched the turbans worn by Indira's assassins.

All of these diverse smells and tastes will eventually blend, with generous helpings of masalas and vinegar and with enough time to ripen, into the pickles of history that Rushdie describes. They're evocative and dangerous, left on the shelves to ferment, or brought down to the table to be sampled.

'Food and the Senses' explores other, more sensual, emotions and experiences. When Radhika Jha's Leela in *Smell* enters the kitchen for the first time and has to learn this unaccustomed, 'womanly' trade via unpleasant smells, she hits upon a classic rite of passage. The lessons she's learning will be refined further, as the women who are proscribed from eating certain foods but not from cooking them for the rest of the family know, in Anuradha Roy's 'Cooking Women'.

But, as with the gelatine that threatens caste taboos in Ruchir Joshi's piece, nothing about food or cooking or eating is entirely innocuous in a country as complex as India. 'Line of Control' looks at the ways in which we divide people into touchable and untouchable, guests into those we can eat alongside and those with whom we cannot share a plate. It's about the prejudices we stir into our lives. Purabi Basu's Radha in 'French Leave' speaks for all women who've ever looked at the kitchen and seen a lifetime imprisonment sentence, when she goes on strike and casts off, for a day, all the other duties and chores incumbent in the persona of wife and mother. And though decades divide Sarat Chandra and P. Sainath, they're asking the same question: Who gets to eat? Who's denied food? What are the systems by which we legitimize denial?

The coveted foods of the Nehruvian years were the ones that you couldn't access except through friends, usually powerful and affluent, who made trips to that place known just as 'Phoren'. Toblerone, the last-minute palliative of the lazy traveller who hasn't bought any gifts, was hugely coveted. Tinned goods had a caste system of their own. Marmite, which will always remain Smarmite in my mind, thanks to Allan Sealy and his Great Trotter, occupied a hallowed niche of its own among the household gods. More recently, Chitra Banerjee Divakaruni was one of the first writers to present the most basic kitchen masalas as the stuff of exotica; transported to a grocery store abroad, spices acquire a resonance that familiarity has blinded us to in India.

It cuts both ways. Browsing in the marketplace, I often think of a remark my father-in-law made at dinner once, as he reached for a baby corn–red pepper stir-fry: 'I'm quite fond of English vegetables.' English vegetables. It had never occurred to me that vegetables could possess a nationality, and yet they did. At the local vegetable markets, a caste system sidelines phalsa in favour of imported raspberries, sweet deep-red carrots in favour of tasteless orange English-style ones. Meenakshi Mukherjea mentions that Bankimchandra, in the first Indian novel written in English, *Rajmohan's Wife*, struggles to express the cooking methods of one culture in the language of another. Finally giving up, he sends a character off to make 'a salad of garden vegetables', though the actual Bengali dish in question must have been quite different, and the vegetables used would have had nothing in common with lettuce, cucumber or tomato.

We stopped saying 'seethed lentils' and progressed, if this be progress, directly to the world of boudin noir and pasta with porcini mushrooms, via Thai food and hawker-style soups, Lebanese haute cuisine and anything else that would attest to the newly globalized palate of the twenty-first-century Indian. But we did it our way, celebrating the joys of fettucine with extra spicy chicken sauce (butter chicken goes Italian), updating that old Indian Chinese standard, Gobi Manchurian, embracing mango salsa and discoursing on the joys of tinda lightly sautéed in olive oil. Today, few writers of Indian origin would use 'seethed lentils' instead of 'dal', or refer to rotis as 'leavened bread'; the need to explain these things has disappeared. 'Masala Mix' brings out the stereotypes of Indian cuisine and examines them more closely via mango yatras and bhelpuri and a confluence of puddings.

'Deprivation' moves away from menus to what's missing; it explores what happens to people who are denied or who deny themselves the right to satisfy one of the two most basic appetites. A young girl learns, in a passage from *Listening Now*, about customs that demand fasts for the welfare of young boys but none for girls. She's close cousin to the slightly older woman in Manjula Padmanabhan's account of a diet, who's learning that being a woman means never having the right kind of body. These women are starved in their souls; the protagonists of Mahasweta Devi's 'Salt' are starved in both body and soul, denied the most elementary and essential of all flavours.

No anthology of this kind would be complete without looking at the role food plays in the lives of Indians abroad. You cannot compile an anthology of Indian food writing without being Indian about it, which entails spying on our neighbour's homes to see what's cooking there. 'Across the Seven Seas' offers only a small sample of the writing from the diaspora, from writers like Naipaul who have ties with India, and from writers who are exploring the rest of the subcontinent. This is just a sampler; to do a more thorough job would require compiling a second anthology.

There are absences in this volume—in the case of one or two pieces we really wanted, permission rights were hard to access and they leave behind gaping holes. For practical reasons, it wasn't possible to put together an anthology that interleaved long pieces with shorter, one-or-two-paragraph anecdotes. Though that meant we missed out on such pithy gems as Amitav Ghosh's description of the condition dear to Bengalis known as 'Gastric', Salman Rushdie's evocation of spices from *The Moor's Last Sigh*, Maharani Gayatri Devi's paean to railway food and Patrick French's anecdote about Jinnah's un-Islamic love for ham sandwiches, it did help us keep this anthology from indulging in the twenty-first-century sin of being overweight.

Some stories are missing because no one thought to write them. The year of the great onion shortage, for example, had one of my feminist friends musing on the irony of north India being plunged into culinary crisis when asked to do without an item of food that was ritually and deliberately banned to most upper-caste Hindu widows. She found it amusing to think that in some small way, the men who prescribed the typical diet for a widow would now have to share in that prescription.

I remember a particular anthology of Indian fiction being compared to a thali. This one has more in common with the buffet, back in vogue these days. Bhelpuri prose, light, spicy and satisfying, shares the same space as Mughal or Anglo-Indian stews, redolent of many simmering ingredients. There is a choice of several main courses or none, for those who prefer to pick at this or that. The menus of the Raj jostle the chalky blackboard etchings of roadside cafes. The starving are, in these pages as in real life, cheek by jowl with the affluent. The separate sections make provision for those who prefer the Bengali, Kerala or wazwaan style, where each item is served up separately, to be tasted in pristine splendour and in a particular order. But if you'd rather mingle bhelpuri with Mrs Sen's nostalgia-laden fish, pile naan and cold buttered toast onto the same plate, wash down baby food and jelly with asli lassi, feel free. As it is, this introduction has gone on far too long for an appetizer; I leave you to enjoy the writers included here, in the knowledge that their skills, far greater than mine, will wipe out any aftertaste left by my own errors.

Nilanjana S. Roy

Note: If there are pieces missing here that you'd like to see in a future edition of *A Matter of Taste*, or food anecdotes, menu misprints, family stories you'd like to share, please e-mail us at india_foodbook@yahoo.com.

INDIVIDUAL PORTIONS

SALMAN RUSHDIE

On Leavened Bread

There was leavened bread in Bombay, but it was sorry fare: dry, crumbling, tasteless, unleavened bread's paler, unluckier relation. It wasn't 'real'. 'Real' bread was the chapati, or phulka, served piping hot; the tandoori nan, and its sweeter Frontier variant, the Peshawari nan, and for luxury, the reshmi roti, the shirmal, the paratha. Compared to these aristocrats, the leavened white loaves of my childhood seemed to merit the description which Shaw's immortal dustman, Alfred Doolittle, dreamed up for people like himself: they were, in truth, 'the undeserving poor'.

My first inkling that there might be more to leavened bread than I knew came on a visit to Karachi, Pakistan, where I learned that a hidden order of nuns, in a place known as the Monastery of the Angels, baked a mean loaf. To buy it you had to get up at dawn—that is, a servant had to get up at dawn—and stand in line outside a small hatch in the monastery's wall. The nuns' baking facilities were limited, the daily 'run' was small, and this secret bakery's reputation was high. Only the early bird caught the loaf. The hatch would open, and a nun would hand the bread out to the waiting populace. Loaves were strictly rationed. No bulk-

This extract is taken from *Step across This Line*, published by Jonathan Cape, London, 2002.

buying was permitted. And the price, of course, was high. (All this I knew only by hearsay, for I never got up at such an unearthly hour to see for myself.)

The nuns' bread—white, crusty, full of flavour—was a small revelation, but also, on account of its unusual provenance, eccentric. It came from beyond the frontiers of the everyday, a mystery trailing an anecdote behind it. It was almost, well, fictional. (Later, it became fictional, when I put the monastery and its secret sisters into *Midnight's Children*.) Now, in the matter of bread, such extraordinariness is not good. You want bread to be a part of daily life. You want it to be ordinary. You want it to be there. You don't want to get up in the middle of the night and wait by a hatch in a wall. So while the Angels' bread was tasty, it felt like an aberration, a break in the natural order. It didn't really change my mind.

Then, aged thirteen-and-a-half, I flew to England. And suddenly there it was, in every shop window. The White Crusty, the Sliced and the Unsliced. The small Tin, the Large Tin, the Danish Bloomer. The abandoned, plentiful promiscuity of it. The soft pillowy mattressiness of it. The well-sprung bounciness of it between your teeth. Hard crust and soft centre: the sensuality of that perfect textural contrast. I was done for. In the whorehouses of the bakeries, I was serially, gluttonously, irredeemably unfaithful to all those chapatis-next-door waiting for me back home. East was East, but yeast was West.*

This, remember, was long before British bread counters were enlivened by the European invasion, long before olive bread and tomato bread, ciabatta and brioche; this was 1961. But the love affair that began then has never lost its intensity; the new exotic breads have served only to renew the excitement.

I should add that there was a second discovery, almost as thrilling: that is, water. Water back home was dangerous, had to

---

* Some of these thoughts found their way into the mind of Ormus Cama, the hero of *The Ground beneath Her Feet*.

be thoroughly boiled. To be able to drink water from the tap was a privilege indeed. In this respect, life in the West has somewhat declined in quality . . . but I have never forgotten that when I first arrived in these immeasurably wealthy and powerful lands, I found the first proofs of my good fortune in loaf and glass. A regime of bread and water has never, since that time, sounded like a hardship to me.

November 1999

My First Buffet Lunch

Yesterday afternoon, a friend invited me to one of these lavish buffet luncheons that the restaurants in the five-star hotels have, at Rs 95 per head or thereabouts.

As this was my first-ever buffet lunch, I was advised on how to go about it. 'Do not eat anything the night before or in the morning. Then you will be able to do full justice to the buffet. Everybody does that,' I was told.

I did as advised and arrived at the restaurant filled with a lot of business types with expense accounts and credit cards. My friend had invited several more guests, and as I was introduced to them and looked around the table, I calculated how much twelve times Rs 95 or thereabouts would be.

The host told me: 'You order the soup, which will be served to you. Then we will go to the buffet table and help ourselves.'

The buffet table looked like there had been a mix-up and somebody had ordered food from Delhi Darbar, Mandarin Chinese Restaurant, Bharat Cafe, Canara Lunch Home and Gulshan-e-Iran, all together.

I followed the others to the cold buffet and a waiter said:

This article is taken from *Busybee: The Best of Thirty-six Years*, published by Penguin Books India, New Delhi, 2002.

'Would you like to try some mussels, sir? They were served only yesterday at a wedding party. And would you like some Russian salad with the mussels? It was made last week for our residents' dining room and has so far been brought out from the cold storage only three times.'

'Yes, please,' I said.

A lady, to whom I had been introduced a few minutes back, suggested: 'Try the cold ham. The last time I was here in April, they were serving the same ham and it was very good. They have got it from Denmark.'

'Nice,' I said, taking some ham on my plate.

A gentleman from Hong Kong was helping himself to chop suey from a large shallow vessel with gas burners below it (next to the chop suey was a dish containing Punjabi parathas). 'Very good,' he said to me. 'I understand the chop suey is a part of the leftovers, specially prepared for the Chinese Year of the Dog.'

The rest of the buffet was also very good. The peas pulao had come from yesterday's lunch at the hotel's Indian restaurant, the chicken in white sauce had made the rounds of all the restaurants, then been put back in the cold storage every night, and finally brought to the buffet lunch. And at least two of the desserts had been prepared at the time the hotel had opened and acquired an Italian pastry chef.

So, finally, when the waiter asked me if I had enjoyed the buffet lunch, I said: 'Yes, I enjoyed all of them. Yesterday's lunch and last week's wedding dinner and last month's lunch from the Indian restaurant. Thank you.'

18 June 1983

Past Times: First Tastes That Lasted Forever

I often see interviewers asking movie stars such questions as 'Which is your favourite role?' Or singers are asked 'Which is your favourite song?' God knows I've asked these silly question often enough myself.

Usually, there's no real answer. That's when journos start getting aggressive and offering their own choices. I recall asking Sting, 'So, what's your favourite song, then?' When he hummed and hawed, I answered the question for him. '*Roxanne*,' I said. 'I don't think you'll ever write a better song.'

Out of politeness (an unfamiliar impulse with Sting when his work is being discussed), he agreed. 'Yeah, it's my favourite,' he said, resignedly. Only later did I realize how rude I had been. It's a little like telling Keith Richards, 'You'll never write a better song than *Satisfaction*.'

In both cases this translates as: 'So, you old fart, have you realized that your first hit was the best and you've spent the rest of your life trying unsuccessfully to equal that creative peak?'

(It is another matter that I was right. Sting will never write a

This essay is taken from *Rude Food: The Collected Food Writings of Vir Sanghvi*, published by Penguin Books India, New Delhi, 2004.

better song than *Roxanne* and 'Keef' has spent his entire career plundering and reworking the riff from *Satisfaction*. The only comparable riff of genius in the Stones catalogue is *Jumping Jack flash* and that, Mick and Keith stole from Bill Wyman anyway.)

But enough of this gibberish.

My point is that when food writers are asked to name their favourite restaurants or their most memorable meals, the question is as difficult to answer. But there is a parallel with rock geriatrics: the best stuff always comes early in our careers.

People always expect me to say that I thought the tasting menu at Restaurant Daniel in New York was amazing (it was not) or that a twenty-two course banquet in Hong Kong represented one of the most memorable meals of my life. But the truth is that now, when I go to a restaurant, I can no longer behave like a simple punter. Part of me is always hard at work: Is the bread any good? Why haven't they poured the wine? Hasn't the fish been slightly overcooked, and so on.

The memorable meals nearly all came when I did no food writing at all and was rarely judgemental about food. And, oddly enough many, if not most, were consumed at extremely unfancy places.

Almost every person has memories of formative taste experiences. In my case, the cuisine of my forefathers (Gujarati) did not leave much of an impression on my palate. The Gujarati food I like is peasant food (a good Kathiawari *bajra rotla* with a raw onion and a chilli or a *thepla* with *kothmir* chutney) and the great classics of Gujarati cuisine (the *kadhi*, the *tuver dal*, *khichi na papad* etc.) require a very deft hand that most cooks lack.

Commercial Gujarati food is nearly always revolting. *Dahi wadi* (now increasingly called *khandvi*) reminds me of bandage, and a *dhokla* is essentially an idli that has failed its entrance exam.

So, my earliest gastronomic memories are of non-Gujarati food. My mother had acquired a taste for bacon cooked very crisp ('like *supari*' she used to joke) from her college days in America and that's still my favourite way of eating bits of dead pig. My aunt, Sushila Subodh (author of the world's best Gujarati cookbook), was one of the few people in Ahmedabad with an oven in the early 1960s, and she taught us all to love pizza.

Otherwise, my favourite dishes came from the restaurants of Bombay. An oily but delicious mutton curry (with boiled egg) from the determinedly unfancy ('This establishment has been graded an eating house Grade III' a board proudly announced) Wilson Restaurant, behind Wilson College. A killer *keema matar* (best eaten with white bread) from—of all places!—the Kwality's at Kemp's Corner. The hot dog at Bombelli's (totally inauthentic— they even sliced a red chilli above the frankfurter—but fun, nevertheless), and *bhelpuri* from Shetty's (no good now, alas).

In Ahmedabad, at my grandfather's house, we ate home-made *dahi batata puri* (which, for reasons that were never clear, Gujaratis like to call *pakodi puri*—though *pakodi puri* is another dish entirely). And fresh fruit ice cream cranked out on a home machine. (Otherwise, it came from Havmore.)

When I think back on the meals and flavours that determined the shape of my tastebuds, it was probably these dishes rather than the creations of Michelin-starred chefs.

Even when we went abroad on holiday, I was never taken to fancy places. I remember eating my first Italian pizza when I was nine (thin crust as distinct from my aunt's American versions) at a cafe by the Fountain of Trevi in Rome. I've never been able to enjoy a fat crust pizza since.

My mother loved meat but my father always regarded my obsession with steak with an amused disdain verging on concern. Still, he indulged me. I remember being taken regularly to the Cafe de Paris in Geneva where the only dish on the menu was an entrecote steak in a delicious cream sauce served with a mountain of slender chips.

Though I recognize that a good steak should not depend on the sauce (and I usually eat my steaks without any sauce at all) I keep searching out the Cafe de Paris Sauce. I found it last month in New York (at a restaurant called—believe it or not!—the Cafe de Paris), and three months ago in (of all places) a cafe on the ground floor of the Isetan department store in Bangkok.

The other formative gastronomic phase in my life was probably university. Because I never ate in college and never cooked, I spent all my time going from restaurant to restaurant. Many of my tastes date from that period.

I discovered South East Asian food in the oddest of locations: at a small cafe called Munchy Munchy run by an overseas Chinese couple (from Malaysia, I think) near the Oxford railway station. The wife did all the cooking behind an open counter and the husband served. They introduced me to *rendang*, to Malaysian curries, to the joys of satay and to noodle soup. They had no liquor licence so you took your own wine and dessert (which was always my all-time favourite, frozen Birdseye cheesecake from the supermarket next door).

There were only five tables, and many evenings my friends and I would be the only people in the restaurant (but there were a lot of us). It almost became our canteen and when it was time to leave Oxford, I gave my hosts a bottle of Bollinger and they gave me the only free meal of my entire time there. (Poor things. They ran a tight ship. And besides they *were* Chinese.)

Though my friends and I made a great show of seeming knowledgeable about restaurants, I doubt now—in retrospect, of course—that we really knew very much about food. In those days there were two great Oxford restaurants: Sorbonne, owned by a Frenchman with a very big dog, and Elizabeth which was—to undergraduate eyes at least—far grander.

Everybody tells me that Sorbonne had much better food but my friends and I much preferred Elizabeth, perhaps because we thought it was fancier. And it used a lot of garlic. I remember our usual starter of prawns with aïoli (I cringe to remember how sophisticated we thought we were dipping boiled prawns into garlic mayonnaise!) and I remember the sorbet au champagne (in retrospect, a lemon sorbet with a touch of champagne).

It is a measure of how gastronomically illiterate we were that when the young Raymond Blanc opened Les Quatre Saisons in Summertown, we went there and pronounced the food 'not in the same league as Elizabeth, just fancified Frog rubbish'.

Within three years Blanc was being hailed as one of England's greatest chefs and Le Manoir aux Quat' Saisons, near Oxford, to which he moved once he made it big, has been incredibly influential in the culinary world.

But we were children then, pretending to be more grown-up than we really were. And sometimes when the fine wines and champagne sorbet got too much for us, we would retreat to such student hang-outs as Browns (where I had my first taste of brown bread ice cream which still lingers on the tongue).

Or we would nurse our hangovers at George's in the covered market, eating the only meal that the British really know how to make—a good fry-up of eggs, bacon, mushrooms, fried bread and baked beans. Washed down, alas, with lousy English coffee.

BOMBAY RESTAURANTS I GREW UP IN

- BOMBELLIS'S: Billed as an Italian (or was it Swiss?) cafe, this had two branches in Bombay in the 1950s and 1960s. The pastries were famous and the food was basic European (fish and chips, mutton crumbed chops etc.) The stand-out was the hot dog which was delicious if completely inauthentic. Two long rolls (rather than one split down the middle) were toasted and placed on either side of a thin pork frankfurter which was itself sliced lengthwise. On top of the frank was placed an entire red chilli, also sliced lengthwise.

- SHETTY'S: *Bhelpuri* was invented by Gujaratis in Bombay who picked up on the principles of UP-style chaat. A restaurant called Vithal usually gets the credit for the invention but the

UP-wallahs who came to Bombay to sell *golgappa*s or *batasha*s (rechristened *pani puri* by Bombay's Gujaratis) quickly made it their own and began selling from stalls on Chowpatty beach. Meanwhile, restaurateurs from Karnataka—chiefly Bunts from Mangalore—opened so-called Udipi restaurants. Sadly they did not serve their own wonderful cuisine (though these days they all specialize in Mangalorean seafood) but made versions of Tamil-style snacks. Shetty's was unusual in that it was probably the first of these restaurants to make its reputation with *bhelpuri*.

THE WILSON RESTAURANT: Just as the Irani restaurants of Bombay have either faded away or begun serving Vegetable Manchurian, the classic cheap-but-terrific Muslim restaurants of the 1950s and 1960s have also died out, victims of the real estate boom. Places like Wilson served oily but basic Muslim curries, the dal was made with stock and boiled eggs were added to nearly everything.

KWALITY'S: The Kwality chain, founded after Independence, by families of cousins with such names as Ghai and Lamba, was unusual in that the restaurants were not owned by the same person but by different members of the extended family. The chain was not noted for cuisine. Most of it consisted of Punjabi restaurant food, a made-up cuisine which no self-respecting Punjabi would eat at home. The Kemp's Corner branch was fairly typical with a Continental section that included things like Chicken Corn Corn. But oddly enough, the *keema* was exceptional.

ROHINTON MISTRY

Gustad's Chicken

Dilnavaz decided to be of no help to Gustad, not while he was embarked on his mad and wholly impractical scheme. A live chicken in the house! Whatever next? Never had he meddled like this in her kitchen. It was true he came sometimes and sniffed in her pots or, especially on Sundays, cajoled her to make a *kutchoomber* of onions, coriander and hot green chillies to go with the *dhansak* simmering on the stove. But in twenty-one years this was the first time he was interfering in kitchen-and-cookery in a very fundamental manner, and she was not sure what it meant or where it was leading.

'Where did we get this basket from anyway?' asked Gustad, covering the chicken with the wide wicker basket that had hung for ages on a nail near the kitchen ceiling. He did not really care to know, just wanting words to flow again between them, get rid of the chill she had been exuding since he got back from Crawford Market with the throbbing, unquiet bulge in his shopping bag.

'I don't know where the basket came from.' Curt and frigid was her reply.

This extract is taken from *Such a Long Journey*, published by Faber and Faber Limited, London, 1991.

He suspected that Miss Kutpitia may have been advising her about omens, but prudence made him return to his peace-making voice. 'At last we have a use for this basket. Good thing we did not throw it away. Where did it come from, I wonder.'

'I told you once, I don't know.'

'Yes, yes, you did, Dilnoo-darling,' he said soothingly. 'Now, for two days it will be a roof over the chicken's head. They relax and sleep quietly, put on more weight, if they are covered with a basket.'

'How would I know? In my family a chicken was always brought home slaughtered.'

'You will taste the difference, trust me, when it is swimming on your brown sauce in two days. With onions and potatoes. Ah ha ha, that brown sauce! So perfect you make it, Dilnoo.' He smacked his lips.

The entire plan had come to Gustad yesterday. He had dreamt of his childhood the previous night, and remembered the dream in detail on waking; it was a day of great gaiety and celebration, of laughter ringing through the house, flowers filling up the rooms—in vases, in strands of *tohrun* over doorways—and music, music all day long: 'Tales From the Vienna Woods', 'Gold and Silver Waltz', 'Skater's Waltz', 'Voices of Spring', the overture to *Die Fledermaus*, and much, much more, playing non-stop on the gramophone, playing in his dream, while his grandmother sent the servants out repeatedly to buy special herbs and *masala* for the feast cooking under her supervision.

There was such excitement and happiness filling his beloved childhood home, the sadness in his heart was acute when he awoke. He could not remember the exact occasion being celebrated in the dream—probably some birthday or anniversary. But live chickens had been brought home from the market by his father, and fattened for two days before the feast. And what a feast it had been.

When Gustad was a little boy, live chickens were standard procedure in his father's house. Grandma would have it no other way. Not for her the scraggy fowl brought home slaughtered and plucked and gutted. Gustad remembered them arriving in a covered basket balanced on the head of the servant who walked behind his father, sometimes two, sometimes four, or eight, depending on how many guests were invited. Grandma would inspect the birds, invariably applauding her son's choice selections as they clucked away, then check off the packets of spices and ingredients against her list.

But spices, ingredients, were only half the secret. 'Chicken if you buy,' she would say when praised for her delicious cooking, 'then you must buy alive and squawking, *jeevti-jaagti*, or don't buy at all. First feed it for two days, less will not do. And always feed best grain, the very best. Always remember: what goes in chicken-stomach, at the end comes back to our stomach. After two days prepare the pot, light the stove, get *masala* ready. Then slaughter, clean, and cook. Quick-quick-quick, no wasting time.' And what a difference that made to the taste of the meat, she would claim, juicy and fresh and sweet, and so much more than the stringy scraps which clad the bones of the scrawny, market-fed birds two days ago.

Gustad's dream about those blissful, long-ago times stayed with him all through the day. For once, he was determined, just once—for one day at least, this humble flat would fill with the happiness and merriment that used to reside in his childhood home. And that day, he decided, would be Saturday. Invite one or two people from the bank for dinner—my old friend Dinshawji for sure—just a small party. With chicken, never mind the extra expense. To celebrate Roshan's birthday and Sohrab's admission to IIT.

As the basket descended over the bird, it peered curiously through the narrow slits in the wickerwork. Safe under the protective dome, it began to cluck intermittently. 'A little rice now,' said Gustad.

'I'm not going to touch the chicken,' snapped Dilnavaz. If he thought she could be tricked into looking after the creature, he was sadly mistaken.

'Boarding and lodging is my department,' he had joked earlier, to win her over. But there was an edge in his voice now. 'Who is asking you to touch? Just put a little rice in a small pan and give me.' His peace-making voice was flagging in its efforts. He had gone straight from work to Crawford Market, and was still in his office clothes: tie, white shirt, white trousers. White except for where the chicken soiled it while he was tying it to the kitchen table-leg with a yard of bristly coir twist. It had been a long day, and he was tired.

Besides, Crawford Market was a place he despised at the best of times. Unlike his father before him, who used to relish the trip and looked on it as a challenge: to venture boldly into the den of scoundrels, as he called it; then to badger and bargain with the shopkeepers, tease and mock them, their produce, their habits, but always preserving the correct tone that trod the narrow line between badinage and belligerence; and finally, to emerge unscathed and triumphant, banner held high, having got the better of the rogues. Unlike his father, who enjoyed this game, Gustad felt intimidated by Crawford Market.

Perhaps it was due to their different circumstances: his father always accompanied by at least one servant, arriving and leaving by taxi; Gustad alone, with his meagre wallet and worn basket lined with newspaper to soak up meat juices that could start dripping in the bus, causing embarrassment or, worse still, angry protests from vegetarian passengers. Throughout the trip he felt anxious and guilty—felt that in his basket was something deadlier than a bomb. For was he not carrying the potential source of Hindu-Muslim riots? Riots which often started due to offences of the flesh, usually of porcine or bovine origins?

For Gustad, Crawford Market held no charms. It was a dirty, smelly overcrowded place where the floors were slippery with animal ooze and vegetable waste, where the cavernous hall of meat was dark and forbidding, with huge, wicked-looking meat hooks hanging from the ceiling (some empty, some with sides of beef—

the empty ones more threatening) and the butchers trying various tacks to snare a customer—now importuning or wheedling, then boasting of the excellence of their meat while issuing dire warnings about the taintedness of their rivals', and always at the top of the their voices. In the dim light and smelly air abuzz with bold and bellicose flies, everything acquired a menacing edge: the butchers' voices, hoarse from their incessant bellowings; the runnels of sweat streaming down their faces and bare arms on to their sticky, crimson-stained vests and loongis; the sight and smell of blood (sometimes trickling, sometimes coagulated) and bone (gory, or stripped to whiteness); and the constant, sinister flash of a meat cleaver or butcher's knife which, more often than not, was brandished in the vendor's wild hand as he bargained and gesticulated.

Gustad knew his fear of Crawford Market had its origins in his grandmother's warnings about butchers. 'Never argue with a *goaswalla*,' she would caution. 'If he loses his temper, then bhup! He will stick you with his knife. Won't stop to even think about it.' Then, in milder tones, less terror-striking but more pedagogic, she revealed the underpinnings from whence this wise dictum rose. 'Remember, the *goaswalla*'s whole life, his training, his occupation, about butchering. Second nature. *Bismillah*, he says, that is all, and the knife descends.'

If she was teased abut it, Grandma would staunchly claim to have witnessed a situation where a *goaswalla* had gone bhup! with his knife into flesh of the human sort. Gustad had relished the gruesome tale in those days, and when he began shopping at Crawford Market, he would remember her words with a nervous amusement. He never could feel quite at ease in that place.

He tried to select a chicken for Roshan's birthday. It was hard for him to tell under all those feathers, as the shopkeeper held up bird after bird for inspection. 'Look at this one, *seth*, good one, this. See under wing. Spread it, spread it, does not hurt the *murgi*, not to worry. See, poke here. How thick, how much meat.' He did this with one chicken after another, holding its legs and dangling it upside-down, hefting it to emphasize the weight.

Gustad watched, thoroughly confused, squeezing and prodding to pretend he knew what he was doing. But each chicken was very much like the next. When he finally approved one, it was the vocal protestations of the bird, seemingly louder than the others, that made him decide. He would have been the first to admit his inexperience with poultry. The number of times he had been able to afford chicken for his family in the last twenty years, he could count on the fingertips of one hand without using up the digits. Chicken was definitely not his area of expertise.

But beef was a different matter. Beef was Gustad's speciality. Years ago, his college friend, Malcolm Saldanha, had taught him all about cows and buffaloes. It was around the same time that Malcolm had helped him hide the furniture from the clutches of the vulturous bankruptcy bailiff.

The loss of the bookstore had turned Gustad's father into a broken and dispirited man, no longer interested in those weekly expeditions to Crawford Market. When his beloved books and his business disappeared, his appetite was also misplaced, somewhere in the labyrinth of legal proceedings. Gustad worried deeply as his father visibly shrank. He did the best he could now as breadwinner, with his meagre income from private tuitions to schoolchildren. But under Malcolm's advice and guidance, the rupees were stretched further than he had imagined possible.

Malcolm was tall and exceedingly fair-skinned for a Goan. He was fond of explaining his colour by telling about the blood of Portuguese colonizers that had mingled with the local stuff. He had thick red lips and slick, gleaming black hair, always parted on the left, brushed back. Malcolm's father, whom Malcolm closely resembled in looks and talents, taught piano and violin, and prepared his students for the examinations periodically held in Bombay by the Royal School of Music and Trinity College.

Malcolm's mother played first violin with the Bombay Chamber Orchestra, and his elder brother, the oboe. Malcolm played the piano for the college choir's practices and performances. He was going to be a professional musician, he said, but his father insisted on the BA to round out his education . . .

Though he was the odd one out, Gustad was always welcomed at Malcolm's home. Sometimes, Mr Saldanha performed a piece for solo violin, or Malcolm accompanied his father, and Gustad forgot his troubles for a while. In those extremely lean days, when every anna, every paisa counted, Malcolm the musician taught him to eat beef and mitigate the strain on his pocket-book. 'Lucky for us,' Malcolm always said, 'that we are minorities in a nation of Hindus. Let them eat pulses and grams and beans, spiced with their stinky asafoetida—what they call *hing*. Let them fart their lives away. The modernized Hindus eat mutton. Or chicken, if they want to be more fashionable. But we will get our protein from their sacred cow.' At other times he would say, mimicking their economics professor, 'Law of supply and demand, always remember. That's the key. Keeps down the price of beef. And it is healthier because it is holier.'

On Sunday mornings, Gustad would set off with Malcolm for Crawford Market, but their first stop was always the church where Malcolm attended Mass. Gustad went in with him, dipping his fingers in the font of holy water and crossing himself, imitating his friend closely, to fit in and not give offence to anyone . . .

Since Crawford Market was only a short walk from the church, they were soon in the great hall of meat. There, Gustad received an overview about beef: its nutritional value, the best ways to cook it, the choicest parts, and, most importantly, the butchers in Crawford Market who sold the choicest parts.

The following Sunday, Malcolm continued the story of Christianity. Saint Thomas was approached courteously by Hindu holy men, by brahmins, sadhus and acharyas, who wanted to know who he was and why he was loitering around these parts. The meeting took place at the sea-shore. Saint Thomas revealed his name, then said, Do me a favour, cup your palms, immerse them under water, and fling water to the sky. They did so, and the water splashed upwards and fell back into the sea. Saint Thomas asked, Can your God keep the water from falling back? What nonsense, Mister Thomas, said the Hindu holy men, it is the law of gravity, the law of Brahma, Vishnu and Shiva, so it must fall back.

Then Malcolm the meat maestro pointed out a most critical point about beef-buying; if the fat had a yellowish tint, it came from a cow, not as desirable as buffalo, whose fat was white. And it was not easy, he said, to distinguish between the two—there was such a variety of traditions, and the light in that huge hall of meat could play tricks, so that very often yellow seemed white. After the first few times, he let Gustad lead the way, to give him practice, he said, practice and more practice, the secret weapon of all virtuosi.

Then Saint Thomas turned to the fishermen and asked, If my God can do it—if He can keep the water from falling back—will you worship Him and forsake your multitude of pagan gods and goddesses, your shoals of idols and deities? And the Hindu holy men whispered amongst themselves, Let us have a little bit of fun, let us humour this Thomasbhai, this crazy foreigner. They said to him, Yes, yes, we will, Thomasji, most definitely.

So Saint Thomas briskly waded out a few feet, cupped his hands, and flung sea-water to the sky. And, lo, and behold, it stayed suspended in the air: all of it: the tiny droplets, the big drops, the elongated ones and the round ones all stood suspended, and refracted the sunlight and sparkled most wondrously, with the perfect glory of the Lord God who created all things. And the crowds gathered on the beach: the fisherfolk, foreign tourists, pilgrims, diplomats, committee chairmen, bankers, mendicants, scallywags, lazy idle loafers, vagabonds, along with the Hindu holy men, all fell promptly to their knees and asked Saint Thomas to tell them more about his God so they too could worship Him.

The last step (after learning to distinguish between buffalo and cow) involved the ability to identify the choicest sections. Malcolm revealed that the neck portion, which the butchers called neckie, was the tenderest, with the least fat, and quickest to cook, thus saving on fuel bills. Neckie was also the sweetest-tasting, and Malcolm assured Gustad that once he learned to appreciate it, he would never return to mutton, not even if he could afford it some day.

Years later, when Gustad was shopping on his own, he was always willing to share Malcolm's wisdom with friends and neighbours. He wanted to train them in the art of beef-eating, so they too could give up the expensive mutton habit. No one, however, was receptive to the idea as he had been with Malcolm. Eventually, Gustad had to abandon all hope of spreading the gospel of beef.

And a time also arrived when Gustad himself shopped no more at Crawford Market, settling instead for whatever stringy bits of goat, cow or buffalo that the door-to-door *goaswalla* of Khodadad Building brought. By this time, he had lost touch with Malcolm and was spared embarrassing explanations about the tenuous, tangled connection between his desertion of Crawford Market and the sadhus' nationwide protest against cow slaughter. It was easier to remain the silent, unknown apostate of beef.

Roshan peered through the cracks in the wickerwork and refused to feed the chicken. She had never seen a live chicken, or even a dead one that had not been cooked. 'Come on, don't be frightened,' said her father. 'Picture it on your birthday dinner-plate and you won't be afraid.' He lifted the basket. Roshan flung the grain and snatched away her hand.

The chicken was used to its new surroundings by now, and pecked busily at the grain, clucking contentedly. Roshan was fascinated by the bird and its movements. She imagined the chicken as her pet. It would be like a dog story in her *English Reader.* She could take it out in the compound for a walk, holding the bristly coir cord like a leash, or it could perch on her shoulder, like the picture in the *Reader* of a green parrot with a boy.

She was still dreaming in the kitchen when Darius and Sohrab came to inspect the chicken. Darius put rice on his palm. The chicken ate from his hand.

'Show-off,' said Sohrab, stroking its wings.

'Does the beak hurt?' asked Roshan.

'No, just tickles a little,' Darius answered. Now Roshan wanted to pet it too and reached out gingerly, but the chicken was suddenly nervous again. It flapped its wings, evacuated its bowel and retreated.

'It did chhee-chhee!' exclaimed Roshan.

Dilnavaz's sorely tried patience ran out. 'See that mess? Everywhere a mess! In the kitchen your silly chicken makes the mess! And in the front room all your books and newspapers, and blackout paper over the windows and ventilators! Dust and dirt and mess everywhere! I am fed up!'

'Yes, yes, Dilnoo-darling, I know,' said Gustad. 'Sohrab and I will make that bookcase one of these days, then all the books and papers will fit nicely. OK, Sohrab?'

'Sure,' said Sohrab.

She looked at them. 'Bookcase is all very fine. But if you think I am going to clean that chhee-chhee, you are making a mistake.'

'By the time Saturday morning comes, there will be a lot more,' said Gustad. 'Don't worry, I will clean.' He took it in his stride, but it was a definite miscalculation. In his childhood home there were servants to clean after the flock.

Sohrab claimed the chicken, holding down its wings, and invited his sister to pet it. 'Come on, it won't hurt you.'

'Look at that,' said Gustad, very pleased. 'You would think he has been handling chickens all his life. Look at the expert way he holds it. I'm telling you, our son will do wonderfully at IIT, he will be the best engineer ever to graduate from there.'

Sohrab released the bird. It dashed under the table, its movements making the roughly-braided coir twist come alive, writhe like a thin, fraying snake. 'Stop it,' he said to his father, clenching his teeth. 'How does a chicken have anything to do with engineering?'

Gustad was taken aback. 'Why are you getting so upset, with just a little joke?'

'It's not just a little joke,' said Sohrab, becoming louder. 'Ever since the exam results came, you are driving me crazy with your talk of IIT.'

'Don't raise your voice at Daddy,' said Dilnavaz. It was true, she realized, they had been discussing it endlessly, making plans and provisions. How he would live in the student hostel at Powai, and come home at the weekends, or they would visit him with a picnic lunch, the college was so close to the lake and the scenery was so beautiful. And after he had finished IIT he would go to an engineering college in America, maybe MIT, and—. But when this point was reached Dilnavaz would say it was time to stop dreaming and tempting fate, because Sohrab had not even started at IIT as yet.

She understood how he felt. Even so, he could not be allowed to shout. 'We are feeling very happy about it, what else? Why do you think your father bought the chicken? After hard work all day he went to Crawford Market. With two grown boys in the house, it is a disgrace that he has to do the *bajaar*. When he was your age he paid his own college fees. And supported his parents.'

Sohrab left the kitchen. Gustad replaced the basket over the fowl. 'Come, leave it alone now, must not be disturbed all the time.'

Around midnight, Dilnavaz awoke to go to the WC and heard the chicken clucking softly. Must be hungry again, she thought, switching on the light. The faint beseeching sounds made her forget how firmly she had spoken against live chickens. She went to the rice jar and knocked over the copper measuring cup. It hit the floor with a clang that woke the flat. Everyone soon assembled in the kitchen.

'What happened?' asked Gustad.

'I was going to the back, and the chicken made a sound. I thought it was asking for more food,' she said, holding out her fistful of rice.

'Asking for more food! How much do you know about chickens that you understand what it is saying?' said Gustad.

Cluck-cluck-cluck-cluck came the muted response from the basket. 'Look, Daddy,' said Roshan, 'it's so happy to see us.'

'You think so?' The child's remark pleased him and erased his annoyance. He patted her hair. 'Since the chicken is awake, you can give it some food, then back to sleep.'

They repeated their goodnight-God bless you's to one another and returned to their beds.

Roshan fed the chicken and played with it all next evening after school. 'Daddy, can we keep it for ever? I will look after it, promise.'

Gustad was amused, also a little touched. He winked at Darius and Sohrab. 'What do you think? Shall we save its life for Roshan?' He expected them to protest and lick their lips in anticipation of the feast tomorrow.

But Sohrab said, 'I don't mind. If Mummy can live with it in the kitchen.'

'Please Daddy, can we keep it, then? Even Sohrab wants it. No, Sohrab?'

'Enough silliness for one day,' said Gustad.

On Saturday morning, the butcher who made deliveries to Khodadad Building knocked at the door. Gustad took him to the kitchen and indicated the basket. The butcher held out his hand.

Gustad was annoyed. 'Years and years we have been your customers. Now for one small favour you want payment?'

'Don't get angry, *seth*, I don't want payment. Something must be put in my palm so I can use the knife without sinning.'

Gustad gave him a twenty-five paisa coin. 'I forgot about that.' He left the kitchen, not anxious to watch or hear the squawk of final desperation, and waited at the front door.

Moments later, the chicken whizzed by his legs and into the compound. The butcher came running after. '*Murgi, murgi*! Catch the *murgi*!'

'What happened?' yelled Gustad, joining the chase.

'*O seth*, I held the string, lifted the basket!' the butcher panted. 'Then string is in one hand, basket in the other, and chicken runs between my legs!'

'Impossible! Tied it myself!' Gustad's slight limp became an ugly hobble when he ran. The faster he ran, the worse it grew, and he did not like people to see. The butcher was ahead of him, gaining on the bird. Fortunately, it had turned right when it emerged in the compound, keeping close to the black stone wall, which led it to a dead end instead of the main road.

Lame Tehmul was there, pacing with his swaying, rolling gait. He dived for the chicken, and, to everyone's surprise, including his own, was successful. He held it up by the legs, waving it at Gustad with frantic glee as it screeched and flapped desperately . . .

'GustadGustadchickenrace. GustadGustadchickenranfastfast. IcaughtIcaughtGustad.' Tehmul proudly displayed the bird by its legs.

'Very good, Tehmul. Well done!' said Gustad, his practised ear sorting out the spate of words. Tehmul's cascading utterances were always bereft of commas, exclamation marks, semicolons, question marks: all swept away without the slightest chance of survival. The verbal velocity only allowed for the use of the full stop. And it was not really a full stop the way Tehmul used it; rather, a minimal halt anywhere he chose to re-oxygenate his lungs.

'GustadGustadrunning race. Fastfastchickenfirst.' He grinned and pulled its tail.

'No, no, Tehmul. Race is over now.' He took the chicken and handed it to the butcher waiting, knife in hand. Tehmul clutched his own throat, performed a slitting gesture and emitted a terrified squawk. Gustad could not help laughing. Encouraged, Tehmul squawked again . . .

Tehmul followed him to the flat. He grinned and waved goodbye. Dilnavaz, Roshan and the boys were waiting by the door. 'The string was untied from the chicken's leg,' said Gustad. 'How that happened is what I am wondering.' He looked meaningfully at them. The butcher returned to the kitchen, the bird firmly in his grasp this time, and Roshan's eyes started to fill. 'Yes,' said Gustad sternly, 'I would like to know very much how. Expensive chicken I buy, to celebrate birthday and IIT, then the string is untied. What kind of thanks is that?'

From the kitchen came the tell-tale screech. The butcher emerged, wiping his knife on a rag. 'Good chicken, *seth*, lots of meat.' He left with a salaam in Gustad's general direction.

Roshan burst into sobs, and Gustad abandoned his line of questioning. All four looked at him accusingly, then Dilnavaz went to the kitchen.

Two crows were peering curiously through the wire mesh of the window. The limp mass of feathers and flesh on the stone parapet beside the tap held their attention. When she entered, they cawed frantically and spread their wings, hesitating for a moment, then flew away.

M.K. GANDHI

Eating Meat

Amongst my few friends at the high school I had, at different times, two who might be called intimate. One of these friendships did not last long, though I never forsook my friend. He forsook me, because I made friends with the other. This latter friendship I regret as a tragedy in my life. It lasted long. I formed it in the spirit of a reformer.

This companion was originally my elder brother's friend. They were classmates. I knew his weakness, but I regarded him as a faithful friend. My mother, my eldest brother, and my wife warned me that I was in bad company. I was too proud to heed my wife's warning. But I dared not go against the opinion of my mother and my eldest brother. Nevertheless I pleaded with them saying, 'I know he has the weakness you attribute to him, but you do not know his virtues. He cannot lead me astray, as my association with him is meant to reform him. For I am sure that if he reforms his ways, he will be a splendid man. I beg you not to be anxious on my account.'

I do not think this satisfied them, but they accepted my explanation and let me go my way.

This extract is taken from *An Autobiography, or The Story of My Experiments with Truth*, published by Navajivan Publishing, Ahmedabad, 1927.

I have seen since I had calculated wrongly. A reformer cannot afford to have close intimacy with him whom he seeks to reform. True friendship is an identity to souls rarely to be found in this world. Only between like natures can friendship be altogether worthy and enduring. Friends lean on one another. Hence in friendship there is very little scope for reform. I am of opinion that all exclusive intimacies are to be avoided; for man takes in vice more readily than virtue. And he who would be friends with God must remain alone, or make the whole world his friend. I may be wrong, but my effort to cultivate an intimate friendship proved a failure.

A wave of reform was sweeping over Rajkot at the time when I first came across this friend. He informed me that many of our teachers were secretly taking meat and wine. He also named many well-known people of Rajkot as belonging to the same company. There were also, I was told, some high school boys among them.

I was surprised and pained. I asked my friends the reason and he explained it thus: 'We are a weak people because we do not eat meat. The English are able to rule over us, because they are meat-eaters. You know how hardy I am, and how great a runner too. It is because I am a meat-eater. Meat-eaters do not have boils or tumours, and even if they sometimes happen to have any, these heal quickly. Our teachers and other distinguished people who eat meat are no fools. They know its virtues. You should do likewise. There is nothing like trying. Try, and see what strength it gives.'

All these pleas on behalf of meat-eating were not advanced at a single sitting. They represent the substance of a long and elaborate argument which my friend was trying to impress upon me from time to time. My elder brother had already fallen. He therefore supported my friends' argument. I certainly looked feeble-bodied by the side of my brother and this friend. They were both hardier, physically stronger, and more daring. This friend's exploits cast a spell over me. He could run long distances and extraordinarily fast. He was an adept in high and long jumping. He could put up with any amount of corporal punishment. He would often display his exploits to me and, as one is always dazzled when he sees in other the qualities that he lacks himself, I was dazzled by this friend's exploits. This was followed by a strong desire to be like him. I could hardly jump or run. Why should not I also be as strong as he?

Moreover, I was a coward. I used to be haunted by the fear of thieves, ghosts, and serpents. I did not dare to stir out of doors at night. Darkness was a terror to me. It was almost impossible for me to sleep in the dark, as I would imagine ghosts coming from one direction, thieves from another, and serpents from a third. I could not therefore bear to sleep without a light in the room. How could I disclose my fears to my wife, no child, but already at the threshold of youth, sleeping by my side? I knew that she had more courage than I, and I felt ashamed of myself. She knew no fear of serpents and ghosts. She could go out anywhere in the dark. My friend knew all these weaknesses of mine. He would tell me that he could hold in his hand live serpents, could defy thieves and did not believe in ghosts. And all this was, of course, the result of eating meat.

A doggerel of the Gujarati poet Narmad was in vogue amongst us schoolboys, as follows:

Behold the mighty Englishman
He rules the Indian small,
Because being a meat-eater
He is five cubits tall . . .

All this had its due effect on me. I was beaten. It began to grow on me that meat-eating was good, that it would make me strong and daring, and that, if the whole country took to meat-eating, the English could be overcome.

A day was thereupon fixed for beginning the experiment. It had to be conducted in secret. The Gandhis were Vaishnavas. My parents were particularly staunch Vaishnavas. They would regularly visit the Haveli. The family even had its own temples. Jainism was strong in Gujarat, and its influence was felt everywhere and on all occasions. The opposition to and abhorrence of meat-eating that existed in Gujarat among the Jains and Vaishnavas were to be seen nowhere else in India or outside in such strength. These were the traditions in which I was born and bred. And I was extremely devoted to my parents. I knew that the moment they came to know of my having eaten meat, they would be shocked to death. Moreover, my love of truth made me extra cautious. I cannot say that I did not know then that I should have to deceive my parents if I began eating meat. But my mind was bent on the 'reform'. It was not a question of pleasing the palate. I did not know that it had a particularly good relish. I wished to be strong and daring and wanted my countrymen also to be such, so that we might defeat the English and make India free. The word Swaraj I had not yet heard. But I knew what freedom meant. The frenzy of the 'reform' blinded me. And having ensured secrecy, I persuaded myself that mere hiding the deed from parents was no departure from truth.

So the day came. It is difficult fully to describe my condition. There were on the one hand, the zeal for 'reform' and the novelty of making a momentous departure in life. There was, on the other, the shame of hiding like a thief to do this very thing. I cannot say which of the two swayed me more. We went in search of a lonely spot by the river, and there I saw, for the first time in my life— meat. There was baker's bread also. I relished neither. The goat's meat was as tough as leather. I simply could not eat it. I was sick and had to leave off eating.

I had a very bad night afterwards. A horrible nightmare haunted me. Every time I dropped off to sleep it would seem as though a live goat were bleating inside me, and I would jump up full of remorse. But then I would remind myself that meat-eating was a duty and so become more cheerful.

My friend was not a man to give in easily. He now began to

cook various delicacies with meat, and dress them neatly. And for dining, no longer was the secluded spot on the river chosen, but a State house, with its dining hall, and tables and chairs, about which my friend had made arrangements in collusion with the chief cook there.

This bait had its effect. I got over my dislike for bread, forswore my compassion for the goats, and became a relisher of meat-dishes, if not of meat itself. This went on for about a year. But not more than half a dozen meat-feasts were enjoyed in all; because the State house was not available every day, and there was the obvious difficulty about frequently preparing expensive savoury meat dishes. I had no money to pay for this 'reform'. My friend had therefore always to find the wherewithal. I had no knowledge where he found it. But find it he did, because he was bent on turning me into a meat-eater. But even his means must have been limited, and hence these feasts had necessarily to be few and far between.

Whenever I had occasion to indulge in these surreptitious feasts, dinner at home was out of the question. My mother would naturally ask me to come and take my food and want to know the reason why I did not wish to eat. I would say to her, 'I have no appetite today; there is something wrong with my digestion.' It was not without compunction that I devised these pretexts. I knew I was lying, and lying to my mother. I also knew that, if my mother and my father came to know of my having become a meat-eater, they would be deeply shocked. This knowledge was gnawing at my heart.

Therefore I said to myself: 'Though it is essential to eat meat, and also essential to take up food "reform" in the country, yet deceiving and lying to one's father and mother is worse than not eating meat. In their lifetime, therefore, meat-eating must be out of the question. When I can, I will eat meat openly, but until that moment arrives I will abstain from it.'

This decision I communicated to my friend, and I have never

since gone back to meat. My parents never knew that two of their sons had become meat-eaters.

I abjured meat out of the purity of my desire not to lie to my parents, but I did not abjure the company of my friend. My zeal for reforming him had proved disastrous for me, and all the time I was completely unconscious of the fact.

FRANK SIMOES

Everything You Ever Wanted to Know about Feni but Were Too Drunk to Ask

I am fortunate in my Goan friends.

The garafaos arrive at a certain time of the year, huge, pear-shaped flagons glazed over with a deep emerald patina, sealed to keep the liquid content as pure and uncontaminated as the morning it was triple-distilled and decanted into each voluptuous garafao. My friend, Steve Miranda, able and honoured President of the Lions Club in Calangute, has sent me two garafaos of caju feni from his own private stock. Brewed on the ancestral estates in North Goa by families who still farm his land and lovingly nurture the plantations of cashew and palm trees, the feni has been distilled in a fashion unchanged for generations. Free of chemicals, fermented as nature intended, in a process which may not be hastened, garnered, drop by exquisite drop in the last distillation, and presented to me each year with a generosity I am never able to repay. Two more garafaos of palm feni arrive the following morning, a gift from Thomas Vaz, scion of Pedro Vincent Vaz & Co., Goa's celebrated clan of bakers and distillers. Wherever good, honestly brewed palm feni is consumed in Goa, more often

This extract is taken from *Glad Seasons in Goa*, published by Viking, New Delhi, 1994.

than not the distinctive pear-shape of his bottle encased in plaited straw and bearing the reassuring legend, 'Big Boss Palm Feni' will make its presence cheerfully felt.

A garafao contains six bottles of feni and Esperanca, our diligent housekeeper, decants each bottle with care. Sun-dried orange peel will be introduced into a few of the bottles of caju; the flavours of orange and caju marry wonderfully well. Green chillies slit along their length in six of the bottles of palm feni will impart to Gita's sundowners just the right touch of tongue-tingling tartness. Twenty-four bottles in all. I shall have to call upon every last ounce of character and self-control to let them lie untouched, maturing for the next six months, when I shall be in great good spirits for the rest of the year. Mere words cannot express my gratitude to Steve and Thomas. May their fenis go from strength to strength.

The Department of Agriculture's official definition of feni is many soulless removes from its ebullient metaphysics; 'Feni (the more accurate rendering, as opposed to the Portuguese 'fenim') has achieved the status of a generic term applying to a wide variety of distilled alcoholic liquors derived from extracts of the coconut palm and the cashew fruit.'

A plague on these purveyors of words without spirit. Wherever the heart of Goa beats, there the living essence of the palm and the cashew are celebrated. The cashew fruit has wrought its benign miracle each golden season for three centuries, while the genesis of the glories of the palm is measured not by the passage of time, but held captured now and forever in the sculpted form of a toddy tapper, high above sand and sea, one with the wind and swaying fronds, seeking the heart of the palm for its abundance and blessings.

The qualities of a happy Goan life find the perfect metaphor in the sparkling crystal depths of a bottle of pure feni. Elemental as the sea, the emerald meadows of ripening paddy, the bells of church and temple calling the faithful to prayer, lore and truth, myth and magic enwrap each potent drop in a mystique which warms the heart, clears the mind and may, freely and generously as the spirit moves one, be entertained and embellished. For feni is to the Goan life what the sky is to a bird, a medium of limitless wonder and potential.

Feni is not a generic term. It is a single, specific description from the Konkani root 'fen', literally 'to froth'. It indicates to the purist (just about all accomplished feni drinkers) that a great-hearted feni, when poured into a glass, should froth a bit, playfully, with just a hint of exuberance, a visual harbinger of the high spirits to come. Clear as vodka, with a slight bouquet in the case of caju, feni may be drunk on the rocks or mixed, as with its Russian cousin, with virtually anything you may care to name.

Source materials derive from two of the most unlikely members of the botanical world, the coconut palm and the cashew fruit. The palm is life and blood to the Goan. Food for the pot; thatch for the home; oil for cooking; tender coconut water for instant refreshment; early morning toddy (the fresh sap at dawn)—no better way to begin the day; and that incomparable gift, feni, all things to all men. The cashew fruit is a mere stripling on the feni scene. Imported by Portuguese from Brazil three centuries ago, it took to the Goan soil with a zesty fertility. Something of a botanical freak, the cashew seed grows on the *exterior* of a gold fruit, heart- or apple-shaped. Feni is distilled from both toddy and the juice of the cashew fruit.

So much for description.

Innate virtues which the Goans have known all about for centuries (presumably by a process of relentless osmosis) have not been revealed by the wonders of science. Palm toddy has been found to be rich in sugars, sodium, potassium, iron, manganese, a host of other minerals, proteins, amino acids, Vitamins B-1, B-2, 6, and trace elements. The juice of the cashew is not to be outdone and throws in for good measure generous helpings of Calcium, Phosphorous and Glucose. Small wonder then that feni is good for you.

On the sound theory that you can't have too much of a good thing, the Goans drink heroic quantities of feni. They drink it at births and wakes, solemnly on Maundy Thursday, never on the Friday and joyfully at Easter; they toast the feasts of their saints with it; they celebrate with generous portions when a favourite sow litters; they drink it before, with and often after meals. Workers in the fields pause at the noon break to refresh themselves with a few quick copitos of feni (Glucose . . . Vitamin B . . . Iron!). They drink it in all ages and conditions; babies are given a few drops dissolved in sugar to ward off the chill; it is rubbed in the joints for gout and rheumatism and generously imbibed by the patient immediately thereafter, recovery being swift and certain. Come to think of it, Goans drink feni whenever they please.

As I learned, to my infinite improvement, one fine January morning in the village of Anjuna. Gita and I were to meet a grand-uncle and aunt who had last seen me thirty years earlier, at my First Communion, doubtless toasting my coming into the age of grace with a glass of feni, or two. We were ushered into a parlour by my grand-uncle. My aunt rose to greet us. They might have stepped out of a cameo, or emerged daintily from an old sepia portrait, a perfect still life from a gracious and distant generation. Their marriage bore witness to well over half a century. They could have been twins, sharing a precious and treasured fragility. Their parlour held the scents of perfumed cachets and old, polished mahogany. A brass bird-cage, with a pair of love birds, swung gently in the wind at an open window. The sea murmured and whispered beyond the casuarinas and the palms. Generations of the family, formal in cutaways and hooped skirts, framed in carved rosewood, posed in attitudes of vast seriousness above the grand piano, reminding us of a venerable and solemn past, when 't's were always crossed and no 'i' went undotted. I could hear my own breathing and I felt I had to speak softly and choose my words with care.

My grand-uncle and aunt sat across from us, ramrod straight (as they had been taught as children), the very soul of gentility and autumnal nostalgia. I remember thinking, not for them the cumbersome annoyances of illness and death; they would, with dignity and good breeding, hand in hand, fade away into the gathering dusk. It was half past ten in the morning and my grand-aunt, in impeccable Portuguese, asked us if we would care for some refreshment.

'Yes,' I said, 'a cup of coffee.' Was there a flicker of amusement in the glance they exchanged? My grand-uncle turned a stern and twinkling eye in my direction. 'We shall drink feni,' he said with a finality that would brook no argument.

The cutglass decanters and glasses were of the finest Belgian crystal. Why two decanters, brimful? I was soon to find out. We drank caju feni and more caju feni. Neighbours uninvited, warmly greeted, appeared magically as if out of the walls. We were introduced. I was embraced and kissed warmly on both cheeks, a long-lost son of the soil, my Hindu Sindhi wife viewed with curiosity and wonder. A third copito? A fourth? I lost count. My grand-uncle and aunt and the neighbours drank with us, glass for glass, noticeably uninfluenced. The ancestors above the grand piano seemed jollier, less lugubrious, as time went on, positively lovable. The love birds sang. Or did I think they did? The decanters were taken away and refilled. The parlour shimmered with goodwill and bonhomie. Laughter invaded the room. Time did not pass. It cavorted and chuckled and did a little jig and flung the hours about without a care. But good a Goan as I am, the years of alienation from the soil of my fathers began to tell.

I rose to leave. The parlour quivered briefly and (feni never lets you down) refocused. Fragile as ever, my grand-uncle and aunt escorted us to the door. My aunt kissed me on both cheeks. 'Give our love to your parents,' she said. Lavender. Gentle. Nostalgic. She had drunk at least half a bottle of feni. So had my grand-uncle. Not a quaver. Firm-voiced. Erect. Sparkling at two in the afternoon. We said goodbye.

Goans drink feni as they please. On festive occasions they please themselves hugely and may even indulge (purists shudder at this) in after dinner derivatives such as Coffee Conserve, double-strength coffee wickedly blended with triple-distilled caju feni. I prefer to stay with pure palm or caju. The standard measure, equivalent to a full two-ounce jigger, is a copito (pronounced kopeeto), a round, full-bodied word, crisply syllabic and never interpreted as it should be, for the copito is a state of mind, an invitation to good fellowship, the equivalent of 'let's have a whale of a time'. It is very bad taste indeed in Goa to take a copito literally. Or offer one as a measure of a drink. For the essence of feni, the true reason for its being, resides first and last in the metaphysics of the belief, felt deeply in Goa, that the breaking of bread and the sharing of a bottle should make brothers of strangers.

As in all happy families brothers may disagree. Individual beliefs are firmly respected even if they differ considerably from your own. You may, of course, *know* that you are invincibly in the right; still, good manners dictate that you keep your views strictly to yourself. Thus, the Goan from Bardez may drink a feni in Salcette even though he suspects from the bouquet that the new fertilizer complex has, without a shadow of doubt, had a peculiar effect on the soil of that unfortunate district. While the Salcettan will drink at any time, or place, of any feni in Goa, but concede to no man on the virtue of the minerals in the Salcette soil; minerals moreover of a certain *quality*, which give to Salcette's feni its singular bouquet and body.

It is true that soil, height, moisture, proximity to fresh or sea water, and many other factors affect the character of a coconut of caju feni. I have an illiterate palate in these matters but many Goans can place the source of a feni from a single sip. Hence you will find a profusion of brands, bewildering to the neophyte eye, labelled with a wanton indulgence in colours, typefaces and illustrations and a lofty disregard for the basic ethics of design. Old Barrel, Red Star, El Nectar (I liked that), Adega da Velha, Real

72, Cocona, Fidalgo, Bando, Golden Barrel, Black Lion. Fancy takes flight; there is an engaging absence of logic, you take your pick or, if adventurously inclined, work your way through with strong heart and stout liver, finding joy where you will.

All of this is purely academic in the village taverna, an institution as natural to its environment as the feni it serves which, more often than not, comes in a discreet amber bottle, without a label, roughly corked. Approach its content with care and respect, for this is likely to be genuine, pure and wholesome, distilled by the villagers for generations, happiest and most true when drunk at home.

The village taverna opens at sunset. Visit. Select a seat by a window with view of cottages, gardens and paddy fields. Get to know the magnificent brew. Allow its liquid alchemy to encourage and revive your tired cells. Time is paced by the tolling of angelus bells, a white dog trotting across green fields, making for hearth and home, the conversation of two farmers enquiring about the health and well being of each other's pigs. Allow the copitos to come as they will. The tavern keeper knows. His disposition, God-given, poured from the happy brown bottle, will lead you gently past sunset and evening star, the flicker of oil lamps in village windows, to quiet introductions and good fellowship as the amber bottle makes the rounds yet again and you are made welcome as guest, friend, boon companion; to laughter and snatches of song as the witching hour approaches; perhaps a plate of prawn, a loaf of bread, the last amber bottle; the house across fields fragrant with dew and the perfume of the delicate white flower which blooms only after dusk, raat ki rani, Queen of the Night. All about you the palms sway beneath a shifting moon, as they have before time began; as they will when a new dawn breaks. Fare thee well, blithe spirit.

SUDHA KOUL

Flesh in the Valley

We might have a modern kitchen now, but I look forward to the formal occasions when our old cook, Sudarshan, now a venerable grandfather, comes back to cook for us. He will never touch a gas range if his life depends on it, and within moments of his arrival the old hearth fires are ablaze once again, crackling as they joyously send fountains of red and yellow embers into the chimney. The flames remember and find their way to the base of an entombed man-tall vessel, heating up the water inside. We now use the hot water from the old bathroom only for doing the dishes in the kitchen, but it feels good to have the medieval water heater called up from retirement once in a while.

Our cook has come to our house to prepare one of the summer banquets given by my grandfather. Any excuse is good enough for Shyamji. We are happy to wait and suffer the torture of enduring a day filled with appetizing whiffs and vapors just for the glory of the meal at night. The more time something takes, the better it always is.

He looks right in place, that old chef, with his crown of red hair and walrus mustache, as he busies himself restoring in a small

This extract is taken from *The Tiger Ladies: A Memoir of Kashmir*, published by Beacon Press, Boston, 2002.

measure a part of life as we knew it just some years ago. When we eat, we have to admit that the quality of the food from these ferocious fires is far superior to anything a modern appliance can produce.

Sudarshan says, 'Real food can only be prepared on traditional equipment. How can I take red-hot out of the gas range?' In Kashmiri excellent, worthwhile, and real are the same word.

Perfectionist and traditionalist that he is, Sudarshan needs the coals for final touches to his dishes and, equally important, for his hookah. He cooks in earthenware pots with concave lids that he seals with dough putty. Then he puts red-hot coals on top of the concave lid, effectively creating an oven of sorts where his dishes acquire their last hours of heat seasoning and flavor. This is just one of his secrets. The daughters and daughters-in-law of our house flatter him and bring him tea and finally persuade him to let them write down some of his recipes. He can neither read nor write but his children are well educated, and that is his accomplishment as well, and he takes pride in it.

'It's gold,' he says of his secret recipes, laughing between puffs at the hookah pipe that he holds in the side of his mouth, 'A poor man's gold. Here, I give it to you. What will you remember?' He knows he is a genius, but like a true artist he loves appreciation. I remember everything, and remember it well. I will inherit all the recipes, and I know just how to prepare them. Decades later I will put all my recollected recipes into a book for my children, and say to myself, 'What will they remember, when Kashmir is like Shangri-la, a matter of myth, an eternal vale, never to be seen again in this life?' To my delight my children can tell the difference between a real *roghanjosh* and a pseudo-concoction. When I replicate some of those family meals in my own home, I close my eyes, surround myself with the aromas, and pretend that I am in Kashmir.

I know exactly how Sudarshan's recipes have to be prepared because that crusty old man has decided quite arbitrarily very early in my childhood that I, the youngest child in the house, am to be his official taste tester. So, on big cooking occasions, on his instructions, I sit on the low wooden ledge separating the kitchen from the shoe-contaminated rest of the house. He, whom everyone fears, looks anxiously at my child's face for signs as I pronounce judgment. Of course, I never say anything about the ingredients because I do not know what he uses or should use, but he checks my pulse by asking if the salt is right. And I am usually on the mark, and although I think I am checking the salt, he relies on my facial expression to judge for himself. I don't know if he does this because he is superstitious, and thinks I bring him good luck. Perhaps he has intuitively guessed that I will grow up to love really good food.

The banquet culminates in the old man appearing with a tray of shoulder lamb chops cooked in milk, saffron, and herbs, then deep-fried in clarified butter and finally decorated with pure silver lead that whispers as he moves the tray around. The trick is to get each piece of lamb to have two long ribs, a layer of lean meat, a layer of soft fat, and a paper-tin skin of tallow on top. Except for the bones every bit of the kabargah piece melts in your mouth. When the guests compliment him Sudarshan is quietly pleased.

We are careful when we talk to him because he has a short temper, and this is why he is also the family pickle maker. Every year at a certain season he comes to our house to fill cream-and-brown ceramic jars with vegetables pickled in crushed mustard seeds, spices, and mustard oil. It is a lengthy ceremony and we prepare for his arrival by sun-drying the vegetables for a couple of days. Then he mixes the vegetables and the pickling spices in a huge round brass tray. Finally, he smokes the jar with asafoetida smoke and stuffs the vegetables and spices into the jars, pounding down the mixture with his hand to expel air.

It takes almost the whole day to accomplish a year's worth of pickles, and the exercise is punctuated with different breads and cups of sweet or salt green tea, that we Kashmiris drink. We add a tiny pinch of soda to the boiling tea, and when we add milk the tea immediately turns salmon pink. We do the master cook the added honor of topping off the tea with a layer of clotted cream from the saucepans of cooling boiled milk that await dispensation in the kitchen. No one ever brings up the fact that he is asked to make the pickles because he is considered to be a hot-tempered man. His red hair is ample proof of this fact, according to us. These are self-evident truths, and we never doubt them.

When our old chef comes to cook for us the hierarchy in the kitchen changes. All our servants, Muslim and Hindu, consider him an Ustad, a master and the most senior, and pay him due respect. Like him most of the kitchen staff came to us when young, sometimes when they were mere children, sent by their families to supplement a village income. In time most of them became like family. My grandparents arranged marriages or better jobs for them and sent them off to set up their own homes. They return often for a visit or when they need help in some matter, or when we call them for help.

After Sudarshan leaves, the junior servants carry the cream-and-brown ceramic jars upstairs to a sunny spot in the attic. There the pickles ferment, and are ready to be eaten at the appropriate season. When ready the pickles should cut a red swathe down a pile of fluffy boiled rice.

The pickles are definitely ready in time for the Winter Moonless Night when we serve the good spirits who surround the house their annual dinner. We cook a special meal of their favorite food and place it outdoors for them, preferably on the wooden steps leading up to the storehouse where the grains are stored. The *yakshas* have a taste for the mortal life and on their feast day expect *khechhri*, rice with mung beans and lamb. Their cuisine travels all the way to England where it is served as kedgeree at breakfast.

We have an indoor deity as well, our house spirit, and he has his own special day. There are many alleged sightings of the deity, mostly in the attic where he lives, usually only by adults seeking to keep children in tow and out of the attic where there are many works in progress. We partake of the meal cooked in the house god's honor after we place his share, topped by a raw fish, on a table in the attic landing.

The fact is that all these tasty offerings go to the neighborhood cats, we know that, but the question of voicing this reality does not arise. Like most Brahmin households we keep neither cats nor dogs in the house, so it is easy for us children to believe that unseen deities consume the offerings. The truth is that no one wants to upset the natural order of things. Even those of us with advanced science degrees dare not tamper with fate by suggesting that the spirits do not exist.

We diligently repeat our seasonal activities year after year, observing good and bad days. We know from tales handed down through the generations that our life in the valley has always been precarious, so we like to assure ourselves of continuity in spite of overwhelming historical odds. We welcome new members of the tribe and honor those passed; it is a thread that passes from generation to generation, like a lifeline from our ancients to our future. When my maternal grandfather passed away, Dhanna honored him by observing his death rituals every year, as did his children. The mountains remained unmoving, mesmerized by their reflection in the lakes, as they watched us mortals go about our business.

Shiva and his consort live in the temple crowning the hill that stands in the heart of town. The Destroyer God depicted by a phallic stone lingam, is ensconced in a stone depiction of the female, and the balance created by the fusion of both energies keeps things quiet. We children have been told in hushed tones that the hill is actually a dormant volcano, although no one can remember the last eruption. The temple is built on the crater. Our valley carries within its tectonic plates the seeds of its own destruction, and we all know that these are always moving around in a subterranean snake kingdom. This movement can blow up in our face anytime, so we pray, the Hindus in our way and the Muslims in theirs, whenever there is an earthquake, and we grow up hearing these chants. All this makes good sense to us; we have many earthquakes, but the volcano remains dormant.

The Muslims have no use for Shiva but we pandits climb the hill and visit the temple as often as we can in the summer. Having made an arduous climb to the crater-top temple, we offer prayers and acquire virtue. But we are famished after the climb, so we rush down on the other side of the hill toward self-indulgence at a picnic on Dal Lake. We are emulating Shiva, combining asceticism and sensuality, perhaps this is why he appeals to us, we are always looking for a good time whenever we can find it. We take good care of our minor deities, but the wedding anniversary of Shiva, which falls in the winter, is the central part of the Kashmiri Hindu calendar.

The menu for this most important holiday is fixed and nothing can be deleted. We cannot give in to whimsical cravings; we only add items that can be repeated every year. Our menu is derived from our winter foods, which are exotic. We eat wild geese, which have flown all the way from Siberia, wild fowl with fluorescent turquoise and gold heads; we eat sun-dried tomatoes, gourds, and eggplants, sun-dried fruits, and dried fish. When we cook dried fish the house is filled with its overpowering odor, and although we joke about it and walk around with our fingers holding our noses, it is a winter dish we relish tremendously. Fresh vegetables and fruits are hard to come by in the winter and have to be captured at the right time in the summer. When the air is the driest and hottest we string up necklaces of fruits and vegetables and hang them to dry in our attic to preserve them for the winter.

Shivratri celebrations go on for several days, just as do our own weddings. On the main day of 'The Perfect Marriage', the one we aspire to, our priest officiates at our family prayers and only then can we partake of the feast prepared for the occasion. The priest starts at home in the old city and works his way through his congregation, finally arriving at our home very late at night. We are quite starved by the time he arrives, but we have to wait, sometimes until midnight. When the services are over we serve the married couple everything we are going to eat, but being deities they also get a whole raw fish, nature unimpaired by human enhancement. Only when this is done can we eat.

Shiva and his consort are everywhere in the valley, but the preeminent deity for us is Shakti, the female consort, the half that breathes life and energy into Shiva. Naturally the Goddess has many more shrines than the God. In a couple of the shrines the gift of choice for the Lady who rides a Tiger is a one-piece offering of the trachea, lungs, and liver of a goat or lamb. The Muslim butcher knows just how to prepare this offering, which we take up to the shrine where the raw meat is whirled into the sky. The flesh and blood whirligig soars into the heavens and it is received within moments, courtesy of circling kites adept at the ritual.

Some of the temples of the Goddess are strictly vegetarian, and to the most sacred of all of these we, growers of paddy, take rice pudding, which we call *khir*, the offering special to this deity. This shrine is a haven of peace. The clear blue-green spring surrounding the temple is in the middle of a garden of chinars. We pray that when we go to Khir Bhawani the spring waters will be clear. When the waters turn dark we are apprehensive because we know that some evil is about to descend upon our valley. The temple precincts are surrounded by Muslim homes and some of these homes have always been vegetarian.

At Shivratri we invite friends of other religious persuasions to our house for meals. We also send fruits and nuts to our house for lunch or dinner. In turn we look forward to eating at their house on the two Eids celebrated by Muslims. For those members of my family who do not eat at a Muslim home, our hosts send a packet of uncooked lamb to our house. Our cooks will prepare the meat, and then it is fine for everyone to eat. Somehow it is the cooking that is a problem. Almost all our butchers are Muslim, and in a heartily nonvegetarian valley, they always prosper.

Our butcher, though hearty-looking, wears a meager beard that he has been encouraging to grow presumably since it first appeared many years ago. He has intellectual aspirations that he nurtures similarly and when he comes to collect his payments he sometimes discusses Sufi poetry with my grandfather in English, perhaps to give himself some much-needed practice.

On one Eid afternoon I am at my friend's house for their annual feast. After a sumptuous lunch as usual we go out into the garden and I find an effigy on fire. The smaller children are running around throwing little twigs at the burning man as he falls on his face.

'What is this?' I ask.

'Oh, it's nothing,' says my friend, her face red with embarrassment. 'I don't know what these kids are up to.'

Just then one of her little cousins runs up to us and says, 'We set fire to Pandit Nehru.'

I cannot make any sense of it, and I feel deeply embarrassed. Our grandmothers are best friends, and our grandfathers rely upon each other. Pandit Nehru is a Kashmiri Brahmin just like us, so I cannot imagine what he must have done to deserve being set afire.

'Why?' I ask.

'He is the Prime Minister of India.'

'Oh,' I say, and to myself I say that it has nothing to do with us being friends. I could not have been quite ten years old and I went home bewildered and afraid. It was my first cognitive encounter with the menacing possibilities of hatred.

Like the ripples caused by a falling chinar leaf on the placid waters of our lakes political resentment creates a stir now and then in our life. The circles of water soon disappear into the nothingness from whence they came. But even though the leaves keep falling with increasing frequency, we naively prefer to believe that it is not inevitable that a frozen season will soon be upon our heels.

Most Kashmiris want a promise to be kept. They want their opinions on their political future to be polled. On the other hand, India has decided that since so many elections have taken place in the valley, it confirms the people's decision to be a part of India. These two ways of looking at the same facts are to fester and grow in the belly of Kashmir, and finally end up in a volcanic eruption that no one's prayers can avert.

We have managed to avert calamity so far, but no one can avert destruction if it is preceded by lack of wisdom. At night at home in my bed I remember the effigy burning and falling to the ground, facedown. I shudder because the cremation of a man standing up is a horrible sight to behold. It is too disturbing an experience to repeat to my family.

When Shivratri comes around in winter my Muslim friend comes over for lunch as usual. Like so many other unpalatable things we have put the burning episode behind us. Shivratri is the most important festival for us and my friend honors our sentiments.

My friend is not the only Muslim who participates with us on this sacred day. The provisions for Shivratri, the pottery vessels, meats, fish, and other ritualistic items are all bought from Muslim traders. We are grown from the same seed on the same soil, and although Muslims have accepted Islam, they have supported our obsession for centuries as well.

Some summers we travel to the Mughal Gardens via the lakes in a houseboat that we rent from a grand old Muslim lady, whom we call Rice Blind. The entire household packs up for a week-long trip on a waterway that takes us through canals, locks, and lakes, ending at the Mughal Gardens. Rice Blind was introduced to us when Tulli came to my grandfather's house as a bride. She is practically one of us and has participated in our household activities all her life. Now she comes to spend a day with Tulli and to help us clean our rice after it is hulled, to separate the chaff from the grain. They talk all the time, sometimes in whispers. The lady cannot see very well, but this does not result in her being kept from a task for which even people with good eyesight sometimes find themselves ill-equipped. She has what it takes, instinct and intuition; both are more powerful than mere eyesight. Our rice is perfectly cleaned, and according to one of our more poetic cooks, blossoms like a lotus when prepared.

Rice Blind used to be a milk-mother in the old days, but now she chaperones those very daughters when they get married. She is prosperous and owns several houseboats, but loves to accompany us on our trips. Her sons are the boatmen. We simply love her as she holds out her arms in an embrace, clasps us to her and offers herself to the fates in exchange for any evil that might befall us. We believe sincerely that fate accepts substitutes.

Summer celebrations are the same for Hindus and Muslims. After hibernating in the long winter we seize the other seasons and stay outdoors and in the sun as long as we can, enjoying our supernaturally exquisite valley. We have everything in common— our food, our music, our language, and humor, our Sufi tradition and shrines, our blossoming fruit trees. Other things we do differently, although nothing comes to mind immediately, except the following of our separate faiths.

Most of all it is the water that seems to provide the common backdrop for all our lives. Our ethos is drenched in water, informed no doubt by the plentitude of deep, wide lakes and beautiful rivers in Kashmir. Superstitions about these waters and their produce are everywhere; we treat our waters with caution.

The waters, though, are far from pure and in some parts near the city quite polluted by human waste. But we do not take the water for granted. Spiritual pollution causes grievous fear and trepidation among Kashmiris. Even as late as the nineteenth century we did not dream of sporting with our water, and only put it to serious and unavoidable use. But a Scottish missionary discovers us, falls in love, stays and eventually manages to persuade his Kashmiri schoolboys to participate in boating races and regattas. The logo for Tyndale Biscoe's school even today is two narrow crew-style crossed oars, but it was a hard-won triumph for him.

Sometimes Rice Blind's sons pull up and anchor the barge poles, and the arklike boat, which is built like a long one-storied house, comes to rest. The boat is furnished with reed mats, and the wooden floors are seasoned with use to a smooth polished shine. My grandfather and his sons go for a leisurely swim in the river, while their still-Eastern women pray inside for their safe return. Mr Biscoe has not managed to convince everyone in the valley: having a bath is a must, but swimming for pleasure might upset water spirits who are always lurking beneath among the swaying weeds and the lotus roots, happy to ensnare and drag down disrespectful Kashmiris. The men leap back on board after a daring swim, and cheerfully if sheepishly pull out the beer that has been surreptitiously traveling the lakes with us. The lake water is cold enough to chill the beer bottles that hang in a net hooked to the boat side. The women love their green tea, but smile knowingly at a couple of the others who linger suspiciously over a metal tumbler.

What meals we enjoy on the boat! Fish are caught, fried, and quickly polished off. The hot sun and the cold beer, the fried fish, the river and all of us on a boat—it is a rare combination of time and place.

We eat off round wide lotus leaves twice the size of dinner plates. I am loath to call them 'disposable', but that is exactly what they are. I can still remember a large drop of water rolling around brilliantly, like mercury, on the velvety emerald-green leaf. Rice Blind's stalwart sons move the boat along with barge poles as we drag our hands in the water, clutching and pulling out the lotus leaves as the houseboat glides through the dark, bottle-green, weed-filled lake.

The process of catching fish provides the greatest excitement for us children, and the adults are no less enthused at the prospect of fresh catch cooked right on the spot. Kashmiris eat river fish, lake fish, and brook trout from the mountains. But being a people obsessed with water we have an enigmatic relationship with fish. I have seen both my grandmothers cook fish with care, anxious that the inviting aroma of frying fish might attract some unforeseen calamity. On the other hand, we serve fish at dinner prior to a traveler's departure, certain that the lingering fishy smell will see him safely to his destination.

Some fish are forbidden to us. We would rather die than touch or even hunger for fish from sacrosanct springs, the residence of mythical snakes. Ours is an honored timeless understanding. The springs are clear green, mysterious, and strangely peaceful, tucked away among the mountains.

Given our preoccupation with fish it is no wonder that Fatha the fishwife is a great favorite at our house, a regular fixture every week. In spring, summer and fall, the fish wife, accompanied by her son, makes the rounds of our neighborhood, opening gates and crying out boastfully 'The best, the sweetest, most unique fish in the world!'

We call them in, mother and child, and the fishwife comes through the garden gate carrying the fish kettle on her head. She sets it down on the granite path leading up to the porch where we choose the fish we want. After a great amount of haggling, laughing, and mock anger, the deal is struck. Then she weighs the fish before taking it around to the garden hose in the back of the house where she will clean it for us. Her little son follows her.

Fatha guts, scales, and cleans the fish at the garden faucet in the backyard. With expert hands she and later her son take a sharp knife to the soft white underbelly of the fish and effortlessly slit it open pulling out the contrasting bloody red entrails. Within minutes the offal is disposed of, the fish washed under the hose and sent into the house in wicker baskets still dripping water.

The fish are sent in to the kitchen whole and then cut into pieces by the kitchen staff who will prepare them for us. We have some favorite fish dishes: my great-aunt's smelts, and fish with tamarind and kohlrabi or daikon radish, and best of all fish cooked with fresh lotus root, as if to provide the fish with familiar surroundings in the hereafter.

One of the first kitchen tasks given to my mother as a brand-new daughter-in-law was to help cut the freshly cleaned fish into steaks. She had hardly been inside her mother's kitchen, being somewhat spoiled as a first child. But eager to please she gladly took the basket. She lifted the basket cover and passed out at the sight of six pairs of fish eyes looking up at her. In spite of this debacle she learned to cook the finest fish dishes for her family. The story is added to others on the family sampler like the motifs on an ivory silk archive, and we hear them all repeated again and again.

GITHA HARIHARAN

The Remains of the Feast

The room still smells of her. Not as she did when she was dying, an overripe smell that clung to everything that had touched her: sheets, saris, hands. She had been in the nursing home for only ten days but a bedsore grew like an angry red welt on her back. Her neck was a big hump, and she lay in bed like a moody camel that would snap or bite at unpredictable intervals. The goitred lump, the familiar swelling I had seen on her neck all my life, that I had stroked and teasingly pinched as a child, was now a cancer that spread like a fire down the old body, licking clean everything in its way.

The room now smells like a pressed, faded rose. A dry, elusive smell. Burnt, a candle put out.

We were not exactly room-mates, but we shared two rooms, one corner of the old ancestral house, all my twenty-year-old life.

She was Rukmini, my great-grandmother. She was ninety when she died last month, outliving by ten years her only son and daughter-in-law. I don't know how she felt when they died, but later she seemed to find something slightly hilarious about it all. That she, an ignorant village-bred woman, who signed the papers

This story is taken from *The Art of Dying*, published by Penguin Books India, New Delhi, 1991.

my father brought her with a thumb-print, should survive; while they, city-bred, ambitious, should collapse of weak hearts and arthritic knees at the first sign of old age.

Her sense of humour was always quaint. It could also be embarrassing. She would sit in her corner, her round, plump face reddening, giggling like a little girl. I knew better than ask her why, I was a teenager by then. But some uninitiated friend would be unable to resist, and would go up to my great-grandmother and ask her why she was laughing. This, I knew, would send her into uncontrollable peals. The tears would flow down her cheeks, and finally, catching her breath, still weak with laughter, she would confess. She could fart exactly like a train whistling its way out of the station, and this achievement gave her as much joy as a child might get when she saw or heard a train.

So perhaps it is not all that surprising that she could be so flippant about her only child's death, especially since ten years had passed.

'Yes, Ratna, you study hard and become a big doctor-madam,' she would chuckle when I kept the lights on all night and paced up and down the room, reading to myself.

'The last time I saw a doctor, I was thirty years old. Your grandfather was in the hospital for three months. He would faint every time he saw his own blood.'

And as if that summed up the progress made between two generations, she would pull her blanket over her head and begin snoring almost immediately. I have two rooms, the entire downstairs to myself now, since my great-grandmother died. I begin my course at medical college next month, and I am afraid to be here alone at night.

I have to live up to the gold medal I won last year. I keep late hours, reading my anatomy textbook before the course begins. The body is a solid, reliable thing. It is a wonderful, resilient machine. I hold on to the thick, hardbound book and flip through the new-smelling pages greedily. I stop every time I find an illustration, and look at it closely. It reduces us to pink, blue and white, colour-coded, labelled parts. Muscles, veins, tendons. Everything has a name. Everything is linked, one with the other, all parts of a functioning whole.

It is poor consolation for the nights I have spent in her warm bed, surrounded by that safe, familiar, musty smell.

She was cheerful and never sick. But she was also undeniably old, and so it was no great surprise to us when she took to lying in bed all day a few weeks before her ninetieth birthday.

She had been lying in bed for close to two months, ignoring concern, advice, scolding, and then she suddenly gave up. She agreed to see a doctor.

The young doctor came out of her room, his face puzzled and angry. My father begged him to sit down and drink a tumbler of hot coffee.

'She will need all kinds of tests,' the doctor said. 'How long has she had that lump on her neck? Have you had it checked?'

My father shifted uneasily in his cane chair. He is a cadaverous looking man, prone to nervousness and sweating. He keeps a big jar of antacids on his office desk. He has a nine-to-five accountant's job in a government-owned company, the kind that never fires its employees.

My father pulled out the small towel he uses in place of a handkerchief. Wiping his forehead, he mumbled, 'You know how these old women are. Impossible to argue with them.'

'The neck,' the doctor said more gently. I could see he pitied my father.

'I think it was examined once, long ago. My father was alive then. There was supposed to have been an operation, I think. But you know what they thought in those days. An operation meant an unnatural death. All the relatives came over to scare her, advise her with horror stories. So she said no. You know how it is. And she was already a widow then, my father was the head of the household. How could he, a fourteen-year-old, take the responsibility?'

'Hm,' said the doctor. He shrugged his shoulders. 'Let me know when you want to admit her in my nursing home. But I suppose it's best to let her die at home.'

When the doctor left, we looked at each other, the three of us, like shifty accomplices. My mother, practical as always, broke the silence and said, 'Let's not tell her anything. Why worry her? And then we'll have all kinds of difficult old aunts and cousins visiting, it will be such a nuisance. How will Ratna study in the middle of all that chaos?'

But when I went to our room that night, my great-grandmother had a sly look on her face. 'Come here, Ratna,' she said. 'Come here, my darling little gem.'

I went, my heart quaking at the thought of telling her. She held my hand and kissed each finger, her half-closed eyes almost flirtatious.

'Tell me something, Ratna,' she began in a wheedling voice.

'I don't know, I don't know anything about it,' I said quickly.

'Of course you do!' She was surprised, a little annoyed. 'Those small cakes you got from the Christian shop that day. Do they have eggs in them?'

'Do they?' she persisted. 'Will you,' and her eyes narrowed with cunning, 'will you get one for me?'

So we began a strange partnership, my great-grandmother and I. I smuggled cakes and ice cream, biscuits and samosas, made by non-brahmin hands, into a vegetarian invalid's room. To the deathbed of a brahmin widow who had never eaten anything but pure, home-cooked food for almost a century.

She would grab it from my hand, late at night after my parents had gone to sleep. She would hold the pastry in her fingers, turn it round and round, as if on the verge of an earthshaking discovery.

'And does it really have egg in it?' she would ask again, as if she needed the password for her to bite into it with her gums.

'Yes, yes,' I would say, a little tired of midnight feasts by then. The pastries were a cheap yellow colour, topped by white frosting with hard, grey pearls.

'Lots and lots of eggs,' I would say wanting her to hurry up and put it in her mouth. 'And the bakery is owned by a Christian. I think he hires Muslim cooks too.'

'Ooooh,' she would sigh. Her little pink tongue darted out and licked the frosting. Her toothless mouth worked its way steadily, munching, making happy sucking noises.

Our secret was safe for about a week. Then she became bold. She was bored with the cakes, she said. They give her heartburn.

She became a little more adventurous every day. Her cravings were varied and unpredictable. Laughable and always urgent.

'I'm thirsty,' she moaned, when my mother asked her if she wanted anything. 'No, no, I don't want water, I don't want juice.' She stopped the moaning and looked at my mother's patient, exasperated face. 'I'll tell you what I want,' she whined. 'Get me a glass of that brown drink Ratna bought in the bottle. The kind that bubbles and makes a popping sound when you open the bottle. The one with the fizzy noise when you pour it out.'

'A Coca-Cola?' said my mother, shocked. 'Don't be silly, it will make you sick.'

'I don't care what it is called,' my great-grandmother said and started moaning again. 'I want it.'

So she got it and my mother poured out a small glassful, tight-lipped, and gave it to her without a word. She was always a dutiful granddaughter-in-law.

'Ah,' sighed my great-grandmother, propped up against her pillows, the steel tumbler lifted high over her lips. The lump on her neck moved in little gurgles as she drank. Then she burped a loud, contented burp, and asked, as if she had just thought of it, 'Do you think there is something in it? You know, alcohol?'

A month later, we had got used to her unexpected, inappropriate demands. She had tasted, by now, lemon tarts, garlic, three types of aerated drinks, fruit cake laced with brandy, bhelpuri from the fly-infested bazaar nearby.

'There's going to be trouble,' my mother kept muttering under her breath. 'She's losing her mind, she is going to be a lot of trouble.'

And she was right, of course. My great-grandmother could no longer swallow very well. She would pour the coke into her mouth and half of it would trickle out of her nostrils, thick, brown, nauseating.

'It burns, it burns,' she would yell then, but she pursed her lips tightly together when my mother spooned a thin gruel into her mouth. 'No, no,' she screamed deliriously. 'Get me something from the bazaar. Raw onions. Fried bread. Chickens and goats.'

Then we knew she was lost to us.

She was dying. She was in the nursing home for ten whole days. My mother and I took turns sitting by her, sleeping on the floor by the hospital cot.

She lay there quietly, the pendulous neck almost as big as her face. But she would not let the nurses near her bed. She would squirm and wriggle like a big fish that refused to be caught. The sheets smelled, and the young doctor shook his head. 'Not much to be done now,' he said. 'The cancer has left nothing intact.'

The day she died, she kept searching the room with her eyes. Her arms were held down by the tubes and needles, criss-cross, in, out. The glucose dripped into her veins but her nose still ran. The clear, thin liquid trickling down like dribble on to her chin. Her hands clenched and unclenched with the effort and she whispered, like a miracle, 'Ratna.'

My other and I rushed to her bedside. Tears streaming down her face, my mother bent her head before her and pleaded, 'Give me your blessings, Paati. Bless me before you go.'

My great-grandmother looked at her for a minute, her lips working furiously, noiselessly. For the first time in my life I saw a fine veil of perspiration on her face. The muscles on her face twitched in mad frenzied jerks. Then she pulled one arm free of the tubes, in a sudden, crazy spurt of strength, and the IV pole crashed to the floor.

'Bring me a red sari,' she screamed. 'A red one with a big wide border of gold. And,' her voice cracked, 'bring me peanuts with chilli powder from the corner shop. Onion and green chilli bondas deep-fried in oil.'

Then the voice gurgled and gurgled, her face and neck swayed, rocked like a boat lost in a stormy sea. She retched, and as the vomit flew out of her mouth and her nose, thick like the milkshakes she had drunk, brown like the alcoholic coke, her head slumped forward, her rounded chin buried in the cancerous neck.

When we brought the body home—I am not yet a doctor and already I can call her that—I helped my mother to wipe her clean with a wet, soft cloth. We wiped away the smells, the smell of the hospital bed, the smell of an old woman's juices drying. Her skin was dry and papery. The stubble on her head—she had refused to shave her head once she got sick—had grown, like the soft, white bristles of a hairbrush.

She had had only one child though she had lived so long. But the skin on her stomach was like crumpled, frayed velvet, the creases running to and fro in fine, silvery rivulets.

'Bring her sari,' my mother whispered, as if my great-grandmother could still hear her.

I looked at the stiff, cold body that I was seeing naked for the first time. She was asleep at last, quiet at last. I had learnt, in the last month or two, to expect the unexpected from her. I waited, in case she changed her mind and sat up, remembering one more taboo to be tasted.

'Bring me your eyebrow tweezers,' I heard her say. 'Bring me that hair-removing cream. I have a moustache and I don't want to be an ugly old woman.'

But she lay still, the wads of cotton in her nostrils and ears shutting us out. Shutting out her belated ardour.

I ran to my cupboard and brought her the brightest, reddest sari I could find: last year's Diwali sari, my first silk.

I unfolded it, ignoring my mother's eyes which were turning

aghast. I covered her naked body lovingly. The red silk glittered like her childish laughter.

'Have you gone mad?' my mother whispered furiously. 'She was a sick old woman, she didn't know what she was saying.'

She rolled up the sari and flung it aside, as if it had been polluted. She wiped the body again to free it from foolish, trivial desires.

They burnt her in a pale-brown sari, her widow's weeds. The prayer beads I had never seen her touch encircled the bulging, obscene neck.

I am still a novice at anatomy. I hover just over the body, I am just beneath the skin. I have yet to look at the insides, the entrails of memories she told me nothing about, the pain congealing into a cancer.

She has left me behind with nothing but a smell, a legacy that grows fainter every day. For a while I haunt the dirtiest bakeries and tea-stalls I can find. I search for her, my sweet great-grandmother, in plate after plate of stale confections, in needle-sharp green chillies, deep-fried in rancid oil. I plot her revenge for her, I give myself diarrhoea for a week.

Then I open all the windows and her cupboard and air the rooms. I tear her dirty, grey saris to shreds. I line the shelves of her empty cupboard with my thick, newly-bought, glossy-jacketed texts, one next to the other. They stand straight and solid, row after row of armed soldiers. They fill up the small cupboard quickly.

HISTORY ON A PLATTER

Mukul Kesavan

Banquet Nationalism

In the week between polling day and the result, Ammi took to the kitchen and produced seven dinners, the like of which hadn't been seen since Lucknow's great days of decadence. The last meal was staged the evening before the results were to be formally gazetted. She invited everyone she liked, generally the same people who had helped her with her election campaign.

The hall was spread with mattresses covered with dhobi-white sheets, and these were arranged around two low tables, less than a foot high, which had been hired for the evening by Haasan. Ammi had originally planned a traditional feast, full of shorbas and kormas, biryanis and sherbets of the sort that had illuminated her expansive childhood, but the menu changed when Haasan argued forcefully that the meal was not meant to commemorate some vanished past but the eclectic present.

So under Haasan's ideological direction we had tomato soup with croutons, jellied hooves, mutton dosas, biryani, fish curried in mustard oil, prawns in coconut milk from Haasan's time in Malabar, potatoes in a thin gruel of haldi and dahi and water, free of garlic or onions—Haasan generously wished to include a sample

This extract is taken from *Looking through Glass*, published by Ravi Dayal Publisher, New Delhi, 1995.

of vegetarian bigotry—which no one ate, and finally, custard. Ammi and I were against the custard but Haasan insisted. Not that he liked custard—he was simply asserting our right to be Anglo-Indian.

And everything on the menu was served up together. Ammi would have served things in courses, but Haasan was her conscience that night. Courses, he declared, were a direct contradiction of her campaign, of her commitment to the present. To eat by courses was to accept the tyranny of chronological time. It was to allow that the past was an appetizer for the present, that the future was our just dessert.

E.M. FORSTER

The Outsider's Thali

After the Rajah had welcomed us we went to the Banquet Room. This again I must try to describe to you.

We all sat on the floor, cross-legged, round the edge of a great hall, the servants running about in the middle. Each was on a legless chair and had in front a tray like a bed tray on which was a metal tray, on which the foods were ranged. The Brahmins ate no meat, and were waited on by special attendants, naked to the waist. The rest of us had meat as well as the other dishes. Round each man's little domain an ornamental pattern was stenciled in chalk on the floor. My tray was arranged somewhat as follows, but 'Jane, Jane, however shall we recollect the dishes?', as Miss Bates remarked.

1. A mound of delicious rice—a great standby.
2. Brown tennis balls of sugar—not bad.
3. Golden curlicues—sweet to sickliness.
4. Little spicy rissoles.
5. Second mound of rice, mixed with spices and lentils.
6. Third mound of rice, full of sugar and sultanas—very nice.

This extract is from *The Hill of Devi*, published by Penguin Books, London, 1965.

7. Curry in metal saucer—to be mixed with rice no.1.
8. Sauce, as if made from apples that felt poorly. Also to be mixed with rice, but only once by me.
9. Another sauce, chooey-booey and brown.
10, 11, 12.   Three dreadful little dishes that tasted of nothing till they were well in your mouth, when your whole tongue suddenly burst into flame. I got to hate this side of the tray.
13. Long thin cake, like a brandy snap but salt.

14. It may have been vermicelli.
15. As for canaries.
16. Fourth mound of rice to which I never came.
17. Water.
18. Native bread—thin oat-cake type.

Some of these dishes had been cooked on the supposition that an elephant arrives punctually, and lay cooling on our trays when we joined them. Others were brought round hot by the servants who took a fistful and laid it down wherever there was room. Sometimes this was difficult, and the elder dishes had to be rearranged, and accommodate themselves. When my sweet rice arrived a great pushing and squeezing and patting took place, which I rather resented, not knowing how attached I should become to the new comer. Everything had to be eaten with the hand and with one hand—it is bad manners to use the left—and I was in terror of spoiling my borrowed plumes. Much fell, but mostly into the napkin, and the handkerchief that I had brought with me.

I. ALLAN SEALY

Trotter Laws

From Victoria, Eugene learnt that curries might be eaten at lunch, but at dinner never, dinner being, for all Trotters of the blood, a formal affair. That lunch was of India (or India Britonized), while dinner was of Britain (or Britain Indianized). That lunch was not a light meal but a heavy one, dinner being, however, no less heavy. That curry, wet or dry, is eaten with a dessertspoon, dessert being eaten with a teaspoon. That mulligatawny soup might precede lunch, but at dinner the soup must be clear, a consommé perhaps of trotters; that a pigeon might swim in chilli gravy at noon, but at night must be roasted; that pickles might accompany the first, but chutneys were for the second; that gulab jamuns might be eaten after the first, but a British pudding must follow the second. That Crumble Custard was a corruption, howsoever apt, of the cook's for caramel custard. That bed-tea was an excellent invention for those who did not go to work, for afterwards one might doze again or chase one's waking dreams until chhota haziri or the small breakfast, which preceded the greater breakfast as the morning star the sun. That spices in the morning were offensive, except for the nutmeg in the sugar-pot. That toast was eaten and

This extract is taken from *The Trotter-Nama*, published by IndiaInk, New Delhi, 1990.

toasts were drunk (a lesson later Trotters forgot). That butter went with toast, not toast with butter, the same law applying to marmalade (a law Little Eugene later forgot). That Smarmite was holy and must be applied sparingly, being English and expensive, but that no Trotter household should be without a bottle. That toast must not be dipped in tea. That eggs were eggs on weekdays but on Sundays became omelettes. That fruit in the morning was gold, in the afternoon silver, but at night lead. That stomach disorders were put right by a dose of effervescent salts in warm water taken in the morning.

GEOFFREY C. WARD AND DIANE R. WARD

English Soup

Despite the reassuring respect shown by his family's former subjects, there was little that was truly princely left to the Rao Raja—except for the spectacular fare said to be prepared in his kitchen. And during my first visit to Alwar, our host promised that the royal cooks would outdo themselves.

That evening, the rich, pungent smells of Indian cooking filled the parlour as I sipped gingerly at a pre-dinner drink, a family speciality brewed in the palace and said to contain the heads of game birds for added zest. (It was bright orange and tasted simultaneously like rose-water and turpentine.) Scores of stylized portraits of the prince's forebears lined the walls, going all the way back to the common ancestor of all Rajput houses, the sun himself. They all seemed interchangeable to me—each had the same turban, round face, big eyes, flaring moustaches, ropes of pearls—but our host seemed able to tell them apart. A portrait of the radiant founder of his clan hung behind his chair, the family resemblance unmistakable.

As the smell of spices filled the room I could hardly believe my luck. I loved Indian food, but in those days it was very

This extract is taken from *Tiger-wallahs: Saving the Greatest of the Great Cats*, published by Oxford University Press India, New Delhi, 2000.

difficult for outsiders to obtain it when dining out. The assumption everywhere seemed to be that we could only survive on the blandest of British fare.

Whether British rule was ultimately good or bad for India is a matter for scholars to decide. But no sane person who ever ate food prepared in the kitchens of the Raj can have any doubts about Britain's culinary legacy: it was universally malign. Never in history has so much bad food been served by so many to so few.

And English food was not only execrable but inescapable. The sahibs had sailed for home seven years before my family arrived in India, but their death grip on Indian kitchens had not even slightly weakened. Whether you dined at the British-run Hotel Cecil in Old Delhi (where Indians were still discouraged from eating seven years after independence), or at Nedou's in the velvet Kashmir Valley of Gulmarg, or at Laurie's in Agra, where dessert was followed by the Taj Mahal by moonlight, the scene and the meal were the same.

There was a big dining room with ceiling fans and dozens of cloth-covered tables, most of them empty. Then as now, Indian dining was labour-intensive. One barefoot bearer in starched *pugree* and white uniform gravely showed you to your table. There was a different man to pull out each chair. Another poured the water (which, of course, you dared not drink). Still others brought the food and served it, sometimes four at a time padding around the table, each serving something different from a silver tray. When they were not bringing food or clearing plates, the waiters stood in a solemn line against the wall watching as you worked your way through the courses. You had the sense always that you were silently being measured against the lofty standards of their former masters, and found wanting.

First came the soup—transparent, tasteless, brown, and brought to the table in a big shallow bowl to ensure that it was not only without discernible flavour but cold. A pale cube of carrot floated in it all alone. This soup was so universally served in India that my brother has suggested it was all prepared in a single cistern somewhere in the Deccan, then piped simultaneously into the kitchens of every club and hotel and rest house catering to foreigners. The subcontinent is the home of mystery, of course, but this theory assumes a brisk efficiency of which India was then, at least, not capable.

The savoury followed, a poker chip of toast upon which rested a single warm sardine. Fresh beef was rarely available for the main course for obvious reasons, and water buffalo is an imperfect substitute, so the choice usually came down to mutton (dry and gray and, as often as not, really goat) or roast chicken (pigeon-sized, sinewy and strangled in the kitchen yard that very afternoon). Both came with matching pallid mounds of English 'veg' and nicely browned roast potatoes—the best part of the meal, hands-down.

A second savoury, often another enshrined sardine, sometimes preceded dessert. Even cooks in very remote outposts could usually manage a good caramel custard, but they too often grew ambitious and proudly offered up instead a big wobbly British 'shape', crenellated with cream and identically sweet and tasteless whether tinted pink or green. The peculiar sucking noise the spoon made as it pulled away a serving of this glistening, unsteady favourite remains with me to this day.

At last the Rao Raja's bearer announced that dinner was ready, and we moved into the cavernous dining room and took our places at a long table. A platoon of bearers began filing in through the kitchen door. There must have been twenty steaming dishes. I remember seeing curried partridges and sand grouse and venison. There were hillocks of saffron rice, garnished with raisins and almonds; bowls of golden *dal*; cauliflower and spinach and potatoes and chickpeas with ginger, and all the pickles and chutneys and hot breads that went with them.

My friends dug in. The servants circled wide behind my chair. Then the kitchen door opened again, and the prince paused, a chicken leg halfway to his mouth, and smiled at me. 'Cooked *especially* for you,' he said, and a beaming servant placed before me another bowl of the universal English soup.

Saadat Hasan Manto

Jelly

At six in the morning, the man who used to sell ice from a push-cart next to the service station was stabbed to death. His body lay on the road, while water kept falling on it in steady driblets from the melting ice.

At a quarter past seven, the police took him away. The ice and blood stayed on the road.

A mother and child rode past the spot in a *tonga*. The child noticed the coagulated blood on the road, tugged at his mother's sleeve and said, 'Look mummy, jelly.'

—*Translated from Urdu by Khalid Hasan*

This story is taken from *Mottled Dawn: Fifty Sketches and Stories of Partition*, published by Penguin Books India, New Delhi, 1997.

Chutnification

My special blends: I've been saving them up. Symbolic value of the pickling process: all the six hundred million eggs which gave birth to the population of India could fit inside a single, standard-sized pickle jar; six hundred million spermatozoa could be lifted on a single spoon. Every pickle-jar (you will forgive me if I become florid for a moment) contains, therefore, the most exalted of possibilities: the feasibility of the chutnification of history; the grand hope of the pickling of time! I, however, have pickled chapters. Tonight, by screwing the lid firmly on to a jar bearing the legend *Special Formula No. 30: 'Abracadabra'*, I reach the end of my long-winded autobiography; in words and pickles, I have immortalized my memories, although distortions are inevitable in both methods. We must live, I'm afraid, with the shadows of imperfection.

These days, I manage the factory for Mary. Alice—'Mrs Fernandes'—controls the finances; my responsibility is for the creative aspects of our work. (Of course I have forgiven Mary her crime; I need mothers as well as fathers, and a mother is beyond blame.) Amid the wholly female workforce of Braganza Pickles,

This extract is taken from *Midnight's Children*, published by Jonathan Cape, London, 1995.

beneath the saffron-and-green winking of neon Mumbadevi, I choose mangoes tomatoes limes from the women who come at dawn with baskets on their heads. Mary, with her ancient hatred of 'the mens', admits no males except myself into her new, comfortable universe . . . myself, and of course my son. Alice, I suspect, still has her little liaisons; and Padma fell for me from the first, seeing in me an outlet for her vast reservoir of pent-up solicitude; I cannot answer for the rest of them, but the formidable competence of the Narlikar females is reflected, on this factory floor, in the strong-armed dedication of the vat-stirrers.

What is required for chutnification? Raw materials, obviously—fruit, vegetables, fish, vinegar, spices. Daily visits from Koli women with their saris hitched up between their legs. Cucumbers aubergines mint. But also: eyes, blue as ice, which are undeceived by the superficial blandishments of fruit—which can see corruption beneath citrus-skin; fingers which, with featheriest touch, can probe the secret inconstant hearts of green tomatoes: and above all a nose capable of discerning the hidden languages of what-must-be-pickled, its humours and messages and emotions . . . at Braganza Pickles, I supervise the production of Mary's legendary recipes; but there are also my special blends, in which, thanks to the powers of my drained nasal passages, I am able to include memories, dreams, ideas, so that once they enter mass-production all who consume them will know what pepperpots achieved in Pakistan, or how it felt to be in the Sundarbans . . . believe don't believe but it's true. Thirty jars stand upon a shelf, waiting to be unleashed upon the amnesiac nation.

(And beside them, one jar stands empty.)

The process of revision should be constant and endless; don't think I'm satisfied with what I've done! Among my unhappinesses: an overly-harsh taste from those jars containing memories of my father; a certain ambiguity in the love-flavour of 'Jamila Singer' (Special Formula No. 22), which might lead the unperceptive to conclude that I've invented the whole story of the baby-swap to justify an incestuous love; vague implausibilities in the jar labelled 'Accident in a Washing-chest'—the pickle raises questions which are not fully answered, such as: Why did Saleem need an accident to acquire his powers? Most of the other children didn't . . . Or again, in 'All-India Radio' and others, a discordant note in the orchestrated flavours: would Mary's confession have come as a shock to a true telepath? Sometimes, in the pickles' version of history, Saleem appears to have known too little; at other times, too much . . . yes, I should revise and revise, improve and improve; but there is neither the time nor the energy. I am obliged to offer no more than this stubborn sentence: It happened that way because that's how it happened.

There is also the matter of the spice bases. The intricacies of turmeric and cumin, the subtlety of fenugreek, when to use large (and when small) cardamom; the myriad possible effects of garlic, garam masala, stick cinnamon, coriander, ginger . . . not to mention the flavourful contributions of the occasional speck of dirt. (Saleem is no longer obsessed with purity.) In the spice bases, I reconcile myself to the inevitable distortions of the pickling process. To pickle is to give immortality, after all: fish, vegetables, fruit hang embalmed in spice-and-vinegar; a certain alteration, a slight intensification of taste, is a small matter, surely? The art is to change the flavour in degree, but not in kind; and above all (in my thirty jars and a jar) to give it shape and form—that is to say, meaning. (I have mentioned my fear of absurdity.)

One day, perhaps, the world may taste the pickles of history. They may be too strong for some palates, their smell may be overpowering, tears may rise to eyes; I hope nevertheless that it will be possible to say of them that they possess the authentic taste of truth . . . that they are, despite everything, acts of love.

AMITAV GHOSH

Tibetan Dinner

It was a while before the others at the table had finished pointing out the celebrities who had come to the restaurant for the gala benefit: the Broadway actresses, the Seventh Avenue designers, and the world's most famous rock star's most famous ex-wife, a woman to whom fame belonged like logic to a syllogism, axiomatically. Before the list was quite done, I caught a glimpse of something, a flash of saffron at the other end of the room, and I had to turn and look again.

Peering through a thicket of reed-necked women, I saw that I'd been right: yes, it was a monk in saffron robes, it really was a Buddhist monk—Tibetan, I was almost sure. He was sitting at the head of a table on the far side of the room, spectral in the glow of the restaurant's discreetly hidden lighting. But he was real. His robes were real robes; not drag, not a costume. He was in his early middle age, with clerically cropped hair and a pitted, wind-ravaged face. He happened to look up and noticed me staring at him. He looked surprised to see me: his chopsticks described a slow interrogative arc as they curled up to his mouth.

I was no less surprised to see him: he was probably a little less

This extract is taken from *The Imam and the Indian*, published by Permanent Black and Ravi Dayal Publisher, New Delhi, 2003.

out of place among the dinner-jackets and designer diamonds than I, in my desert boots and sweater, but only marginally so.

He glanced at me again, and I looked quickly down at my plate. On it sat three dumplings decorated with slivers of vegetables. The dumplings looked oddly familiar, but I couldn't quite place them.

'Who were you looking at?' said the friend who'd taken me there, an American writer and actress who had spent a long time in India and, in gratitude to the subcontinent, had undertaken to show me the sights of New York.

I gestured foolishly with a lacquered chopstick.

She laughed. 'Well, of course,' she said. 'It's his show; he probably organized the whole thing. Didn't you know?'

I didn't know. All I'd been told was that this was the event of the week in New York, very possible even the month (it wasn't a busy month): a benefit dinner at Indo-Chine, the in-est restaurant in Manhattan—one which had in fact defied every canon of in-ism by being in for almost a whole year, and which therefore had to be seen now if at all, before the tourists from Alabama got to it. My skepticism about the in-ness of the event had been dispelled by the tide of paparazzi we'd had to breast on our way in.

Laughing at my astonishment, she said, 'Didn't I tell you? It's a benefit for the Tibetan cause.'

More astonished still, I said, 'Which Tibetan cause?'

'The Tibetan cause,' someone said vaguely, picking at a curl of something indeterminately vegetal that had been carved into a flower shape. It was explained to me then that the benefit was being hosted by a celebrated Hollywood star; a young actor who, having risen to fame through his portrayal of the initiation rites of an American officer, had afterwards converted to Tibetan Buddhism and found so much fulfillment in it he was reported to have sworn that he would put Tibet on the world map, make it a household word in the US, like Maalox or Lysol.

'The odd thing is,' said my friend, 'that he really is very sincere about this: he really isn't like those radical chic cynics of the sixties and seventies. He's not an intellectual, and he probably doesn't know much about Tibet, but he wants to do what little he can. They have to raise money for their schools and so on, and the truth is that no one in New York is going to reach into their pockets unless they can sit at dinner with rock stars' ex-wives. It's not his fault. He's probably doing what they want him to do.'

I looked at the Tibetan monk again. He was being talked to by an improbably distinguished man in a dinner jacket. He caught my eye, and nodded, smiling, as he bit into a dumpling.

Suddenly I remembered what the dumpling was. It was a Tibetan *mo-mo*, but stuffed with salmon and asparagus and such like instead of the usual bits of pork and fat. I sat back to marvel at the one dumpling left on my plate. It seemed a historic bit of food: one of the first genuine morsels of Tibetan *nouvelle cuisine*.

The last time I'd eaten a *mo-mo* was as an undergraduate, in Delhi.

A community of Tibetan refugees had built shacks along the Grand Trunk Road, not far from the university. The shacks were fragile but tenacious, built out of bits of wood, tin and corrugated iron. During the monsoons they would cover the roofs with sheets of tarpaulin and plastic, and weigh them down with bricks and stones. Often the bricks would be washed away and the sheets of plastic would be left flapping in the wind like gigantic prayer-flags. Some of the refugees served *mo-mo*, noodles and *chhang*, the milky Tibetan rice beer, on tables they had knocked together out of discarded crates. Their food was very popular among the drivers who frequented that part of the Grand Trunk Road.

In the university, it was something of a ritual to go to these shacks after an examination. We would drink huge quantities of *chhang*—it was very dilute, so you had to drink jugs of it—and eat noodle soup and *mo-mos*. The *mo-mos* were very simple there: bits of gristle and meat wrapped and boiled in thick skins of flour. They tasted of very little until you dipped them into the red sauce that came with them.

The food was cooked and served by elderly Tibetans; the young people were usually away, working. Communicating with them wasn't easy for the older people rarely knew any but the most functional Hindi.

As we drank our jugs of *chhang*, a fog of mystery would descend on the windy, lamp-lit interiors of the shacks. We would look at the ruddy, weathered faces of the women as they filled our jugs out of the rusty oil-drums in which they brewed the beer, and try to imagine the journey they had made: from their chilly, thin-aired plateau 15,000 feet above sea-level, across the passes of the high Himalayas, down into that steamy slum, floating on a bog of refuse and oil-slicks on the outskirts of Delhi.

Everyone who went there got drunk. You couldn't help doing so—it was hard to be in the presence of so terrible a displacement.

It was an unlikely place, but Tibetans seem to have a talent for surviving on unlikely terrain. Ever since the Chinese invasion of Tibet, dozens of colonies of Tibetan refugees run businesses in woollen goods, often in the most unexpected places. In Trivandrum near the southernmost tip of India, where the temperature rarely drops below eighty degrees Fahrenheit and people either wear the thinnest of cottons or go bare-bodied, there are a number of Tibetan stalls in the marketplace, all piled high with woollen scarves and sweaters. They always seem to have more customers than they can handle.

Once going past the Jama Masjid in Delhi in a bus on a scorching June day, I noticed a Tibetan stall trucked in between the sugar-cane juice vendors. Two middle-aged women dressed in heavy Tibetan *bakus* were sitting in it, knitting. The stall was stacked with the usual brightly coloured woollen goods. The women were smiling cheerfully as they bargained with their customers in sign language and broken Hindi. A small crowd had gathered around them, as though in tribute to their courage and resilience.

I found myself looking around the restaurant, involuntarily, for another Indian face, someone who had been properly invited, unlike me. I suppose I was looking for some acknowledgment, not of a debt, but of a shared history, a gesture towards those hundreds of sweaters in Trivandrum. I couldn't see any. (Later someone said they'd seen a woman in a sari, but they couldn't be sure; it might have been a Somali robe—this was, after all, New York.)

When I next caught the monk's eye, his smile seemed a little guilty: the hospitality of a poor nation must have seemed dispensable compared to the charity of a rich one. Or perhaps he was merely bewildered. It cannot be easy to celebrate the commodification of one's own suffering.

But I couldn't help feeling that if the lama, like the actor, really wanted to make Tibet a household word in the western world, he wasn't setting about it the right way. He'd probably have done better if he'd turned it into an acronym, like TriBeCa or ComSubPac. And sold the rights to it to a line of detergents or even perhaps a breakfast cereal.

TiBet (where the Cause is): doesn't sound too bad, marketable even.

FOOD AND THE SENSES

RAJ KAMAL JHA

Baby Food

There's not much in the fridge, let me remember. Just a couple of potatoes, old, with things, some curly, some straight, coming out of their skins. A bottle of ketchup, its cap stuck because of the crust. There's a lettuce, cut and chopped, its leaves dry, what remains of its head quivers every time the fridge coughs.

There's not much in the kitchen cabinets either. Or in the spice jars, just two sticks of cinnamon, smelling like my breath when I have fever. There's one egg, an onion, I could scramble it, fry it, but I'm too tired to cook now, there's a pouch of toned milk I got two days ago. That should do.

I will have to get up in five minutes, take a break, let the pen rest for a while, the ink on its nib breathe in the night air, let the words sleep before they are called once again to perform to our bidding. For there's a long way to go.

First, I have to wash the smell of the hospital from my face, my hands. In my hurry to get down to these stories, I forgot to remove my socks; the nylon and the sweat, the water heater doesn't work, the water must be cold.

How long will you remain in that towel? No, I'm not going

This extract is taken from *The Blue Bedspread*, published by Picador India, New Delhi, 1999.

to disturb you now, when you wake up in the morning, we'll change you, clean you up, get breakfast ready.

Once upon a time we had the Calcutta Milk Corporation Van, white and blue, dented, strips of steel bent and jutting out, but it came tearing down the street as if it was brand new. It lurched, shuddered over pot-holes, the milk inside was kept in aluminium cans so the driver didn't care, let them rattle against each other. So that half an hour before sunrise, the Van woke up the neighbourhood, first the pigeons in the cage, then the birds in the trees and then all of us.

The Van stopped a few years ago, now they've set up a milk booth down the street where people begin lining up one full hour after sunrise, their eyes wide open as they drop coins and wait for the light to turn green, for the milk to flow, precisely measured, gurgle into their steel cans, drip drip at the end, the froth collecting at the top of the jar, spilling over when they put on the cover. I skip all this, I buy the pouch.

I shall boil this milk; I've seen mothers on TV test the milk against their wrists, I shall do the same and when it's cool, when I am sure it won't hurt your lips, I shall feed you the milk, I shall pour the milk into your mouth carefully so that the rim of the spoon, its steel edge, doesn't scrape your gums. And I shall hold the spoon close to my chest so that if you wish to, you can imagine I'm your mother and the milk flows, drop by drop, from her breast.

Maybe my hands will shake, I am not a young man any more, your head may jerk and the spoon may tilt, the milk will run down my shirt but it doesn't matter, it's milk, cool to the touch, I can always wash up later. What's important is you don't miss your mother tonight.

ANURADHA ROY

Cooking Women

One monsoon in the 1960s, my father's oldest brother died. His portrait hung in a room at the centre of our house, where all the pictures were. It showed just his face, looking up at a camera that had surprised him by appearing from the back. His bumpy forehead was creased with a baffled frown that seemed to ask why his picture needed to be taken. A week later, coming down our red stairs after an afternoon amble on the rain-slicked terrace, he stumbled and fell. The many-windowed room that the stairs landed upon was deserted; the bedrooms that led off it were empty. Twelve people lived in that house, but nobody heard him crumpling at the foot of the stairs. As he fell, one of his hands jammed in the wrought iron banisters.

Four days later, I was born, a month before I was due. There was no celebration, relatives didn't crowd to catch a glimpse of the new baby. They were shaking their heads over the young widow and her fatherless children. Even Johnson's Baby Powder couldn't quell the deathsmell from tuberose, incense and boiled-up deathtime food. My father sat with his remaining brother, working out how far two salaries could stretch without snapping.

This essay is taken from *Outlook*, 8 March 2003. It was the winning entry in the third *Outlook*-Picador Non-fiction Contest.

Less money and more mouths to feed, one of them mine. In an early memory, I am sitting on the floor, ringed by bell metal plates of rice and *daal* and faces beyond imprisoning me. 'Now we'll eat you up whole,' someone says laughing, 'if you don't finish what's on your plate.' I rushed for refuge from those communal meals to our own set of rooms upstairs. I thought our two rooms were the nicest in the house. The one with four long windows overlooking a tree-fringed road was where we did all our living. Like the windows in *Charulata*, ours were made for peeping through, their wooden shutters let me observe the world below unseen. Torn away from the windows for unwanted naps I lay looking up at iron rafters cloudy with cobwebs; when I turned, ceramic electric switches formed a row of black-and-white doodle faces in one corner. It was in this room that my father's mother, who died before I was born, before my father married, had been kept through her long mysterious illness. The picture room had a cut-out mounted portrait of her—large, almost two feet high. It showed a seated woman, her skin the colour of tea, man-like hands folded tight. Her brown lips sagged at being imprisoned within a glass case. Perhaps her bad humour had something to do with her being an inert dinner guest at many games of House-House.

Real dinners? That was in our other room, which was actually an enclosed verandah, a portion of which had been further sectioned off. In one part, there was a bed. This part was my brother's and mine. My mother cooked in the smaller portion behind the partition dividing the room. She had attempted making the dull grey plywood partition garden-like by painting large yellow and white daisies on it. For water in her little food room— it was never grand enough to be thought of as a 'kitchen'—there was a metal drum with a little brass tap, and a bucket below to hold the spill. The cloudy water in the bucket, floating with slimy peel and tea leaves, had to be emptied out several times a day.

Our sectioned-off, make-do food room was a rebellion. The

real kitchens in the house were on the ground floor, alongside the dining room and formal sitting room, which we seemed to enter only when a compounder came around to dot forearms with smallpox vaccine. We stayed away from them. In the early years of my childhood, all meals emanated from the ultimate real kitchen downstairs. Here, my aunts and mother would cook for the extended family, aided by a helper, and a maid called Dolly'r Ma because she was supposed be the mother of a girl called Dolly. We awaited the day Dolly would accompany Dolly'r Ma, but when the daughter finally showed up it turned out she was called Kamini.

The ultimate real kitchen was large but dark, with a low sooty ceiling, and mud-coloured platforms rising from a mud-coloured floor. The cooking here was done on coal-fire stoves fashioned out of what looked like metal buckets thickly coated with yellow clay. The coals that went into it were fanned and blown upon in the courtyard outside until they lit to a red glow. After this, they were moved in, towards utensils lying in wait for them.

Vegetables and fish were bought afresh each day, refrigerators still being the preserve of the adventurous rich. Each day's fish was first inspected in the courtyard corner, against the wall which had a small water tank by it, about three feet deep. Most of our fish was 'bought dead'. Tradition decreed, however, that some kinds of fish had to be cooked 'just killed'. The eel-like *shingi* and *magur* and the energetic thrashing *koi* that seemed to have some inkling of their fate came gazing up from their small water-filled containers, daring anyone to butcher them. They were thrown into the tank to swim around, falsely secure in their new home. As the crows lined up along the walls like impatient mendicants before a temple, Dolly'r Ma would begin cutting and cleaning the fish out in the courtyard. She sat surrounded by bowls of water and a plate onto which she piled the cut fish. She clenched the fish firmly with both hands, her foot holding down the wooden slat supporting the vertical blade of the bonti. The fish slid against the sharp blade, their scales flying in a gaudy aluminium shower. Dolly'r Ma's hands grew slippery with blood. She scooped out the innards, taking care not to burst the bile pouch that could tinge the fish with its bitterness. The crow calls grew more urgent. Sometimes I saw Dolly'r Ma push some of the innards and a piece of fish under her sari. She would look sidelong with a pleading smile, silently begging my complicity. Mostly, one of my aunts would stand watching her all through the cutting.

My mother, being the newest bride and wife to the youngest son, was not trusted to cook in the ultimate real kitchen. 'What do they cook in your part of the world, anyway? Just potatoes and roti,' my middle-aunt Shanti would remark. For Calcutta Bengalis, my mother was 'as bad as a Bihari' for having lived all her life in Rajasthan. She was thought just about good enough to cut the day's vegetables. Every morning, she sat on the floor surrounded by brinjals, potatoes and greens bulging out of hessian bags. She placed two basins of water by her side and began with the potatoes, holding each carefully against the blade of the *bonti*, guarded against the day she sliced off a bit of her finger with the peel. She was twenty-six. In the humid, gossip-laden confines of the kitchen the melancholy wail of peacocks played nonsensically in her mind, Byron and Swinburne still faintly audible in the distance in lecture notes and *Palgrave's Golden Treasury*. In Jaipur, now, she would wear her best chiffon sari, put a fragrant *champa* in her hair and go off to teach in her school. She would pool money with her friends and sigh in a cinema over the glint in Gregory Peck's eyes. Surrounded by damp vegetables, she fed on images.

At times when Shanti was away, my widowed aunt Parvati, the unacknowledged chef among sous-chefs, taught my mother to slice potatoes into fine sticks quicker than anyone's eye could follow her hands. And for the banana flower she would coat her hands with oil so its black ooze slid off under hot water. She would do most of the cooking as my mother watched. Even now, when my mother shows me how to make *maacher jhaal* the way my father's family ate it, she explains, 'Your aunt said, let it cook at a rolling boil, only then will the true flavour of the fish burst out.' I never saw my aunt eat the fish curries she made. That didn't make me pause. What did intrigue me though was a practical point. How did she cook what she must have forgotten the taste of? She made egg and mince-stuffed cutlets, prawnmalai, hilsa, and waited looking at us until we took a mouthful and told her how it had turned out. Her own cutlets were made of boiled beetroot, as close as she ever got to the colour red. She was even forbidden anything with onion or garlic in it. She had to ensure she didn't eat food that made her feel over-energetic. Lust lurked not far behind garlic. Starved of the delights, she cooked for us. I wonder now about the memories on which she fed to sustain her spartan frame. My aunt's skin had become translucent by her fifties. She had always been spare and hollow-cheeked, now her body began to cave inward. Crumpled map-paper covered the knotted green veins that went up and down her emaciated arms. There were many women like her among our extended family. They would sometimes sit down together, to their special food, after all of us had eaten and gone. Their chuckles and gossip would drift disjointedly for hours into our restless, sultry afternoon naps in darkened rooms.

Every week my aunt seemed to be fasting, so she ate even less. Each fast had a different set of rules. I envied her diet then. She might eat just fruit the whole day. Since rice was always forbidden on fasting days, sometimes she would eat *loochis*, which she would fry for herself after everyone had eaten. With the *loochi* there would be a simple potato, stirred around in oil. She could make even the staider among vegetables aspire to uncomplicated glory. She would cube the potatoes small, and sauté them lightly in mustard oil to which a red chilli and a mix of whole spices had been added. Then, it was covered and cooked, with green chillies and salt. My own food, whatever it had been, could not compare. Some fasts called for leftovers from the day before, everything cold and stale. At such times I never sat around while she ate, begging a share. For someone who consumed so little, my aunt's existence depended upon the production of food. The more long-winded the recipe, the more she seemed to relish it. She would grind soaked lentils and add spices to them, usually asafoetida and aniseed. Then, she'd carry the mixture to the terrace and climb precariously up to the water tank in her billowing, starchy sari, making the sturdy cement tank look as if it was a ship about to embark with its improbable sail. She would spread a torn piece of an old muslin sari, as thin as the skin of milk with all the washing it had gone through, and place balls of the ground stuff on it. The sari, weighed down by pickle bottles maturing in the sun, would remain there for a couple of days, until the *boris* were little stones, ready for frying.

On winter afternoons, she would make pickle out of a wild plum that looked like a cherry. This is a fruit we called *kul*; in north India it's called *ber*. There are many kinds of *kul*, but this kind, the most delectable, has almost vanished from big city markets. It was small, deep orange, and sweet and sour all at once. The pickle was a gooey mixture of mustard oil, mollasses, a five-spice mixture, asafoetida and chilli. It would mature gently taking in the lemony colour and warmth of the winter sun until it was just right.

In the dark leafy back garden that encircled the kitchen courtyard were neem, guava and *bel* trees. There was also an *amra* tree, another fruit that hung in the cusp of town and country— it hasn't survived big cities and branded fruit—a green, sour fruit, with crisp white flesh that encloses a thorny seed. It could be made into chutneys but was tastiest raw, dipped in rock salt and chilli. *Amra* and *kul*-scented afternoons were the domain of women and children. In *Pather Panchali*, young Durga and her little brother Apu steal a bit of mustard oil and salt from their mother's scanty supplies to make themselves a raw mango chutney, out of mangoes stolen from a neighbour's orchard. The episode has all the thrill and danger of a bank robbery. Mid-afternoon licks of *amra* and *kul* always had that tinge of the illicit, a guilty union of self-indulgence between adult and child, whether the fruits were stolen or not.

Amra and *kul* united us with our mothers; *bel* was the enemy. It takes adulthood to enjoy the odd flavour of this hard-skinned gourd. My mother didn't seem to like it either, and, fortunately for us, paid scant attention to its digestive properties. My aunt would urge glasses of its sherbet on us, it'll cool your stomachs down in this heat, she would say. She would scoop out the messy orange pulp of the *bel* and press it through a sieve, then stir sugar and water and a little lemon into it. It would be kept covered and ready to be drunk in the evening, to take the dust and weariness off bus rides from school and workplaces. Like papaya, the bel has an unmistakeable memory of vomit in its smell. You have to grow into it. Just as there is one mysterious moment when youth flies out of the window and Danish Blue stops smelling of death in sweaty socks, so too there comes a time when *bel* starts smelling sweet and cool.

Once in a while my aunt would pack up some of the food she had made, and go to her brother's house to spend the day. This was her only outing, other than her yearly visit to the Durga Puja pandal nearby or to a family ceremony. She took us along, my brother and me, sometimes. We walked to the end of the road and took a tram to the Kalighat tram depot. Kalighat depot was like a small magical train station in the middle of a city street, with narrow tracks snaking in and out, empty trams clanging up and down. Here, we waited impatiently for the sweet-seller, whose tantalising cry we could hear in the distance: *'Logensh, chaatny logensh, nebu logensh . . .'* Would he come to us? Would the tram leave before he made it to our seats? When he came, the man had a large glass jar out of which he scooped sweets with a teaspoon, and deftly packed them in a twist of newspaper. We ignored the lime and orange lozenges, saving the ten-paise coins my aunt had handed out for the chutney ones, black, sour and sweet all at once. We were then ready for the tram to go.

When we reached the alleyway where my aunt had lived as a girl, she would show us a lamp post. 'What happened here?' we'd ask, though we already knew. 'My cousin was tied to this pole,' my aunt said, 'and the Muslims put a knife into his stomach and took out his intestines.' She would say this without any agitation. I thought of fish. We looked hard and hopefully at the pole for signs of blood, but there were none. Instead it had a hammer-and-sickle-painted poster on it saying 'Brigade chalo'. 'Many people got killed, the drains were running red with blood,' she went on as we walked up the alley to the house. I thought of fish. And then, 'Now don't be greedy here, alright? What I've cooked is for them, not us.' At home, when we sat down on the red floor to eat, everyone got served the same food. The meal reflected the law of averages: nothing was cooked that could not be afforded by all. But Shanti came from an affluent family. At times I would notice her slide extra bowls across to her son and her husband. Usually it was something covetable, like lobster or crab, and we would try to look away. One afternoon, as I pretended to nap, I overheard my parents arguing. 'I've had enough,' my mother was saying, 'I won't sit there and watch that boy getting fed what our children can't have.' My father sagely and sleepily said it didn't matter. It would teach us the value of good food and the ways of the world. 'There's no need for them to learn so soon,' said my mother.

These rumblings went on a few weeks. I don't know what extra bowl of food finally prompted it, but I heard some raised voices in the ground floor one day. After this, meals were cooked in three separate kitchens. My mother's domain, as the juniormost, now became the impromptu food room upstairs, with a kerosene stove. She cooked her rebellion on a high flame: she began adding onion and garlic even to vegetables. Strains of Rajasthan and *Mrs Beeton's Cookbook* entered our now unpredictable meals. Sometimes, we would get an omelette, sometimes *sattu* with yogurt.

My aunts divided up the real kitchen. Refrigerators and cooking gas were around the corner, the days of communal meals were over.

No one in Calcutta would know where our house is any longer. Its wrought iron grills must be part of some fake antique villa, its venetian shutters pulped to plywood. Termite tunnels had consumed the walls. It was scorched sooty by the wet sea wind and the heat, an aubergine ready to be crumbled by the property-hungry. Only its floor had remained untouched by time and our indigence, shining redder and cooler than watermelon juice.

Charms of Life

Some tastes of childhood you never forget. I remember the taste of early morning chapattis with tea. The chapattis would be prepared in a corner of the old dining table itself, the tablecloth carefully folded back. Then, hot from the tava, Polson's butter would be applied on them, and a sprinkle of sugar. Then folded in a messy roll, the hot melting butter streaming out, I would dip it in tea and eat.

It is a taste I regularly try to recall; sometimes it works, most of the time it does not.

Chapattis are no longer made at home, forget on the dining table. I get them sometimes from restaurants where I may have been eating the night before. Sometimes from the houses of friends, where I may have been invited for dinner, and to whom I tell shamelessly that in the night, as also in the afternoon, I eat rice, chapattis I eat only in the morning with tea. So they pack some and give me. Sometimes, in Gujarati houses, they give me chapattis with methi inside. That is also a childhood taste.

I do not warm them in the mornings. I have learnt that through experience, because if you warm them, they become crisp like

This article is taken from *Busybee: The Best of Thirty-six Years*, published by Penguin Books India, New Delhi, 2002.

papads. And I eat them with Amul butter, which is not the same thing as Polson, nowhere near it. Amul has its own place; it is meant for pau bhaji (or my friend, Captain Dandekar, of the Cannon Pau Bhaji Stall at VT) and chicken makhanwalla (murg makhanwalla).

I also remember, though this was between childhood and adulthood, eating brun-maska (or bun-maska) and tea at various Irani restaurants—the Byculla Restaurant and Bakery, the Regal Restaurant, also at Byculla, the Stadium Restaurant at Churchgate.

The brun would be crisp and hard; you dipped it in the tea to soften it. Normally, I would finish one cup of tea in the brun only, then order another cup to drink. And the bun would have raisins in it. I do not know if the Byculla Bakery still does it; their buns would have biscuit crosses on top, like hot-cross buns.

For that matter, the loaves of bread used to have tiny biscuits on them, which is another childhood taste; we would be given one little biscuit per child to eat.

These days, most people prefer to eat pre-sliced and packaged breads, indigestible and lacking the aroma and taste of bread. I still prefer the *ladi*, the small loaves of bread, warm and soft to the touch, made by my friend, Zend M. Zend, of Yazdani Bakery in Cowasji Patel Street.

But teatime has lost its charms, without chapattis, without methi rotis, without Polson butter, without authentic breads. I have to wait till the late evening, when a bottle of Scotch is opened among friends, for some charm to return to life.

6 November 1986

Initiation

The kitchen was long and narrow with one large window at the end. The view outside was exactly the same as from the bedrooms. The electric stove was ringed with dark brown grease that glowed in the yellow light from a bulb suspended above it. Next to the stove was a sink filled with dirty dishes in grey oily water. I moved quickly towards the window. Beneath it, there was an oasis of order. On a little wooden table painted yellow, there stood three bowls of vegetables—purple brinjals, red tomatoes and creamy yellow potatoes.

Amma was already sitting there, peeling and slicing vast quantities of potatoes. I sat down beside her and began to peel them too. They were slippery and twice the knife slipped out of my hands. I realized that the potato was not the benign vegetable I had imagined it to be. It gave off a white milky liquid as you cut it which gradually ate into your hands. After a while my hands began to burn and tremble. I turned to Amma. 'I can't peel anymore. My hands hurt.' She looked at me uncomprehendingly. I held out my hands so she could see how red they were. Slowly understanding dawned on her face. She began to laugh. 'Your hands hurt after just eight potatoes. Oh maa, how will you look

This extract is taken from *Smell*, published by Viking, New Delhi, 1999.

after a family? At your age I was already a mother.'

I stared at her mottled face in disgust. Suddenly it was no longer the face of a person, but that of a senseless fate. 'My mother taught me to read, not cook,' I snapped. But this made her laugh even harder. 'Well, you won't have much use for that here,' she said, wiping tears from her eyes.

After that we worked in silence. Amma sliced potatoes faster than I could peel them, and while she waited for me to finish, she sang old film songs. When I handed her a potato, the singing would stop for a while. Then it would begin again. My fingers burned, my wrists and neck began to ache, and my peeling got slower and slower.

Finally, Amma took over the rest of the potatoes, and let me go wash my hands.

The sink smelled of rotten food and stale spices. Little mustard yellow and saffron globules of oil floated on the surface of the water. I averted my eyes and turned on the tap. The water gushed out and hit the dirty dishwater with a slap, causing some of it to splash onto my chest and face.

'Amma,' I burst out, 'these are yesterday's dishes, are they not?' She didn't reply. 'Why haven't you cleaned them?'

'I'm an old woman,' she replied sulkily. 'My fingers hurt in cold water.'

'But you could empty the sink and fill it with hot water,' I pointed out.

She gave me a look full of resentment, and muttered something in a language I couldn't understand.

'What did you say?' I asked in Gujarati.

'I said do it yourself,' she replied. 'You ate my food last night. So now you can help with the washing.'

I tried a last desperate tactic. 'I don't know how to wash dishes.'

'Anyone can wash dishes,' she scoffed. 'Come hurry up and do it. Since you can't even chop potatoes, I'll finish them and the

onions while you do the dishes. Then we'll do some cooking.'
She gave me a sly smile, 'Be quick, or else your Aunty Latha will
be angry.'

I knew I had lost. Reluctantly I went over to the sink and
taking a deep breath, plunged my hands into the filthy water.
Lumps of half-dissolved food brushed against my hands and
disintegrated. The stench was horrible—the water had embalmed
all of last night's flavours, but now they were rank and disordered,
fighting with each other to stay alive. I felt my gorge rise.

The dishes were slippery. I pulled one out to get a better look.
It was encrusted with congealed fat. As the hot water warmed the
sludge in the sink, the fat began to melt. Soon my arms were
covered in a patina of red-brown fat right up to my elbows.
Embedded in the grease, the smell entered my traitorous pores
with ease. Suddenly I remembered the old perfume from Zanzibar
that my grandfather had given me when I was ten. It had smelt of
wild roses and honey, with a touch of musk, and had come
embedded in a pot of grease.

Taking refuge in the memory, I washed the dishes as fast as I
could. I let the water out of the sink, scooped out the sodden
unrecognizable remains of the food and scrubbed the sink
vigorously with detergent, ignoring the pain as the chemicals ate
into my chafed fingers. I felt soiled and longed for a bath, but my
aunt stood blocking the kitchen door.

'I'll just go and wash. I've been washing last night's dishes.' I
looked pointedly at Amma.

My aunt ignored my remark. 'I'm glad you're making yourself
useful. Before one knows how to cook, one must know how to
clean.' She looked at Amma, and the two women exchanged a
smile.

I saw the smile and felt anger flare within me. 'Excuse me,
Aunty,' I said as coldly as I could, 'I need to take a bath.'

She didn't budge. 'You can do that later, when you have finished.
Now I will show you how to cook.'

'But I smell,' I stared at her rebelliously.

'No matter,' she replied.

Amma had finished cutting the vegetables. They were sitting on the table beneath the window sill. Aunty Latha pulled out a white ceramic bowl covered with a piece of gauze from the fridge. 'The first thing you must learn is to prepare the spices. You can either crush them into a fine paste, or you can fry them whole. If you crush them, then there is no problem; you can use them any way you like.' She pulled aside the cloth, and looked inside. 'Or else you can fry the spices in oil first and let the heat free the smell.' She handed me the bowl and reached into the cupboard. I looked into the bowl. There were finely chopped pieces of ginger and whole tear-shaped cloves of garlic, already peeled. The bowl almost fell from my suddenly nerveless fingers.

'Aunty Latha, you . . . you eat garlic?' I asked her tentatively, still unable to believe that what I was holding was in fact garlic. Her back stiffened and she turned around, 'In cold countries you need all the garlic you can get to keep you warm. At least we cook it. These barbarians,' she looked out of the window, 'eat it raw.' She pushed the bowl into my stomach. 'Now you crush,' she ordered, and turned her back to me once more.

I didn't have the courage to argue. Everything was different. My life had changed so fast: what did it matter if my aunt, or I for that matter, ate garlic? I remembered my father telling me about how food was divided into three types—*satvik* which encouraged detachment and contemplation, *rajasik* which promoted vigour and action, and *tamasik* which generated heat or passion. Passion was what was most to be feared because it gave birth to anger and lust, which destroyed families. Garlic, my father used to tell us, was the epitome of *tamas*. That was why he, like other Gujaratis, wouldn't let us eat it. But suddenly I felt free of his disapproval. My father was dead. I had no family now. So of course I could eat garlic!

I looked around the kitchen for an implement to crush with. Not finding anything I settled for the handle of a large heavy knife. '*Aiee*,' Amma screamed when she saw what I was doing. 'You stupid girl,' said my aunt. 'Amma, show her where the mortar stone is.' Amma went over to the large cupboard built into the wall, rummaged in a corner piled high with plastic bags, and pulled out a large stone with a bowl-shaped hollow in the centre. Inside this hollow was a heavy pestle of the same stone. She grabbed the bowl of spices from my hands and threw some into the hollow. Then she took the pestle and using the heavy end, began to pound away at the spices. In less than a minute the room was filled with the hot heavy odour of garlic and ginger, a velvet blanket that coated my senses, making my body feel heavy and languorous. I watched Amma's body quiver as she pounded on the stone. I wanted to do it myself, to feel the rhythm of the pestle in my hands beating into that smooth hollow, liberating the pungent essence of the ginger and garlic. In a daze, I took the stone from her and began pounding myself. The smell of the paste made me feel hungry and satisfied at the same time.

In the kitchen my aunt was a different person. Her movements were crisp, filled with sudden energy. I watched mesmerized as her hands opened like flowers and closed around the onions, nor letting a single morsel drop in the process. She sniffed at the paste I handed her and shook her head. 'Not enough salt,' she said. Without looking up, she stretched her arm above her head. Her fingers closed around a plastic jar of salt. She took out a pinch between two huge fingers and sprinkled it over the paste. Then she added some green chillies and sesame seeds. She took the pestle and ground the spices a little more, no longer pounding away at them but moving the pestle around gently in the hollow. Subtly the smell of the spices sharpened and became tinged with a hint of lemon. Aunty Latha began to speak as she worked away at the spices, 'You know, Leela, each spice has a special smell. The challenge is to marry the spices together. As in life, some marriages last well—like your uncle's and mine. We are matched nicely. Other couples are not so lucky. My sister has got a horrible husband. He never listens to what she says.' She smiled, looking suddenly coy, 'Not like my Krishenbhai at all, her husband.' She shrugged her shoulders and her flesh rippled.

On the stove, the oil was hot. Aunty Latha walked over to it quickly and threw in the onions and the paste. The smell exploded into the air. I fell back against the little table by the window. My aunt, meanwhile, was peering into the pan, stirring vigorously. Her double chin was lit up from below by the blue-yellow flames. 'Come here, Leela, and stir this,' she called.

I went over to the stove and grasped the flat spoon-like implement she was using. 'Keep turning the onions till they become transparent,' she commanded and swam away to the other side of the room. I peered into the mist that arose from the pan. The steam wet my face like a warm kiss. I moved the little white cubes around gently in the frying pan. Suddenly a new odour hit me, completely different, an ugly death smell. I jumped away from the stove, as if I had been slapped in the face. The spoon slipped out of my hands and clattered to the floor. Within half a second my aunt had crossed the six feet of space between us and was upon me. 'What is the matter?' she asked. 'What happened? Did the oil burn you?'

'No. No it's . . . it's just the smell, that's all. I was surprised.' I felt a fool even before the words were out. Quickly I shut my mouth and looked nervously up into my aunt's face.

But instead of being angry, she smiled, genuinely amused this time. The smile transformed her face. 'I see now that your mother never did teach you to cook. I thought you were lying.' She grabbed another spoon and began to stir the onions vigorously. They had stopped making their hissing noise and were slowly turning brown. 'But no matter. Your instinct was right—listen to the smell, it will tell you things,' she said, stirring away. 'Onions give off smell with water. That is what stings the eyes and makes them cry. So we fry them to get rid of the water.' She paused and looked at me.

'To begin with, the onions fight back. They hold on to their water, afraid to die. They sing a song, they shout at you and curse you. And they give a terrible smell. Then the fire and the oil have their way and the onions give up. The smell leaves the onions like a dying breath leaves the body, and enters the rest of the food.' She paused dramatically, 'The onion's smell is the smell of dying.' I stared at her in surprise. Aunty Latha's face had become soft and her eyes glistened in the afterglow of her smile. 'You will be a good cook, my child,' she said . . .

By six in the evening, we were finished. Five types of vegetables, two kinds of dal, three meat and chicken dishes, rice, papads and puris sat upon the little table by the window waiting to be eaten. Three types of sweets were unpacked and placed there as well. If last evening's meal had been rich, I thought wryly, this was three times as sumptuous. The house was afloat in the smells of almond, fried meat, pineapple raita and other delights. My cooking-sensitized nostrils felt buffeted by the hordes of new and rich smells. 'That is good,' said Aunty Latha finally as she surveyed our work. 'Now go, bathe and get ready quickly. The Ramdhunes will be arriving at any moment.'

Ruchir Joshi

Shrikhand

It was damn funny ya. Unlike yours it wasn't . . . urrr . . . imported, it was . . . what do these BJP buggers call it? . . . yeah, it was fuckin' swadeshi . . . home-made. . . indigenous technology.

I didn't tell you then but you know after I broke up with Priya? Remember Sherman apartments and Zeenie? Well, the hell with Zeenie aunty, but do you remember me telling you about Sandhya? Sandy Agarkar the deadly Ghaatan? Remember I told you she really liked you but you were useless because you went back to Cal so, like, she and me did it? Well, what I didn't tell you was that she also went down on me the night before I left for Penn State.

Unh-huh.

Arre don't get like that ya Paresh, it was just a blow-job, okay? Like what ya?

I know I got what should have been yours, but wait, listen to this and you won't feel so bad.

I don't feel bad yaar, Patel, this was almost twenty years ago, right?

Right, but I can also see your face now, bugger. Anyway, so we

This extract is taken from *The Last Jet-Engine Laugh*, published by HarperCollins *Publishers* Limited, London, 2001.

did everything, and we went all the way and all that . . . BUT. She wouldn't give me head. I'd ask, she'd come close, but no cigar. You know, just at the last moment, HORNY Ghaatan as only Ghaatans can be, but no mouth, she'd pull out.

So? How did you do it?

Patience, man. So like, I thought. Now you have to understand that Sandy was a sporting type and she believed in honour on the field. And also, if she bet you something and she lost, she would deliver, come hell or high water. Honourable that way too. Once we bet on a Davis Cup match and she lost and the bet was she would get me the keys to Hiranandani's Porsche for a night. And she did. She made her maid servant sleep with Hiranandani's darwaan and one weekend, when Hiru was in Singapore, yeah?, she got the fucking keys one night, middle of my exams, but a deal is a deal, yeah?, so we wailed on that sucker 911 all over town before parking it back. So that way she was solid.

So I made a plan. Anyway she was getting a bit senti about my leaving, otherwise she'd never have bet head, but I sort of worked her into it.

How many days' work went into this?

Well if you put a proper time-motion analysis on it . . . I guess . . . well, you would have to say from beginning to end about twenty working days, total.

Ei, Viral? When was the last time you spent twenty whole days on a project?

Last year, setting up the finance for a machine-tools plant in Canton, but do you want to hear this story or not? So then, maybe shut up? This is what I did. Willingdon squash ladder, okay? This guy Abhay Mathur, who for three years had been killing everyone that came near him—inside Willingdon Club or out—later he once stretched Jehangir Khan, really, nearly beat him in a tournament in Leeds, he was that good. So this Mathur was at the top of the ladder. And there was this mad chap, mad Assamese bugger called Bora, Bidyut Bora, we used to call him Bidiot

Bore-a, who thought he was better than Mathur even though Mathur had, like, pulverized him three times. I mean Bora was on 4 or something on the ladder but after Mathur he was probably the best in the club. He had this kind of mad energy, yeah?, like he would as soon kill you as smash an unreturnable cross-court backhand. And he could nick that ball from absolutely anywhere, which Mathur could also.

Now Bidiot was in good form that time and seething to take on Mathur yet again. And Mathur being this quiet imperious type, would play it by the book. You had to be within two numbers to challenge, like if you were 5 you could challenge 4 or 3, but not 2?, unless 2 sportingly agreed to give you a match. And Mathur, though he wasn't chicken, was in no hurry to give Bora his chance, so like every time Bora would ask, he would refuse politely. So, fingers crossed, I waited for Bora to take out Shambhu, who was on 3, which Bora obligingly did.

First thing I did was to take the jubilating dumbfuck aside and convince him that he should wait before challenging Mathur. Make him nervous, I said, let him wait, like, like I'll tell you when to challenge Mathur? At first Bore-a kept asking, 'But vhy yaa Vidal? I can beat him now,' but finally he scratched his head and said, 'Okay yaa Vidal, I'll do dat.' Dumbfuck, brand manager in ITC now, bloody fags sell themselves and he takes the credit, fucking complete moron.

So soon after that, one day when Sandy and I were knocking about on the courts, I casually said I thought Bora was getting better than Mathur. Sandy screamed with laughter. I stayed serious and then pretended to get angry. Then I blurted out the bet, not like I had planned it but like I had just thought of it? In my fury? You know, like—fine baby, why don't you put your money where your mouth is—what I should have said was mouth where your mouth is—if Bora beats Mathur what will you give me? Oh, anything you want Viri, anything at all. Anything ya? Ya. Okay, so fine, you will suck my cock till I come, is that okay with you?

That'll be the day asshole, but yeah. Sure. Okay. Bet. And boy she was deep in it.

You bastard.

Yup, that's me . . . uh . . . let me correct that Paresh—point of order—I'm a byaastrurrd, not a bawstud? But anyway, so next I started working on Mr Abhay tight-ass Mathur. Playing with him everyday, giving him psych-advice, telling him how great he was but not overdoing it, you know?, just halka. Then, one day I just let drop that he should make his point with this idiot Bidiot. It was getting annoying, some fucking chink-eyed semi-tribal thinking he could beat Abhay Mathur and going about saying it to all the chicks. 'I'll kill him ya,' says Mathur. 'What's the big deal in that, Abhay? You've done it thrice already. So this time you whip him 9–0, 9–0, 9–0 and you know what? He'll come back next week and challenge you again—bloody dhiint that he is.' 'So what should I do?' 'Make your point,' I say. 'How?' says tight-ass. I scratch my head, I pretend to think about it, I make a few sounds like I'm rejecting stupid ideas—nothing but the best for my dost Abhay—and then I come up with it.

'Why don't you . . . no . . . no . . . too risky . . .' 'What? What? What's too risky?' 'Nahi yaar, you can't take the chance.' 'What? Tell me! Tell me!' So I tell him. 'What if you say to Bora, look Bora I'm getting a bit bored with all your big talk, I'll play you left-handed, and if I beat you, you will shut up and never challenge me again? Gentleman's Word?' Both these clowns were big into Gentleman's Word you see, Bora because his haw-haw dad owned some tea estates and Mathur' cause his dad was some corrupt ex-ICS-IAS on the boards of some feeding Brit companies.

So what did Mathur say?

Oh, Mathur loved it. 'Now *that*, you clever Gujju bastard—bashtudd—is a brilliant idea.' Then I tried to dissuade him, not too hard, halka, like. And the more I tried, the more convinced he became that thrashing Bora left-handed was the thing to do.

And did he? No, obviously not.

Well. He came close, the son-of-a-bitch. Best of five, he lost the first two games, worked it out and won back the third, all left-handed, almost won the fourth but finally Bora just overpowered him, blood-rushed him on deuce, for the crucial two points. I mean, watching that match, I sweated more than the two of them put together.

Then what happened?

Oh. Bora like, gave up squash after that? He was now on top of the ladder and there was nothing in the gentleman's agreement to stop Mathur challenging him back—right-handed this time— and so Bora resigned from the ladder and took a trip back to Dibrugarh. Business Called.

Viral. Fuck the squash. Sandy, what happened with Sandy? . . .

Ah that. Well, that chick was zapped. Couldn't believe it. When I told her she just got into her Fiat and drove from Nepean Sea to Haji Ali at ten thirty at night to see the ladder for herself. Came back with tears in her eyes. Mouth tightly shut, wouldn't let me even kiss her that night.

We kept fucking and all, but finally she gave like . . . when? This was almost a month before I left but there was no agreement on the delivery schedule, so she kept pushing it back, kept pushing it back, till my last night. That morning when her parents are out, she takes me into her room and we do it there for the first time, screw, that is. Damn strange. Till now it was always in some friend's flat or at my place or even in the Fiat, but this time we are in her room? You know those 'Love is . . .' posters? Well they looked damn funny when you are on your back and Sandy is rollercoasting on you, 'Love is . . . giving her the coffee mug the right way 'round', yeah right, she also had one Neil Diamond poster and this litt-tul picture of Vinod Khanna on her bedside table, right next to some heavy American novel she was pretending to read, what was it? Oh yeah, Portnoy's something? Philip Roth? . . . And this was the eighth floor and Ai and Daddy were out but could come back anytime and the maid, same Porsche-wali maid, was guarding the fort, making a lot of noise cleaning up outside, and the sea was making a lot of noise and Sandy, Sandy always made a lot of noise?, and my Jethro Tull tape—

My Jethro Tull tape, thank you.

Yeah, oh yeah, your tape, what was it?

Yeah well, that tape was dragging, but it was great. At the end of it she says like a goodbye, you know? 'I'll miss you Viri but . . . just go and have fun!' You know, that sort of thing? I start to point out that something's owing. She says, 'Don't worry baby, I'll see you before you go . . .' and gets me out of the house just as Mrs Agarkar comes up the lift. 'Hello beta, all packed?' 'Yes aunty, almost done.' 'We will miss you dear, don't forget to leave a little part of you behind for all of us.' 'Yes aunty, I will try.' 'Especially for your mother.' 'Yes aunty.'

So that night, right?

Right, so that night she comes over. The flat's in chaos, packing, checking tickets, passport, visa, shoes, trying on warm clothes on a hot monsoon night, my mom's organized like this huge meal, puris, undhyu, khandvis, patras, shrikhand, you name it. Mom-Dad's friends all there, half the Union Carbide Bombay top brass, all the fucking relatives, friends, people from the building—it's a riot—Viral beta is going to America, right? Jesus God. In the middle of this Sandy walks in, wearing a sari.

Sari? Sandy?

Yeah man, Sandy. In a sari. Pure traditional Ghaati, green and gold silk, probably her mother's, looking total pride of Maharashtra. No tight jeans, no bloody skimpy halter-top, no little t-shirt, no tennis shorts, bloody sari and long-sleeved matching gold-ish blouse. No ponytail, hair open, bindi even. Green eyes wide and innocent, come to see off friend. All the relatives cream, sort of 'Vahu, vahu' in their eyes? I've like forgotten about the bet, I'm trying to get ready for a continent to come and sit on me. But not Sandhya. A bet is a bet. So she waits for her chance and it comes during the aarti. Parents do this like big puja with a long, long aarti. Sandy knows because she's been to a couple before. And everyone knows I can't stand the smell of incense and even though the puja is for the departing scion of Patel family I ain't going anywhere near that stuff till it's over.

So like the puja starts in the drawing room? And Sandy and me are in the kitchen—my mom's kitchen. Food all laid out for, like, a buffet,' cause there are too many people. Sandy goes around picking up different bits of food and tasting them. My mother hated this.

Mine too. Einthoo.

Yeah, makes it einthoo, you know how it is, so I get nervous, and like tell her to, like, stop? Sandy stops and looks at me. Then she takes a spoon and scoops off a good chunk of the lime and chilli pickle. She puts it in her mouth and then she comes and gets down on her knees in front of me.

Yes. Now, Bhatt, no one's ever, you know?, like done this to me before? . . . So, so . . .

No, Viral, oh no.

Oh yes. Aarti going on full force, just a door between us and the crowd, and Sandy pulls it out and takes it . . . like into her mouth? I get hard man, I am hard already, I don't feel anything at first, and she is quick, business-like, job to be done—do it. And cool, Jesus she was cool. Like, like once a strand of her hair gets in the way? So she stops, peels the hair off my dick and just carries on . . . phooph . . . and by now my knees have gone but I'm still standing up somehow. I'm, like, holding on to her shoulders, her gold blouse? And then I come and Sandy does this quick little thing with her lips and takes it all in. And then my mom's voice like right next to the kitchen door, 'Viru-beta! Kyaan chhu beta, aihya-aaaw!' and this girl is up and away. And me, I just shove my dick back into my pants, zip, and turn to grab the door.

Luckily my mom goes away, looking for me in my room. And Sandy's cheeks are all puffed up? Like when you're gargling? So . . . she begins to circle around the kitchen and I don't get it. She stops near the table and takes a quick look at the door, and then she bends over the Shrikand bowl and lets go . . . I say Sandy . . . what the hell—

I'm like gagging, the words don't come out almost, and Sandy coolly says, 'The deal was come in my mouth, no one said anything about swallowing,' and then you know what she does, the bitch? She then takes a serving spoon and mixes it all in. She was always good in the kitchen, Sandy, and Ghaatis you know they also have Shrikand, so by the time she's finished the fucking bowl is nicely decorated again, exactly like it was, you know, like fat white sworls, and the white mixing in the white and the goddam bits of pickle mixing with the little bits of pista and badaam on top . . .

My father had three brothers and four sisters. Of the four sisters Vasundhara, the one just after him, my Vasufoi, was the most beautiful. When Vasufoi was fourteen she was taken to be photographed. This was standard practice in the Bhatt family—all the daughters had their portrait taken just before they got married. 'Beta, we will lose you, but this daughter will always stay with us,' my grandmother used to say when the framed picture arrived from the photographer.

'Those photos would hang there like photos of dead people,' my father told me one time when we were in the darkroom. 'I mean, we knew that Tara was around the corner in Jethabhai Poel, Chandra and Vasu were half a mile away near Dilli Darwaja, much later Mrudula went to Mumbai . . . and they would all come home quite often, but the girls in those photographs were dead.'

Why isn't there a photo of Vasufoi?' I asked once, when I was ten, and received no reply, then I saw the glint of his teeth in the light of the enlarger and realized that my normally stern-faced father was grinning.

The photographer's studio was in Chakli-naka. That day they made Vasu up as if for her wedding, which was still two weeks away. Mahadev was interested in photography and went along with Vasu and Vrajendramama to the studio. The photographer, a portly man with a thin moustache and thick glasses, was called Hirabhai Dave. His speciality was making ordinary Amdavad girls look prettier than they actually were.

When they reached the studio, Hirabhai ignored Vasu completely. He first greeted Vrajendramama effusively as you would an old and valued customer, then next he greeted Mahadev and for a brief moment Mahadev felt like a man. 'Yes yes, photography, interest in photography, very good, it's a very new thing but soon it will rule the world. Good boy. You can watch.'

This was 1932 and photography was already more than a hundred years old but Mahadev was fascinated.

The studio consisted of a front room on the ground floor of an old haveli, the place where business was done. Up a short flight of stairs, two back rooms, one where the photographs were actually taken and then an adjacent little, black, cupboard-like space where they were developed and printed. The framing was done by Khalid Mian at Dilli Darwaja but Khalid Main didn't exist in Hirabhai's explanations to his clients because most of them would have been horrified at the thought of their daughters being touched, even in a photograph, by a Muslim man, old and skilled though he was.

Hirabhai's front room: a desk, a chair, a new fan suspended from the ceiling, moving slowly, circling in wonder as if it had just discovered electricity, as if it was not sure yet of this mysterious thing that set it spinning. The room was lit by a fifty-watt Sylvania bulb poking out of a flower-shaped shade made of smoked white glass. The shade held to the wall by a holder attached to a curving pipe of brass, perky, and, unlike the fan, brightly confident in the knowledge that 'electric' existed and would power it forever.

Under the fan and light was a row of bhagwans and bhagwanesses: Vishnu, Shiv, Brahma, Parvati, Amba, Saraswati, Lakshmi, Ganesh and, punctuating all these, various images, big and small, of Krishna. None of them photographs, all lithographs because they were in colour. Under the gods the photographs, black and white, sample brides, sample bridegrooms, sample patriarchs sitting, surrounded by well-organised peaks of families, flanked by wives standing next to chairs, sons and daughters sitting at feet, older ones standing next to wives. All lit brightly, but also lit by the light of an uneasy self-regard. Flies landing, for some reason, on the photographs, never on the lithographs, glued to the photographs but never on the patriarchs.

Finally, Hirabhai turned to Vasundhara, pushed his spectacles back and looked her up and down. When Hirabhai's head tilted up Mahadev could see two fans turning, one in each eye. When Hirabhai looked down you could see another kind of glint behind the chashmas. Hirabhai held Vasu lightly by the chin and moved her head around as if he was shifting the gears of a small and delicate car. Mahadev began to dislike this man. Hirabhai had a thin and scabrous voice and, though he would never live to hear it, there would be an exact replication of that sound decades later. His voice sounded like the Nambudiripad-6CX colour fax/printer/scanner when its power supply was fluctuating.

'Aah. Dikri, it's your marriage is it?'

Mahadev felt like saying, 'No, looking at you, one would think it is yours,' but he kept quiet. Vasu looked down, saying nothing. The ghumta of the sari hid her face but from the pull of her shoulders Mahadev could see his sister was furious.

'She is a bit thin,' said Hirabhai, turning to Vrajendramama with his diagnosis. 'But I have ways to remedy that, don't worry.' Vasu kept looking at the ground.

Hirabhai led them up the narrow wooden stairs that led to the studio. An assistant was dusting a big painted curtain that stretched across the back wall. It was what Hirabhai called the Mahal Curtain—the painting was of a series of grand arches stretching away in perspective with the light coming in from the left, an odd mix between a Mughal mahal and a Baroque palace.

'Not the Mahal,' said Hirabhai curtly, printer jamming, 'she will drown in that. Pull out the Mona Lisa Akash.'

The assistant stopped his dusting and brought out a little stool from somewhere. He got up on it and with the flourish of a magician yanked away the Mahal. The decorated pillars crumpled sideways as if a soft earthquake had hit. The arches became wavy, revealing briefly the lines of paint of which they were made, and then disappeared.

'Ah,' said Hirabhai.

'Oh,' said Vrajendramama, 'this is new.'

'Yes, only the second time I am using it. I have just ordered it from Poona. It will be a novelty.'

The palace had left behind a voluptuous sky, dawn or evening light, clouds impossibly rounded, gold, pink, yellow, red, with a small, dark brown landscape—some odd relation to a scene near some river in Italy—taking up the bottom third of the painting.

Hirabhai led Vasu to a high stool-like chair in front of the backdrop and sat her down, his hands staying on her shoulders a fraction longer than necessary. Vasu gave an involuntary shiver.

'She must look like she has had fresh air,' Hirabhai rasped as he took the covering off his camera.

The camera was a Thornton Packard, with an 80 mm Zeiss lens. Mahadev's growing dislike for Hirabhai mingled oddly with an emotion that he had never felt before. Looking at the view camera, Mahadev found himself caught between desire for the object and revulsion for its owner.

The box of the camera was crafted from some dark brown wood. The corners were precise. The sides had a straightness that only vilayati things seemed to achieve. The wood had a muted sheen that contrasted beautifully with the gleaming silver of the lens body. The lens itself pulled Mahadev's eyes in, pulled them through the sparkle of the front element into a dark and deeply pleasurable cave. It was a cave from which Mahadev would take many years to emerge.

As if to spite Mahadev's gaze, Hirabhai quickly put a burkha of black cloth over the camera body and then flipped half of the cloth over his own head, joining the hated and the loved under one covering. This caused Mahadev almost physical pain. The half human, half wood, steel and glass thing looked like a mismatch from an English picture puzzle book. Vrajendramama smiled at his niece and nephew, proudly, as if he had just husbanded this strange creature into existence. After a while the creature made a muffled scratching sound.

'Light,' is what Hirabhai had said and the assistant pulled down two huge switches one after the other. Her new bangles jangling, Vasu instinctively put her arm over her eyes because the lights were so bright they hurt. After a pause Hirabhai made the same sound again and the assistant put the lights off. Mahadev and Vasu looked at each other and suddenly found themselves trying to suppress a common, insurgent grin.

Hirabhai emerged from under the cloth and shook his head as if to clear it, then he turned back to his camera and looked it over carefully, almost like a mother checking her child for mosquito bites. He flicked away an imaginary speck of dust from the aperture ring and turned to the assistant, who handed him a sealed plate. Hirabhai took the beige squarish package and immediately brought it to his mouth, his forehead puckering into a frown which pushed down behind his glasses to screw shut his eyes. Getting his teeth into the right position, Hirabhai began to gnaw at the package.

Later, when he began drowning himself in photography books, Mahadev would come across the travel journal of a sales representative of the Forbes Photographic Co. of Manchester:

> Apropos our new half-size plates, we have been instructed
> to take the greatest care against revealing, even inadvertently,
> the substance from which the package seal is made.
>
> Photographers in this country have the habit of using
> their teeth, scissors probably being beyond the grasp of
> most, to tear open the seal before placing the plate in the
> camera. While it may not be a problem for a Mohammedan
> photographer, knowledge of the fact that we find gelatine
> derived from beef to be the most effective sealant for our
> plates may cause more than a mild disturbance amongst
> photographers who are of the Hindoo conviction.
>
> My superior, Mr Downey, was at some pain to remind
> those of us being sent to India that the mutiny of 1857 had
> erupted from just such a 'provocation'—the rumour that
> cartridges supplied to the sepoys, cartridges which they
> were supposed to rip open with their teeth, had been
> sealed with extracts of beef and pork, each respectively
> anathema to the Hindoo and the Muslim.
>
> While the thought of rebellious photographers did not
> keep me from sleeping soundly on the ship (photographers
> the world over being generally less martially inclined than
> soldiers), I do confess to a slight trepidation on my first
> sales visit, which was to the Daruwalla Portrait Studio near
> the Taj Mahal Hotel in the Kolaba area of Bombay.
>
> This trepidation proved unfounded when Mr Daruwalla
> invited me to share a meal that had freshly arrived from his
> wife's kitchen. When I politely enquired what we would
> be eating, the man cheerfully informed me that we were
> about to be served the best beef stew in the city! For Mr
> D., as it turned out, was neither a Hindoo nor a
> Mohammedan but a Parsee . . .

Thinking back on all the gods and goddesses in Hirabhai's front room, Mahadev would feel a gleeful satisfaction because he remembered clearly that the beige packet that Hirabhai dismembered had the legend *Forbes Photographic Co.* printed on it in big bold black letters.

The assistant took the empty packet away while Hirabhai slipped the plate and covering into the camera with the skill of a pickpocket.

Hirabhai turned from the camera and said yet another isolated word: 'Mamra.'

The assistant scurried down the stairs and disappeared. Hirabhai went into a huddle with Vrajendramama and Mahadev could not hear what was being said. Vasu stared into nothing, her imminent capture on film now putting an invisible barrier between her and Mahadev. Mahadev moved closer to the magical camera.

There were words engraved around the ring that went around the lens, magical foreign words, black and neat against the shining steel: *Carl Zeiss, Jena* and then 80 mm, f4.5. On the body of the lens itself were two rings with other numbers, equally neat, equally mysterious, the two rings looking as if they had paused, caught by an outsider in the middle of an arcane, secret, dance. Mahadev's hand moved involuntarily towards the rings.

'Eeaank!' shrieked Hirabhai. 'DON'T touch!'

Mahadev snatched his hand back and moved away.

The assistant thumped up the stairs and came in holding a paper packet. Hirabhai took it and went to Vasu.

'Now beta, listen carefully. These are not to eat, do you understand? Put them in your mouth and keep them there, do you understand? After I finish, you can eat them. Now open your mouth.' Vasu looked at Hirabhai as if he had gone mad, but then she opened her mouth. Hirabhai took the packet and began pouring the puffed rice into Vasu's mouth.

Vasu took in as much as she could and then shook her head but Hirabhai continued.

'A little more dikri, just a little more, those cheeks need to be filled out so you look healthy.'

Vasu's eyes opened wide with the effort not to choke but Hirabhai showed no sign of sympathy. After an impossible amount had gone in, he stopped.

'Now close your mouth,' he said and watched as Vasu complied. He stared at her for a long time, took her by the chin and turned her head a tiny bit. 'Stay exactly like this,' he said, and skipped back to his camera.

The assistant switched on the lights and Vasu shut her eyes.

'Open your eyes, open your eyes,' said Hirabhai.

'Beta, eyes open,' parroted Vrajendramama.

'Okay dikri, now look at the camera as if you are looking at your husband. With love and devotion,' instructed Hirabhai, now standing next to the camera, his body tense as if he was about to pull the trigger of a starting gun for a race.

'Love, beta, devotion,' said Vrajendramama.

'One,' said Hirabhai. 'Two.'

Vasu glanced over at Mahadev, who had his hand clapped on his mouth. Mahadev met Vasu's eyes at the exact moment Hirabhai said, 'THREE!' and yanked the sliding cover off the plate.

I see the picture the moment the barman switches on a light behind the bar. Then he helps me a bit more by switching on a sign advertising the place. 'Braganza's Beach Hut' it says in red letters, and underneath it, in smaller writing, 'Authentik Goan Seafood'. The dim wash of light on Viral's face increases by about half a stop but it is all I need, because in my F3 I have the new Kodak 3200 ASA that I'm testing. I pick up the camera and look through the viewfinder. Viral has now begun ordering beer chasers to the feni and he knocks' back a little glass and then reaches his nose into the beer mug. I wait till he is in mid-swig before asking him a question I already know the answer to.

'So Viral, did you eat the shrikhand?'

A photographer can only do so much to make a great picture. The rest is up to the universe. What I wanted was Viral spewing beer with an unspecified beach behind him. When I finally printed what I got, it was one of the most amazing images of my life. What I got was Viral bending forward, eyes wide and looking at me over the rim of the mug, Patel pupils catching the glint of the lights behind me, the spew from his mouth somehow forming two blurs that bracket his face while leaving the features clear and—and here is where the universe, or god-cheez, comes in—behind him, at the exact moment the shutter opened, a wave hitting a rock on the beach and forming a halo of spray. The spray is slightly darker than the beer, but on the black and white film it's a grey that belongs to the same joint-family of white. In the photograph it looks as if Viral Patel has swallowed the sea and is spewing it out.

Viral shakes his head and flecks of beer fly out of his hair. He chokes and coughs as the laughter fights to find its way back out of his gullet.

'Fuh—fuhk—ffuck no. Fuck no man. Fuck no—you know I don't eat shrikhand.'

I know. I know Viral hasn't touched shrikhand since my seventh birthday party when he was six and a half.

'Noh . . . no . . . but Sandy had to eat it.'

'Hunh? Kem?'

'Kem? Kem, because Mamma Patel offered it to her first. She says, my mom, says to Sandy—Beta, Viral doesn't eat shrikhand so you have to eat it for him. Sandy says no aunty, please, I am not feeling well. Mom says—what, notfeelingwell-notfeelingwell, we are all upset Viru is leaving but still you have to have shrikhand. In our house either the son has it, or a kanyaa has to have it. Sandy says please, no aunty please. Mom says—it will make you feel well, it is shrikhand after all, and none of us will have it until you have it. It's like Sandy's already the daughter-in-law, right? Ghar ni Vahu, right? Mamma Patel vs. young kanyaa Agarkar—it's a no contest and Sandy knows it's like, checkmate. So my mom takes the spoon, scoops up a bit and shoves it into Sandy's mouth. Then one more, because you never have just one spoon of anything in my house. Sandy swallows, oh boy, she swallows fast. I can still remember her face as she tries to keep it down.'

'Kanyaa, huh?' I say, grinning.

'Yeah, and she did look pretty virginal in that sari.'

We both start to laugh. In fact, we both start to do the jet-engine laugh that we'd invented in class 6, when we were eleven. The Bhatt-Patel jet-engine laugh was famous in Calcutta. One of us would start a whine and the other would pick it up and then we'd be flying, making a sort of high-pitched scream punctuated by real guffaws until we lost control and rolled on the ground, finally electrocuted by full laughter. Our enemies used to hate that sound and so did our friends. And teachers and parents it drove completely crazy.

We start well—two grown men trying to reproduce the falsetto taste of childhood. Viral goes high. I go high. We climb, but suddenly the laugh loses power halfway through take-off. The guffawing, which I was king in, is now impossible for me, and Viral chokes every time he tries the whine. Our throats are too brittle, we have swallowed too much life, too much feni, talked many hundred thousand more words since the last jet-engine laugh. Both engines go down for different reasons and both of us peter out into silence.

LINE OF CONTROL

MULK RAJ ANAND

Bread for the Sweeper

A glance in the direction of his sister, and Bakha walked slowly away from the house of God. '*Posh, posh*, sweeper coming,' he suddenly remembered his warning call, as he just avoided touching a barefooted shopkeeper who was running like a holy bull from shop to shop. When he had thus unconsciously passed through the congested iron-monger's bazaar, past a humanity whose panting rush in its varied, rather hybrid clothes, neither English nor Indian, he took for granted, he found himself standing outside an alley which spread like a yawn between a fruit shop and an old perfumer's. Beneath the emptiness in his inside lay suppressed a confusion arising from the overpowering contradictions of his feelings. But outwardly he was calm and unperturbed. He stood still for a moment, to exercise his sense of direction, as he had been walking almost in a coma. 'To the house in this alley for food,' he said to himself and turned into the lane.

A stray dog, thin, flea-bitten and diseased, was relieving itself. Another which was all bones, was licking at some decayed food on a refuse-heap that lay blocking the drain. Right across the passage further up lay a cow. Bakha observed the dirt and filth that

This extract is taken from *Untouchable*, published by Penguin Books India, New Delhi, 2001.

lay about, casually. But the animals seemed to infuriate him. He approached the dogs, and jumping sharply surprised them into making off with a squeak and a squeal. The bovine insensibility of the cow that lay stretched before him was, however, hard to break through. Lest he should be accused of disturbing the holy mother by the rich owners at whose doors she lay stretched, he held it by the horns to protect his legs against its well-known ferocity, and picked his way across. More heaps of rubbish littered all over the small, old brick pavement meant to him only more reminders of his sister's careless performance of her duties that morning. He excused her, however, by thinking of her suffering. Nobody who had been insulted as she had, could be expected to do her work properly. He didn't want to confess that his defence of her was unreasonable, in that she was supposed to have been here before she went to clean the house in the temple. A huge din of coppersmiths hammering and rehammering copper in their irregular little dark shops engulfed him and he walked more comfortably for a while, for the noise was pleasant, even cheering from a distance, and helped to drown his conscience with regard to his sister's negligence. Deeper in the square, however, the 'thak, thak' that issued from the collection of shops became unbearable. He would have rushed into the little sub-alley where he had to go and call for food but that the ablutions of a devout Hindu on the platform of the street well in the middle of the lane offered the prospect of Bakha getting well sprinkled with the holy water that rained off from the well-oiled body, naked save for a loin-cloth. Bakha waited until his holiness had emptied a canful of water on his head and slunk into the empty gulley, where two fat men could hardly pass each other. He felt calmer because it was cool here and the noise of the copper beaters was fainter. But the test of his nerves was yet to come. For being an outcaste he could not insult the sanctity of the house by climbing the stairs to the top floors where the kitchens were, but had to shout and announce his arrival from below.

'Bread for the sweeper, mother. Bread for the sweeper,' he called, standing at the door of the first house. His voice died down to the echo of 'thak, thak, thak', which stole into the alley.

'The sweeper has come for bread, mother! The sweeper has come for the bread,' he shouted a little louder.

But it was of no avail.

He penetrated further into the alley, and standing near a point where the doors of four houses were near each other, he shouted his call: 'Bread for the sweeper, mother; bread for the sweeper.'

Yet no one seemed to hear him on the tops of the houses. He wished it had been the afternoon, because he knew that at that time the housewives were always downstairs sitting in the halls of their houses, or on the drains in the gulley, gossiping or plying the spinning-wheel. But the vision of a number of them squatting in the gulley and wailing with each other's aprons over their heads, or beating their breasts in mourning for the dead, came before his eyes and he felt shy.

'Bread for the sweeper, mother,' he shouted again.

There was no response. His legs were aching. There was a lethargy in his bones, a curious numbness. His mind refused to work. Feeling defeated, he sat down on the wooden platform of a house in the lane. He was tired and disgusted, more tired than disgusted, for he had almost forgotten the cause of his disgust, his experiences of the morning. A sort of sleepiness seemed to steal into his bones. He struggled hard against it by keeping his eyes open. Then he lightly leaned against the hard wood of the huge hall door as a concession to his fatigued limbs. He knew that his place was on the damp brick pavement on the side of the drain which carried water from the filth-pipes of all the houses. But for a while he simply didn't care. Bringing his legs together he crouched into a corner and gave himself up to the soft urgings of the darkness that seemed to envelop him. Before long he had succumbed to sleep.

Unfortunately for his tired body, it was an uneasy half sleep that he enjoyed, the hindrances in the labyrinthine depths of his unconscious weaving strange, weird fantasies and dreams . . .

'*Alakh, alakh*'[1] came a call and awoke him. The dream completely faded out in the glare that the sunshine cast leaning over the tall houses. Bakha knew it was noon and that just at that time every holy man and beggar seeks the doors of the devout for alms which he has earned by the dedication of his person to God. Almost at once he collected himself together, rubbed his eyes and felt: 'I shall soon get bread.' He knew that the housewives sat waiting for the ash-smeared sadhus (ascetics) and did not eat their food before dispensing hospitality to the holy men. 'I shall soon get food,' he thought, and he looked up at the sadhu without getting up. The man was staring down at him. Bakha fell back into the drowsy listlessness of a moment ago.

'*Bhum, bhum, bhole Nath*,'[2] cried the sadhu in the peculiar lingo of sadhuhood, shaking the bangles on his arms, which brought two women rushing to the terraces of their house-tops.

'I am bringing the food, sadhu ji,' shouted the lady at whose doorstep Bakha was at rest. But she stopped short when she saw the sweeper's body knotted up on the wooden platform outside her house.

'You eater of your masters,' she shouted, 'may the vessel of your life never float in the sea of existence! May you perish and die! You have defiled my house! Go! Get up, get up! You eater of your masters! Why didn't you shout if you wanted food? Is this your father's house that you come and rest here?'

Bakha got up as abruptly as the woman's tone had changed from kindness to the holy man to cruelty to him. And rubbing his eyes and trying to shake off the lethargy that lay thick like hot air about him, he apologised.

---

1 An invocation of the ascetics.
2 Idem.

'Forgive me, mother. I shouted for bread, but you were perhaps busy and didn't hear me. I was tired and sat down.'

'But, you eater of your masters! Why did you sit down on my doorstep, if you had to sit down at all? You have defiled my religion! You should have sat there in the gulley! Now I will have to sprinkle holy water all over the house! You spoiler of my salt! Oh, how terrible! You sweepers have lifted your heads to the sky, nowadays! This bad luck on a Tuesday morning too! And after I had been to the temple! . . .' She saw the sadhu waiting and checked her copious flow of remonstrance and abuse. Bakha didn't look up to her but he knew she was dark with anger.

'Be patient, sadhu ji,' her voice came again. 'I shall just go and get you your food. This eater of his masters has even burnt the bread I was baking by detaining me here.' She retreated from her vantage point on the terrace.

Meanwhile the other woman, as quiet as she was heavy, came down the stairs with a handful of rice in one hand and a chapatti in the other. The first she put into the holy man's bag, the second she handed over to Bakha, adding kindly: 'My child, you shouldn't sit on people's doorsteps like this.'

'May you live long and all your family prosper!' said the sadhu as he received the alms. 'Isn't there a little lentil of which you could make the holy man a gift?'

'Yes, sadhu ji,' she said, 'to-morrow, from to-morrow, you shall have lentil! I am busy cooking.' And she rushed upstairs saying she was busy cooking.

The owner of the defiled house came down now, as voluble as she was short of volume. She stared eagle-eyed at Bakha and remonstrated: 'Wah! You have wrought strange work this morning, defiling my home!' Then she turned to the holy man and heaped a steaming hot vegetable curry and a potful of cooked rice onto the sadhu's black skull of a begging-bowl. 'Please accept this,' she said, 'the house is all right; he didn't really pollute it. I wonder if you have a cure for my son's fever which you could bring me.'

'May the gods bless you and your children,' said the holy man. 'I will bring you some herbs in the morning.' And he turned his back after having exacted his dues for looking after the souls of his disciples.

'May you die,' the woman cursed Bakha, thinking she had acquired enough merit by being good to the holy man and wouldn't lose much of it by being unkind to the sweeper. 'What have you done to earn your food to-day, you or your sister? She never cleaned the lane this morning, and you have defiled my home. Come, clean the drain a bit and then you can have this bread. Come, do a bit of work now that you have defiled my home.'

Bakha looked at the lady for a while. Then cowed down by her abuse, he set to work to sweep the gutter with a small broom which, he knew, his sister always hid under the wooden platform where he sat.

'Mother,' shouted a little child from the top of the house, 'I want to go to the lavatory.'

'No, you can't go,' replied the mother, who stood superintending the sweeper's work. 'You can't go upstairs, it will lie there all day. Come here, come downstairs, quick, and go here in the drain. The sweeper will clear it away.'

'No,' insisted the obstinate boy, who felt shy to sit in a public place.

His mother rushed up to fetch him. She had forgotten to give Bakha the bread she had brought for him. On reaching the top of her house she sent her son without the bread, and since she didn't want to undertake another journey down, she called to Bakha while he was in the middle of his job.

'*Vay* Bakhya take this. Here's your bread coming down.' And she flung it at him.

Bakha laid aside the broom and tried hard to be the good cricketer he usually was, but the thin, paper-like pancake floated in the air and fell like a kite on to the brick pavement of the gulley. He picked it up quietly and wrapped it in a duster with the other bread he had received. He was too disgusted to clean the drain after this, especially as the little boy sat relieving himself before him. He threw the little broom aside and made off without saying a thank-you.

'Aren't they a superior lot these days!' exclaimed the lady, disappointed at not receiving a courtesy. 'They are getting more and more uppish.'

'I have finished, mother,' her son shouted.

'Rub yourself on the ground, my child, if there is no one to give you water at the pickle-maker's next door,' she said, and she went back to her kitchen.

SUKETU MEHTA

Black-Collar Workers

The slaughter will continue for three days. Thousands of goats
and cattle have been brought to Madanpura, in central Bombay,
for the Bakri Eid festival. Girish has been invited for the feast by
his good friend and occasional business partner Ishaq, another
young entrepreneur, and Girish and I set out in a taxi. The
streetscape as you approach Madanpura becomes heterogeneous,
kaleidoscopic. A sign just before the overpass at Bombay Central
heralds 'Dr Ganjawala, Anaesthesist'. On the main street of
Madanpura, you see a bone-setter next to a hotel next to a chemist
next to an eatery making kebabs on coals next to Ishaq's STD
booth, where people can make long-distance calls. There are
thousands of small workshops here making blowlamps, belt
buckles, textile machinery parts, and a myriad of small but essential
items that keep Bombay's economy humming. The roads are in
danger of being overwhelmed by the Bihari slums spilling out
over the sidewalks on either side. The back alleys have lots of
mosques, one for each sect. There are boundaries everyone knows
that separate the Muslim and Hindu areas. Before the riots, there
were many Hindus in the Muslim area and vice versa. After 1993,

This extract is taken from *Maximum City: Bombay Lost and Found*,
published by Viking, New Delhi, 2004.

the minority community on each side started selling out and leaving. The segregation is almost complete. 'Mini-Pakistan', people in the city call Madanpura.

Sitting in the rough but air-conditioned office of Ishaq's stove-parts factory, his cousin Shahbuddin, a movie-star-handsome doctor in his twenties, explains to me the meaning of Id-ul-Adha. 'When Allah Mia called on Ibrahim to sacrifice his son, Ibrahim took him to the mountain. He closed his eyes, raised the sword, and when he was ready to bring it down, he saw a goat standing in his son's place. The festival means that you have to sacrifice to god something that is dear to you.'

We go outside.

A young bull is led to an open space in front of the factories. It belongs to a pipe-fitter who is extra-grateful to god this year, for he has narrowly escaped extortion by a gang. They phoned him and then came to his factory, looking for him. He wasn't there then, but the gang told his workers they would shoot him if he didn't pay two lakh. The pipe-fitter called Ishaq. Ishaq and his men waited for the gang, armed with iron rods. But the gangsters didn't show up, and the pipe-fitter bought a bull for twenty thousand rupees and is about to give a public demonstration of his thanks to god.

The children are brought out. 'The children should see,' says Dr Shahbuddin. The animal is toppled to the ground and its head yanked back, its legs tied up. A one-year-old child is placed on the bull, then lifted up again. The imam asks in whose name the sacrifice is to be offered and is given a piece of paper. He reads seven names aloud and says a prayer. Then a man, not a professional butcher, draws a knife across the beast's neck. I am watching from a ladder leading to Ishaq's office, so I have a vantage point as the throat opens up, the blood gushes out, and the suddenly white arteries quiver madly. The animal's body moves involuntarily; the head is jerking, the feet are twitching. 'The meat will keep trembling at home,' one of the men says to another. The muscle movements might continue for over an hour, during which time the meat will be dressed and put on the table, ready to be cooked. On the kitchen counter it may suddenly spasm, especially the outer muscles.

In the broad street behind the factory, the road is sloppy with blood. I see another bullock being dragged by a gang of men. A rope has been put through its nostrils, and they are trying to topple it over. They tie up its front and rear feet and push. The beast goes over, but somehow it struggles and gets up again. With a jerk, the bull is splayed out again. One of the men holds its mouth closed. Another comes up with a foot-long sharpened blade. The spectators crowd around; it is still early on the first day. There are lots of very young children. The bull struggles a bit, there is a deep rumble from the depths of its being, and then the blade is drawn with one swift motion across a vein. A torrent of blood gushes out, they pull its head and body in opposite directions, and the whole neck is open to the street, blood streaming out in bucketfuls, all over the clothes of the professionals. The fresh blood has an unreal colour about it, as if it is paint; it is not the deep red of a few moments later but a light, bright pinkish-red. A bucket of water is brought and splashed into the bull's exposed throat, to keep the blood from clotting. The head and the body struggle separately. They leave it there for a few moments for the blood to drain out, then commence cutting the carcass. When a sac in its stomach is cut, it releases gobs of warm dung, mixing with the blood and the entrails. Next to it, another bull's carcass, its skin cut away, suddenly releases a stream of yellow liquid; fifteen minutes after it has lost its head, the torso is pissing.

As the fur and the skin and the flesh are cut away in layers, the animals' bodies reveal treasures in multiple vivid colours: the brownish-red of the liver; the elegant white and red stripes of the inside of the rib cage; the brown, white and black of the fur; the crystal of the eyes; the pure cream of the intestines, unfurled. I see the marvellous arrangement of the bull's body within and without, the complex cornucopia of its insides, the fine differentiation of the organs, each admirably suited to its purpose. All these had been working in tandem a minute before, and now each part is freed from the yoke of the mind and acts independently, twitching, pissing, growing, hardening. Now they will go their separate ways. After one bull is slaughtered, the children pull at the white fat inside its body; it stretches like an elastic sheet. A man pokes the open eye of the dead animal; its mouth suddenly opens in reflex, showing a line of teeth. The man repeats his gesture; the mouth opens again.

One thing surprises me: Of the thousands of animals, live and dead, in these streets, there is no sound. No bleating of the terrified goats, no bellowing of the cattle. The killing takes place right next to the live beasts; a massive bullock goes on chewing grass while another is brought to its side right next to it. Similarly with the goats. Don't the animals sense something, the stink of slaughter all around them? Aside from a slight trembling that I see in one goat, and a curious silence, there is no reaction. They look, if anything, depressed. One bull allows itself to be brought to its side and lies there waiting for the knife with its eyes open. When the blade is drawn across its throat, it doesn't even struggle.

Grinning children run barefoot through the blood-deep streets holding the freshly cut heads, all the eyes open. There are groups of municipal garbage collectors who take away the waste entrails, the dung-filled stomach sacs. Huge dumps are filled with these carcasses. A man stands inside a municipal garbage container, cutting a big animal's insides, disposing of the remains right inside the container around his feet. Cats and dogs are having a feast on the leftovers. At the corner there are the knife sellers, and a man on a bicycle with a knife-sharpening wheel attached. As he pedals, the wheel spins; as he holds the blade at an angle to the wheel, a stream of sparks flow in one direction.

The Muslims of this area are sensualists. On festival days and weddings, the older folks take a napkin, anoint it with attar, put a pellet of opium on the tip, and stick it inside their ear. Then they can be high all evening. On the streets outside, the children of the Bihari slums, dressed in their best—like one little boy in a brown suit with a black bow tie stitched on—are being given rides in small hand-turned Ferris wheels. Men are playing games on the sidewalk. A ring is tossed over a group of toys and gadgets; if your ring lands and completely encircles, say, a deck of playing cards, the deck is yours. The narrow streets are slippery with blood and shit, the filthiest time of the year in the filthiest part of the city. On the road leading to the factory I notice a dead squashed rat covered with flies. An open manhole reveals huge red cockroaches ringing the tunnel. The animal hides are stacked and put in front of mosques for charity. Men walk about with reddened shirts; they look as if they've been playing Holi.

According to the laws, cattle are supposed to be slaughtered only in the Deonar abattoir. A truckful of policemen looks on as the bulls are slaughtered in front of their eyes. The cattle that I see are all bullocks, though the doctor says, since the cow is cheaper and more delicate, they prefer that meat, and some are smuggled in against the laws and slaughtered here. 'It is against the feelings of the other community,' he says. 'If they find out, in an hour there would be a riot.'

There is none of the usual Western avoidance of the fact of death behind the dressed-up food on the plate; the animal is brought in live, and you see the before and after. You see exactly which part of the animal's insides a cut of meat comes from. You see the beast struggle to stay upright as it's brought down; you see its eyes open wide as the men sit on its body; you see the desperate gasping and trembling of the body after the blood has left it. Before this, I have seen killing only on the Discovery channel. But now here it is: in full view, in the open street, in the broad daylight. When I see my first bull slaughtered I feel sick inside; I want to go and stop it. I have been a vegetarian for some eleven years. But I cannot tear myself away. I climb over a handcart, to get a better view. I look at my blue denim shirt as the man hacks at the bull's carcass with an axe. A bright-red droplet of blood has landed on the blue and stands there, solid. I am afraid to touch it. After a while it turns black, and then it is harmless, just another black speck.

The freshly killed meat is supposed to taste better than the flesh killed in distant countries, many months or years ago. Hunters must get this charge, but it is nothing like this; the rifle confers the privilege of distance. This is the most direct form of hunting, where you plunge the knife straight into the neck of the struggling animal and rip its body apart with your own hands. The men are all eager, happy to participate in the killing and the carving up. The labourers in Ishaq's factory are in a good mood. This is the beginning of a three-day holiday, a holiday in the city, for there isn't enough time to go back to the village. All day long, there is just the killing and the feasting. All the poor will be fed, and fed well, on fresh meat; three-quarters will be distributed to them. The bullock meat is tough, and most of it is made into seekh kebabs and mincemeat. The goat meat is more tender. The chickens in their cages in the market are safe for the next few days.

It is hot, baking hot, and the meat lies in the open streets. After the carcasses are cut, they are left on the street or in the gutters where they have fallen. Then they are dragged over the surface of the road on their way to people's homes or to the Gulf countries, to which a lot of the meat is exported. I don't see a freezer anywhere. By mid-morning a lot of this will be in people's stomachs, the one animal going into the other. In the workshop, I see a man wring out a long tube from a goat's inside; a shower of hard black droplets of dung falls out into a bucket. Then he chops up the edible parts of the goat and throws them in the same bucket, where they mix again with the dung.

There will be feasting for three continuous days. 'In the evening of the third day,' says the doctor, 'we go out to a hotel and eat vegetarian food.'

Inside his factory, Ishaq shows off his pet goat. He is feeding the goat mutton. He laughs. 'It will eat anything.' Its diet over the last year included tea and cigarettes. He has developed feelings for the goat. On the day after tomorrow he will slaughter it.

I see children leading baby goats—kids—through the lanes, petting them, feeding them lettuce leaves. A worker in Ishaq's factory, dressed in white just before he steps into the washing pit to kill a goat whose horns have been painted green, says these animals are lucky, because they are being killed for religion— 'they are happy'—whereas all the others are killed just for food. That's why they aren't making any sounds, he says. He goes into the pit and hacks at the goat's throat, and the blood pours out on his white clothes, making him red all over.

In his village, the doctor says, he has killed goats dear to him. 'It is best to sacrifice a goat that you have raised from infancy, that you have developed love for.' At the moment of sacrifice, he says, the religious sentiment overpowers the reluctance to kill the one you love. 'Not what they do here: buy the animal the day before, that they don't even know, so the only sacrifice is of your money. All this blood you see today—Allah doesn't like that.' They are eating mutton right now, Shahbuddin and Ishaq, dipping chunks of pav into the meat. It is liver. Some people prize the liver, others the heart, others the thick soup that is made of cattle hooves, which is supposed to give strength to the eater; the doctor prefers the muscle of a cow's udder.

Shahbuddin says, 'If animals could speak a human language, then very few would be cut.' He is trying to defend the practice. He believes he has a soft heart, he says, and so these things affect him. But his religion believes that every single thing on earth was created by Allah for the enjoyment of man, and so if animals weren't meant to be slaughtered and eaten, what are they here for? 'If someone can prove to me that animals aren't created for the use of human beings, I'll give it up.' He asks me, 'Some people believe it's okay to kill a chicken but not a goat. Why is that?' I answer that it's because the goat has a greater capacity for pain. But to an ant, responds Shahbuddin, its pain is as great and its life has the same value as that of an elephant. 'But you may ask me why I won't eat meat that's not halal. You may say that the meat is the same; what's the difference if one has a prayer said over it?' He is willing to admit doubt into his belief system. At any rate, he is thinking about the slaughter going on outside, and ever so gently he is addressing my unasked questions.

Mahesh

Kashipur was a small village. The zamindar was even smaller. But he was such a tyrant that tenants were mortally afraid of him.

It was the birthday ceremony of his youngest son. Tarkaratna, the priest, had performed the rituals at the zamindar's house and was returning home at noon. It was the end of Baisakh but not even the shadow of a cloud could be seen in the sky. It was as though the burning sky was raining down fire.

A huge field spread out before the priest. It was rent asunder by the scorching sun and the earth's life-blood oozed out in the form of smoke through the gaping cracks that criss-crossed the field. One felt dizzy as one looked at the serpentine columns of smoke rising to the sky.

Gafoor, the weaver, had his hut at one end of the field. The mud walls had caved in, the courtyard had touched the public street and the family's privacy was at the mercy of the passers-by.

Tarkaratna stood in the shade of a tree and called out, 'Hey, Gafra, are you in there?'

Gafoor's ten-year-old daughter, Amina, came out—'Why are you calling him? He is down with fever.'

This story is taken from *Image and Representation: Stories of Muslim Lives in India*, edited by Mushirul Hasan and M. Asaduddin, published by Oxford University Press India, New Delhi, 1999.

'Fever! Call the bastard. Scoundrel. The mlechcha!' The noise brought Gafoor out, shivering with fever. A bull was tethered to the old acacia tree that stood by the ruined wall. Tarkaratna pointed towards it and said, 'What is this? Don't you know that this is a Hindu village? And the zamindar is a Brahmin?' His face had turned red in anger and the glare of the sun. Such a countenance could only voice harsh and cruel words, but Gafoor simply stared uncomprehendingly at the invectives and rage directed at him.

'I saw it tied there in the morning and it's still there. If the bull dies, the master will bury you alive. He's no ordinary Brahmin!'

'What can I do, Babathakur? I'm down with fever for the last few days and can't take him out to graze in the field. I feel dizzy and fall down.'

'Untie him. He'll graze by himself.'

'How can I do that, Babathakur? People haven't threshed all their crop yet. It is standing in the field. The straw has not yet been gathered. The dikes are burning—not a blade grass on them. If I let him go, he'll stray into someone's harvest or grab the straw of another.'

Tarkaratna seemed somewhat pacified. 'All right, don't untie him. But you can at least tether him somewhere in the shade and give him some straw to munch. Has your daughter cooked rice? Why don't you give him a tub of boiled rice-water?'

Gafoor gave no reply. He looked at Tarkaratna dumbly and heaved a deep sigh.

'Don't you have even that much? What did you do with your share of straw? Sold all of it to fill your stomach? Didn't you keep even one bundle for the bull? The butcher!'

Gafoor became speechless at this unjust accusation. After a few moments he said slowly. 'I got a bit of straw in my share this year, but the master claimed it all as my last year's arrears. I wept, fell at his feet and said, "Sir, you're my lord and master. Where else can I go? Give me a bit of hay. There's no straw in my roof. We—father and daughter—will somehow patch it up with palm leaves and pass this rainy season in one room. But our Mahesh will die if there's no fodder.'"

Tarkaratna was amused: 'Indeed! So you call him Mahesh. What a joke!'

The taunt escaped Gafoor. He continued, 'But the master didn't take pity on me. He gave me rice which lasted barely two months. But all the straw was stacked to his own stock. Mahesh didn't get any.' Gafoor's eyes brimmed over. Tarkaratna remained unmoved by his plight. 'What a strange fellow you are! You owed him money, shouldn't you pay up? Is it the zamindar's duty to feed you while you stay at home doing nothing? You're living in the kingdom of God. You don't realize it and malign the master because you're lowborn.'

Gafoor was ashamed. 'I'm not maligning him. We never do, Babathakur. But tell me how can I pay up? We till about four bighas of land on a share-crop basis. The crop hasn't been good for the past two years, the paddy dried up in the field. My daughter and I couldn't manage even two square meals a day. Look at the hut! When it rains we spend the nights huddled together in a corner—we can't even stretch our legs. Look at Mahesh! All his ribs have come out. Babathakur, please lend me some straw so that he may be fed properly for a few days.' Gafoor fell at the Brahmin's feet. Tarkaratna stepped back quickly as though lightning had struck him. 'Damn you! Are you going to touch me?'

'No, Babathakur. I won't touch you. But do lend me some straw. I saw you have four stacks. If you lend me two bundles, it'll make no difference. We don't care if we die starving. But he's a helpless, dumb creature. He only stares at us and tears trickle down his eyes.'

Tarkaratna said, 'You want to borrow. Tell me how will you pay back?'

Gafoor's hopes were raised. He said eagerly, 'I'll pay back by any means, Babathakur. I won't cheat you.'

Tarkaratna clicked his tongue and mocked Gafoor: 'I won't

cheat you! I'll pay back by any means. Lousy fellow! Keep off. I'm getting late for home.' He smiled to himself and moved forward. But he had to retrace his steps. 'Damn it! He's brandishing his horns. Will he butt me?' He asked angrily.

Gafoor stood up and indicating the bundle of wet rice and fruit in his hand said, 'He can smell that and wants to eat a morsel.'

'Wants to eat? Indeed! Like peasant, like bull. Can't manage hay, but must have rice and banana! Take him away from the street and tie him up somewhere else. What horns! He'll gore someone to death one of these days.' So saying Tarkaratna beat a hasty retreat.

Gafoor turned away from him and stared silently at Mahesh whose deep, black eyes were filled with hunger and pain. 'He didn't give you even a handful. They have so much, yet they don't give even a little. Let them keep it all.' His voice choked and large drops of tears flowed down his cheeks. He came closer, stroked Mahesh's head, throat and back as he muttered, 'Mahesh, you're my son. You've looked after us for the last ten years and now you're old. I can't give you a square meal. But you know very well how much I love you.'

In response Mahesh stretched out his neck and closed his eyes with pleasure. Gafoor rubbed his tears on the back of the bull and said in the same low tone: 'The zamindar snatched away your food. He is greedy enough to auction the pasture that stands beside the burning ghat for money. Tell me how shall I provide for you during this barren year? If I let you loose, you'll eat up other people's paddy or their banana trees. What shall I do with you? You've no strength left in your body—no one wants you. They want me to sell you out in the cattle market . . .' Tears began to roll down his eyes and then he fetched a sheaf of old, discoloured straw from the roof of the broken hut. 'Eat it quickly, my son. If you delay, then . . .' said Gafoor softly, placing it before Mahesh.

'Father . . .'

'What's it, daughter?'

'Come, the food is ready.' Amina came to the doorstep, looked before her for a moment and said, 'Have you again pulled out straw from the roof for Mahesh?'

He had feared this. 'It's old straw—it was falling off anyway,' he said shamefacedly.

'Father, I heard you pulling it out.'

'No daughter, it wasn't exactly . . .'

'But you know that the wall will crumble . . .'

Gafoor was silent. He knew very well that everything was lost except his hut and at this rate it would not last the next rainy season. But what was the way out?

'Wash your hands and come and eat. I've served your food,' said the daughter.

'Bring the rice-water, let me feed him first.'

'There's none of it, father. It dried up in the pot.'

No rice-water even! Gafoor sat there mutely. Even the ten-year-old girl understood that it could not be wasted during those bad days. He washed his hands and went in. Amina had served rice and some leafy vegetables to her father in a brass plate while she ate out of a clay one. Gafoor looked at his plate and said haltingly— 'Amina, I feel feverish. Is it right to eat rice in this condition?'

'But you said that you were very hungry,' Amina said anxiously.

'Probably there was no fever, then.'

Gafoor shook his head, 'The fever will increase if I eat the leftover rice.'

'Then . . .'

Gafoor thought deeply for a while and then seemed to have found a solution to the problem.

'Darling, why don't you give it to Mahesh? Can't you boil a handful of rice for me in the evening?'

Amina stared at her father's face for a while. Then she lowered her head and nodded . . . 'I can, father.'

Gafoor's face brightened up. It seemed as though someone else was watching this little play-acting between the father and the daughter.

A week later. Ailing Gafoor was sitting mournfully in the courtyard. Mahesh had not returned since the day before. As Gafoor was too weak to move, Amina had been looking everywhere for Mahesh since morning. She returned home in the late afternoon.

'Father, can you believe that Manik Ghosh and others have taken Mahesh to the police station!' she said.

'Are you crazy?'

'Yes, father. It's true. His servant said to me—tell your father to look for Mahesh in the pound at Dariapur.'

'What did he do?'

'He strayed into their garden and spoiled the plants.'

Gafoor sat there like a statue. He had imagined many other probable mishaps concerning Mahesh, but not this. Poor and harmless, he had never feared that any of his neighbours could be so revengeful. Least of all Manik Ghosh who was known for his devotion to cows and Brahmins.

The daughter said, 'The sun is about to set, father. Won't you fetch Mahesh?'

'No,' said Gafoor.

'After three days, they said, the police will sell him in the cattle market.'

'Let them.'

Amina had no idea about the cattle market. But she had often noticed how her father would get upset at the mention of the cattle market in connection with Mahesh. But today he just went out of the house slowly without uttering a word.

In the darkness of the night Gafoor came to Banshi's shop. 'Uncle, you'll have to lend me a rupee,' he said, slipping down a brass plate under the seat. Banshi knew well its weight and other properties. Gafoor had pawned this at least five times in the last two years to borrow a rupee each time. Banshi did not object to it that day either.

The next day Mahesh was seen at his usual place—the same acacia tree, rope, pole, grassless manger and the same tearful gaze of blue, eager eyes filled with hunger. An elderly Muslim was examining him closely. Not far from there Gafoor sat silently on the ground, huddled up. After scrutinizing the bull thoroughly, the old man took out a ten rupee note from a knot in his shawl and began to unfold it, stroking it with his hand again and again. Then he took it to Gafoor and said: 'Here you are. I'm not keeping anything from it. Take the whole amount.'

Gafoor stretched out his hand to take the note, but kept sitting without uttering a word. But he stood bolt upright when the two persons accompanying the old man went to take hold of the rope.

'Don't you touch the rope. I warn you!' he growled.

They were stunned. 'Why?' asked the old man.

Gafoor answered angrily, 'He's mine. I won't sell him. That's why'—and he threw away the bank note.

'But you took the advance yesterday,' they chorused.

'Take it back,' he flung the coins at them.

The old man tried to pacify him. 'You're playing this trick to wangle two rupees more, aren't you? Hey, give two rupees to his daughter. Is it all right now'?

'No.'

'No one will pay even half a rupee more, you know.'

'No!' Gafoor shook his head vigorously.

The old man lost his temper—'What do you mean? Only the hide will fetch some money. What else is there?'

'Tauba! Tauba!' Gafoor let out a filthy invective and then ran into his hut. 'Leave the village immediately. Otherwise I'll get you all beaten by the zamindar's men,' he warned them from inside in a shrill voice.

Seeing him in this state the men went away. But soon he was sent for by the zamindar. Gafoor realized that the master had been told about it.

There were quite a few persons sitting there. Shibu Babu, the zamindar, was furious. 'Gafra, I don't know what punishment will be adequate for you. Do you realize where you're living?'

Gafoor said with folded hands, 'We know. We don't have the means. Otherwise I would have paid any penalty you deemed fit.' All were taken aback. They always regarded him as a short-tempered and stubborn fellow. Gafoor continued in a tearful voice, 'I'll never do such a thing again.' Shibu Babu said kindly, 'That's enough, don't behave so crazily again.'

All those present there shuddered as they came to know about the incident. They were convinced that a great disaster had been averted because of the master's piety and strict rule. Tarkaratna was there. He gave a discourse on the religious connotations of the word 'cow' and enlightened everyone as to why these faithless mlechchas were not allowed to stay within the village precincts.

Gafoor did not say a word. He took as his desserts all the abuses and humiliation heaped on him and returned home contentedly. He begged rice-water from neighbours and fed Mahesh. He ran his hand gently over Mahesh's head, horns, and the whole body and whispered words of affection into his ear.

It was the end of Jaishta. The heatwave that began in Baisakh had now become terrible. One look at the sky and one could feel its relentless severity. There was no trace of mercy anywhere. It was difficult to imagine that someday this sky would appear soothing to the eyes again, with transparent clouds pregnant with moisture. It seemed as though the blazing firmament would continue to rain fire on the earth, ceaselessly and pitilessly, till everything had been burnt to a cinder.

Gafoor returned home at noon on such a day. He was not used to working as a day-labourer and it was only four or five days since the fever had left him. Though he still felt weak and exhausted, he went out in the strong sun to look for work that day, but without success. Hunger, thirst, and bodily exhaustion had nearly blinded him. Standing at the courtyard, he called out, 'Amina, dear, is the food ready?'

His daughter came out of the hut and leaned against the wall without a word.

Her silence infuriated Gafoor. 'Is the food ready? No! Why?'

'There's no rice, father.'

'No rice? Why didn't you tell me in the morning?'

'I told you last night.'

'I told you last night,' mimicked Gafoor, contorting his face. 'How could I remember what you told me last night?' He was mad with rage. 'Indeed, there's no rice! What do you care if your sick father eats or not. You must eat five times a day. From now on I'll lock up the rice when I go out. Give me a pot of water— I'm dying of thirst. Now don't tell me there's no water, either!'

Amina stood there with bowed head. When Gafoor realized that there was no water in the hut to quench his thirst, he lost all self-control. He rushed towards her and slapped her fiercely in the face. 'Wretched girl! What do you do all day long? So many people die—why don't you?'

The girl did not say a word. She took up the earthen pitcher and went out in the sun quietly wiping her tears. Gafoor was cut to the quick the moment she went out of sight. He alone knew how he had brought up the motherless child. He knew that it was not the fault of his quiet, affectionate, and dutiful daughter. They could not afford two square meals a day even when the little store of rice lasted. If they ate just once on some days, they could not manage even that much on other days. Not only was it untrue but impossible to eat rice five times during the day. He also knew the reason why there was no water. The two or three water tanks of the village had dried up. The little water that was left in Shibu Babu's private tank was not meant for the public. People had dug up wells at the bottom of some other water tanks, but there was such a rush and scramble there that the little girl could not manage to reach them. She would stand there for hours on end begging and if someone took pity on her and poured a little water into her vessel, she would return home with that. Perhaps that day no one had had the time to take pity on her amidst the scramble. His eyes brimmed over with tears. At this juncture the zamindar's messenger arrived like an angel of death.

'Gafra, are you in?' he yelled out.

'Yes. What's it?' retorted Gafoor in a shrill voice.

'Master has sent for you. Come.'

'I've yet to take my meal. I'll come later.'

The messenger could not bear this insolence. He called him an obscene name and said, 'It's master's order to drag you there, beating you with shoes.' Gafoor lost self-control a second time. He returned similar compliments and said, 'No one is a slave in the Queen's reign. I pay rent to live here, I will not go.'

But in the world it is not only futile for the small to invoke a mighty authority, it can be dangerous as well. The saving grace is that the feeble voice seldom reaches the ear of the mighty—otherwise Gafoor would have lost both his livelihood and his peace of mind. There is no need to describe in detail what happened afterwards. Suffice it to say that when he returned home from the zamindar's court after about an hour and lay down quietly, his limbs were swollen. The chief cause of his misery was Mahesh. After Gafoor had left home in the morning, Mahesh had broken loose from the tether and strayed into the zamindar's garden trampling the flowers. Then he had spoiled the rice left to dry in the sun and when they tried to catch him he had pushed the landlord's youngest daughter and escaped.

It was not the first time that such a thing had happened. But he was usually forgiven in view of his destitution. If he had come in time, fallen at the zamindar's feet as before and begged his forgiveness, he probably would have been forgiven. Instead he had claimed that he paid rent and was no one's slave. Such insolence on the part of a subject was too much for the zamindar Shibu

Babu to bear. Gafoor underwent the punishment and humiliation without protest. He reached home and sat numb and listless. He had forgotten thirst and hunger, but his heart was burning like the scorching sun outside.

Gafoor had no idea how long he spent in that listless state. He was rudely shaken out of his stupor by the piteous shriek of his daughter from the courtyard. As he rushed out of the hut he saw Amina lying prostrate on the ground. The earthen pitcher she had been carrying lay broken and Mahesh was sucking like a desert the water that poured from it. Gafoor went completely out of his mind and seizing the ploughshare that lay close by, he struck Mahesh violently on his bent head.

Mahesh tried to raise his head just once, then suddenly his thin and starved body fell to the ground. A few drops of tears rolled down his eyes while blood glinted from his ears. His whole body shook twice and then, stretching his hind legs as far as they went, Mahesh breathed his last.

Amina burst out weeping—'What have you done, father? Our Mahesh is dead.'

Gafoor neither moved nor answered. He stared unblinkingly at a pair of motionless, deep, black eyes.

The news spread and in two hours the tanners living on the outskirts of the village came charging over. They tied Mahesh to bamboo poles and carried him to the disposal ground. Gafoor shuddered and closed his eyes as he saw the shining knives in their hands, but didn't say anything.

The neighbours told him that the zamindar had sent for Tarkaratna for his advice. He would be compelled to sell his hut to meet the expenses of the penance. Gafoor made no reply but remained there squatting, his chin resting on his knees.

At midnight, Gafoor woke up his daughter and said, 'Amina, let's go.' She had fallen asleep in the yard. She rubbed her eyes as she sat up, 'Where, father?'

'To work at the jute mill at Fulbere,' said Gafoor.

The girl stared at her father in disbelief. Despite their poverty, her father repeatedly declined to go to Fulbere. She had heard him say time and again that there was no religion, no honour and privacy for women there.

Gafoor said, 'Hurry up, daughter. We've a long way to walk.' Amina was going to take the water tumbler and her father's brass plate but Gafoor asked her not to. 'Leave them, my child. They'll pay for the penance of our Mahesh.'

Gafoor set out holding the hand of his daughter in the darkness of the night. He had no one to call his own in the village; he had nothing to say to anyone. As he crossed the courtyard and reached the acacia tree, he stopped dead in his tracks and burst out crying loudly. Lifting his head to the star-studded black sky he said— 'Allah, punish me as much as you like . . . But Mahesh died with his thirst unquenched. They did not leave the tiniest patch of land for him to graze on. Don't forgive the persons who robbed him of the grass and the water that are your gifts to all creatures.'

—*Translated from the Bengali* 'Mahesh' *by M. Asaduddin*

French Leave

It was almost dawn, yet not quite. A gentle breeze blew. Radha could sense the orange and white splendour of the shefali tree and its fragrance from where she lay in bed.

Last night Radha had had no quarrel, no stormy words whatsoever with her husband, mother-in-law or sister-in-law—no argument at all, unlike all the other days which made up her life.

Her body was not abnormally hot, so needless to say she did not have a fever. Nor did she feel unwell or fatigued in any way.

It was not raining outside. The sky was a clear, deep blue.

The weather was neither too warm, nor too cold to bring discomfort. Radha's only son, Sadhan, was perfectly healthy.

Husband and son were still asleep next to her.

Nevertheless, Radha suddenly decided that she would not cook today.

She was absolutely determined not to cook today.

No, she was not going to cook today.

She called the sun and said, 'Rise late today because I want to stay in bed for a long time.'

She did not get a chance to talk to the dark as it had already

---

This story is taken from *The Stream Within: Short Stories by Contemporary Bengali Women,* published by Stree, Kolkata, 1999.

gone before she had made her decision.

So Radha told the birds, 'Please don't stop your morning songs. I want to lie awake in bed and listen to your music.'

She called the clouds and said, 'Help the sun. Hide him in the folds of your flowing sari.'

Looking at the shefali tree she advised, 'Don't drop your flowers upon the earth. Imagine it is still dark.'

She told the dew, 'Form yourself into droplets and gently settle on the grass.'

The sun listened to Radha. He did not rise for a long time.

The clouds spread themselves to cover the clear blue sky.

The birds sang over and over the first songs of the day.

The flowers clung to their stalks and made the shefali tree resplendent.

Dewdrops continually wet the grass and filled it with love.

Radha leisurely turned over in bed and lay there.

Meanwhile there was chaos in the household. All the members had somehow been late in getting up today.

Sadhan forgot his multiplication tables and handwriting; he fidgeted and kept looking outside.

It was time for Radha's husband, Ayan, to be off to the village market.

And her sister-in-law was going to be late for school.

Her mother-in-law had finished her morning prayers and was waiting expectantly for her first meal of the day.

But Radha was still in bed.

For Radha will not cook today.

No, she is not going to cook today.

Radha will not cook today.

'What's wrong? What on earth is the matter?'

'Will you force us all to fast today?'

'What exactly is going on?'

All three, son, mother and daughter, questioned her in the same tone.

Radha couldn't be bothered.

She left her bed and stepped onto the floor at a leisurely pace. Lifting to her hip the pitcher that stood in a corner of the room, Radha made her way to the pond, very slowly.

'Will my son go to work on an empty stomach?'

Radha was silent. Her husband was surprised.

'It's time for me to leave for school, Bouthan.'

Radha was silent. Her sister-in-law was worried and upset.

Radha went and quietly sat on the steps leading down to the pond, dipping her feet in the water.

Behind her the voices were not merely in chorus; they were shouting the house down.

Her mother-in-law had already managed to gather a few neighbours with her loud wailing. Radha remained unmoved. She sat quietly, gazing at the water.

A shoal of small fish—punti, bojuri, khalisha, kajoli—came and swarmed to her feet.

'Oh, please go away. I haven't brought food for any of you today.'

But they somersaulted joyfully around her feet. They were glad to have Radha near them and did not ask for more.

Radha looked up at the sky. The sun smiled meaningfully and asked her. 'Are you angry with me?'

'Why couldn't you have waited a little longer?' Radha asked reproachfully.

'If you take one look at the paddy fields you'll realize why I couldn't wait a minute more.'

Radha looked across the pond to the wilting fields. 'Will they survive?' she asked anxiously.

'If you smile once on them the fields will surely revive.'

Radha stood up. She twirled around, laughing loud and freely, her arms flung out wide.

Radha laughed and laughed and laughed.

The green fields seemed to wake up at once; the crops raised their heads.

Radha suddenly discovered her husband had come and was shaking her shoulders violently.

Radha's mother-in-law was weeping bitterly.

But Radha still went on laughing. She laughed and laughed and laughed. Her laughter trilled and sang.

A gentle breeze blew in rhythm with her laughter.

The water of the pond tripped about in little waves, and broke upon the pond's edges in chuckles.

The birds chirped and chattered in wonderful harmony.

The fish danced in the water and tumbled about, flitting from the surface to the depths and back again.

The flowers made friends with the leaves and tossed their heads in unison.

Radha laughed and laughed and laughed.

Her enraged husband snatched the rice pot and smashed it on the ground leaving for the weekly market on an empty stomach.

Her mother-in-law's curses and wails grew shriller and shriller.

Her frightened sister-in-law crept away to a neighbour's house.

Her son, Sadhan, slowly came and stood near the edge of the pond.

But Radha will not cook.

No, Radha was not going to cook today.

Radha will not cook today.

Radha suddenly felt dizzy. She wanted very badly to vomit but controlled herself.

She quickly sat down. Then she stood up again. Radha was well aware that she was not ill. She has simply felt a sense of giddiness which originates from the most normal physical process in life. So she was not scared.

'Ma, I am hungry.'

The voice seemed to reach her from a distance, 'Ma, I'm very hungry.'

Radha felt something big stir in her heart. Upon the calm sea of her mind, huge waves suddenly reared up in the furious dance of the storm. Holding her son close, she looked with a steady gaze upon the water.

Then she looked up at the sky, at the sun.

Then at the trees, birds, flowers and leaves.

She closely observed her surroundings.

A crow flew by and dropped a small ripe papaya in Radha's lap. She peeled it with both hands and put it into her son's mouth. It could hardly fill Sadhan's stomach.

Radha called a kingfisher and said, 'Go and fetch the largest seed-head from the water lilies in the middle of that pond for my son.'

It was a big seed-head. Enough to feed a hungry mouth. But Radha's son would eat only a little of it.

'Ma, I am very hungry. Won't you cook today?'

Sadhan was four years old. He was absolutely famished. How could he be satisfied with what she had just given him?

'Ma, won't you cook?'

She felt her heart was breaking. Perhaps she would not be able to hold out much longer.

But she still said, 'No.'

Radha will not cook.

No, she was not going to cook today.

Radha will not cook today.

Pressing Sadhan close to her heart, Radha left the pond and went into the orchard. She sat cross-legged on the grass and made her son lie down on her lap. Then she looked all around cautiously. There was no one to be seen. The leaves of the jackfruit and *jamrul* trees rustled in the wind and seemed to encircle Radha gently. She slowly uncovered her breasts. Under the clear sky her firm and well-formed breasts gleamed in the sunlight. Radha put the left nipple into her son's mouth. With her right hand she continually caressed Sadhan's forehead, eyes, head and hair.

Unused to breast-feeding, Sadhan was puzzled for a few moments at this unexpected gesture. Then gradually he began to draw upon his mother's nipple in his mouth with great enthusiasm. First softly, then with a little more force and finally with all his strength Sadhan tried to suck in his best and safest food from his mother's body.

Radha was worried. She waited eagerly for something to happen, but nothing did. What would she do now? Straightening her back and stretching her legs, Radha sat more comfortably. She looked all around. Gritting her teeth, she bit her lips in determination and wished—exercised all her will power. And then it happened that very moment. Like a gurgling waterfall, her body trembling with pleasure, something flowed out of her breasts, brimming over the banks like flood waters.

Radha looked at her son. Sadhan giggled.

Bubbling white milk flowed from his busy lips and dripped on the ground.

Radha laughed. Sadhan laughed too.

Clouds hid the sun. A shalik rested on one leg. A soft breeze blew.

Radha laughed.

Sadhan laughed too.

Radha has decided that she will not cook today.

She is absolutely determined not to cook today.

Radha will not cook today.

—Translated from the Bengali 'Arandhan' by Sarmistha Dutta Gupta

ABDUL BISMILLAH

Guest is God

It was unbearably hot. The blast of hot winds blowing across the city had caused several deaths. The roads were like a tawa on the chulha. The rich had khas screens on their doors. These were kept wet by the servants who splashed them with buckets of water. Shopkeepers had their thick curtains drawn. Barbers, food-vendors, and lottery ticket sellers sought refuge under the overbridge waiting for the sun to set. Some others sat huddled in rickshaws avoiding exposure to the sun. Everyone's handkerchief was dirty because of the constant wiping of sweat. The rural folk wrapped up their faces with thick towels or gamchas—they could be mistaken to be dacoits. Pedestrians without umbrellas held up handbags or handkerchiefs to cover their heads. Vendors hiked the price of drinking water from five to ten paise.

The heatwave disrupted the city's social and economic life. People felt severely constrained yet were helpless. They even carried onions in their pocket to protect themselves from the hot winds. Salman Saheb's wife had also put a small onion in his pocket, though he pretended not to know. He was sure that onions had nothing to do with the looh.

This story is taken from *Image and Representation: Stories of Muslim Lives in India*, edited by Mushirul Hasan and M. Asaduddin, published by Oxford University Press India, New Delhi, 1999.

With a suitcase in his hand, Salman trudged on towards Mishrilal Gupta's house. Though he felt like covering his head or his face with the towel, he could not bring himself to do so. Gupta's house was not all that far. Or so he thought.

This was his first trip to the town. He remembered Gupta's house number but not its location. And yet he hoped to get there.

Mishrilal Gupta was once Salman Saheb's neighbour in their small town. He was known for his radical views—the first in his family to eat meat and drink tea in a Muslim restaurant. The town had separate Hindu and Muslim places to eat, just as there is a Hindu University in Benaras and a Muslim University at Aligarh. Though nobody prevented anyone from eating where he pleased, it was not common to do so in those days. Salman Saheb's neighbour Zaki Saheb would buy sweets from a Muslim shop but not from Shivcharan Halwai. Why? Because Shivcharan did not wash himself after a pee.

The town had one school where Sanskrit was taught. Salman Saheb memorized Ramah-Ramau-Ramaah and the entire gamut of Sanskrit conjugations. The upshot was that he did not read Urdu. Likewise Mishrilal's father Girdharilal Gupta studied Urdu and not Sanskrit. For one, he was a Vaishya. Besides, the madarsa had no provision for learning Sanskrit. So when Salman Saheb moved to the city for higher education, he opted for Sanskrit hoping to secure a teaching position in a college. But this is not how things turned out. He was now teaching history in the newly-opened Islamia Middle School in his hometown.

While preparing for his Intermediate examinations, Mishrilal received lessons in Sanskrit from Salman Saheb. So he regarded him as his guru and touched his feet as a mark of reverence. Now that he had graduated and was preparing for a competitive test, he invited Salman Saheb to visit him. But Salman Saheb decided to spring a pleasant surprise on him by keeping his arrival date a closely-guarded secret. He would simply knock at his door, he said to himself.

Mohalla? Yes, yes, Gopalganj—House No. B-562; Radharaman Mishra's house, about half a mile from the railway station.

'Bhai Saheb, what's the way to Gopalganj?' he asked a shop-keeper. Without bothering to spit the paan juice out of his mouth, the shopkeeper produced a gurgling sound and managed to tell Salman Saheb that he had overshot the house. He was told to turn back, reach the electric pole, and enter the nearby lane.

A hot blast hit Salman Saheb as he emerged from the shopfront. Shielding his ears with his palms, he felt somewhat relieved at the thought of the onion in his pocket. Oh yes, that's the lane. Looking at the electric pole he entered the lane. Block A was on his right; so Block B should have been to the left. But it was Block H. He kept going, thinking that B might be adjacent to A. Instead he found himself in front of M Block. And C turned out to be to his left! He was baffled and confused.

'Can I help?' asked a gentleman who noticed his uneasiness. He was banging a charpoy, killing bed bugs as they fell on the ground. Salman Saheb crushed a small bug that made its way into his shoe and asked—'Where is B-562?' 'Oh, you mean Mishraji's house? That's in Old Gopalganj. Go this way till you come to a temple. Turn right. Then ask someone.' Salman Saheb moved on after a 'thank you'. As he turned to the right near the temple he noticed four or five buffaloes tethered there and a girl was trying to draw the attention of the bangle-seller.

'Is this Old Gopalganj?' he asked. She had no time to reply, her attention riveted on the bangle-seller's pushcart. Salman Saheb trudged on.

After some moments he reached a set of tall, old-fashioned houses. The shade from them kept the pebble-strewn street cool. Naked children played around. Salman Saheb thought of resting for a while but ultimately decided to move on.

A boy was running towards him dragging a fat mouse with a string tied to its tail. He tried to brush past him and seemed unconcerned with what was happening around him.

'Where is B-562, Mishraji's house? Do you know?' The boy pointed his finger indifferently at a house and off he went.

Salman Saheb took a deep breath and stood before the tall house pointed out by the boy. Two women were perched on a charpoy discussing the Punjab problem and offering their own solutions.

'O Bittan's Amma, thank your stars that we're in India. What would have happened to us if we were living in Punjab!'

'Is this Radharaman Mishraji's house?'

Salman Saheb expected them to rise in deference, as was usual in his town. But no. This was, after all, a city.

'Mishraji lives in Jawahar Nagar. Only his tenants live here'— one of them volunteered the information and fell silent.

'Why do you want to meet him?'—the other asked scratching her head.

'A boy named Mishrilal Gupta stays in his house. I've come to see him.'

'Go up the stairs. He lives in the second room.' The woman continued to scratch her head.

Salman Saheb went in. It was dark and the staircase was barely visible. He spotted a water tap and then the staircase while groping in the dark. Then he went up the stairs haltingly. He imagined Mishrilal having a nap and waking up in a huff by the loud sound of his knock. He would then open the bolt still blinking and then hasten to touch his feet.

'Who's there?' a female voice enquired at the end of the staircase.

'Is Mishrilalji in?'

'Wait a minute.' The abrupt tone indicated that the woman was busy with her chores. He stood in front of the doorless entrance wondering what he should do when a middle-aged, fair-complexioned woman appeared. She had only a petticoat and a bra on and hurried from the veranda into the adjoining room. She quickly wrapped herself in a sari and came out still trying to fasten the hook of the blouse.

'This way please.' Salman Saheb entered as though he had not seen the lady a while ago, a pretension that went well with the person who stood there without feeling embarrassed.

Salman Saheb's eyes fell on a freshly discarded wet sari near the drain pipe on the veranda. The smell of Jai toilet soap filled the air.

'Mishrilalji stays in the adjoining room. But he is not in at the moment. He went out this morning. Where are you from? Please be seated.' The courteous lady placed a cot before him and went in. After a few moments she came out holding a steel tumbler with water and some gur on a saucer. She placed the saucer on the cot and stood there.

'Drink some water. It's terribly hot today!'

She went in again, this time returning with a palm-leaf fan that she placed on the cot. Salman Saheb helped himself to some gur, drank water, and began fanning himself leisurely.

'I hope Mishrilal isn't out of town.'

'I don't think so. He must be around. Maybe he has gone to a movie or to a friend's house. Usually he spends most of his time in this room.'

Salman Saheb looked at his watch. It was about three past noon. He felt tired and stretched his legs on the cot. Seeing this the woman brought him a pillow.

'Please relax for a while. Guptaji will certainly get back by the evening.' She put her wet sari in a bucket and went down.

As Salman Saheb lay on the cot, he took out the onion from his pocket as it was hurting and slipped it under the cot. He dozed off thereafter. He dreamt of his school teachers having a fight and the Headmaster reprimanding Satya Narain Yadav, the physical training teacher. When Salman Saheb wanted to defend Yadav, his colleagues pounced on him. Just then he woke up.

It was late evening. The light of the dim electric bulb spread to the veranda. A stove was alight. The lady was cooking. The smell of Jai soap at noon was now replaced with the aroma of cumin seeds.

'Mishrilal hasn't returned yet!'

'Well, how can one tell where he's gone? He is usually cooped up in his room on most other days,' said the woman as she offered him tea in a steel tumbler.

'Oh, why did you bother?'

'No bother at all. We drink tea every evening.' Salman Saheb accepted the tumbler as the woman turned to the stove.

Just then a gentleman, freshly bathed, appeared stroking his sacred thread. With a gamcha wrapped around his waist, he entered the room reciting the Hanuman Chalisa. Soon, the scent of joss sticks merged with the aroma of cumin seeds.

Salman Saheb peeped into the room where household goods were neatly arranged. The walls were adorned with pictures of gods and goddesses of the Hindu pantheon—Rama, Krishna, Hanuman, Shankar, Parvati, Lakshmi, Ganesh, and so on. On one side a placard bore the inscription—'Ram Manohar Pandey, Assistant Telephone Operator.' He held a joss stick in his right hand while his right elbow rested on the left palm. Sitting thus, he swayed his hand in a circular motion spreading the scented smoke around and, at the same time, reciting some shlokas from the Gita. His pronunciation left much to be desired. A dirty ceiling fan revolved slowly.

The lady of the house finished cooking sabzi and had started on chapatis. Salman Saheb thought of leaving. He decided to move to a hotel and look up Mishrilal the next morning. It was getting late and there was still no sign of him. He stood up.

'I should go. I'll visit him tomorrow,' he said picking up his suitcase.

'Where to?'

'To a hotel.'

'Why a hotel, Bhai Saheb? There is enough room here. The meal is ready to be served. Please eat and then go to bed. Guptaji is sure to return. Even if he does not, stay overnight and leave tomorrow morning. No, no, I won't let you go. Come, take off your shoes and freshen up. I'll serve food straightaway.'

'No, Bhabhiji, I've caused you enough trouble,' Salman Saheb did not hesitate to address her as Bhabhi.

'It's no bother. Please eat.' Salman Saheb could not refuse. He took off his shoes, had his wash, and waited. By now Pandeyji was through with his puja. Perched on a chowki he began examining some documents. Salman Saheb was sorry that he had neither greeted him nor exchanged pleasantries.

'Bhai Saheb, won't you join me?'

'No, please go ahead. I'll eat after a while.' He answered hastily and turned to his papers.

'Please be seated. You must be starving. He'll eat later. He had some snacks after office. You were asleep then.' The woman placed the thali on a pirhi and a water-filled lota and a glass by its side.

Salman Saheb began eating. He was very pleased. In his small town a Brahmin wouldn't offer food to a stranger without knowing his religion and caste. But it was different in a city like this. True, this is not such a big city and, for all you know, many people here may still cling to the traditions of rural areas. But this is a city nevertheless. Educated people tend to be progressive and not narrow-minded in their outlook. They are religious without being orthodox.

That's what he thought while eating. He relished the brinjal, the somewhat raw mango pickle, and the rotis soaked in ghee. Such rotis were not baked at home where they produce giant-size half-baked chapatis on the inverse tawa and then kept them wrapped in a piece of old cloth.

His hostess offered to him yet another puffed up roti.

'Are you from Guptaji's village?' Salman Saheb raised his head. Pandeyji was through with his papers and was now peeling a mango. His tone was business-like.

Pandeyji beckoned his wife inside and gave her three slices of mango for Salman Saheb.

'Are you his brother?' Pandeyji asked dryly.

'No, he is my student!'

'Are you a teacher?'

'Yes'.

'Where do you teach?'

'In my own town.'

'Are you also a Gupta?'

'No.'

'A Brahmin?'

'No, I'm a Muslim. My name is Muhammad Salman.' After this introduction he began eating. Pandeyji raised his eyes, turned towards his wife to find her looking at him curiously. They wanted to exchange notes but . . .

Salman Saheb waited for his roti. But the woman was nowhere near the stove. She got busy inside the house looking for something. He then helped himself to the mango.

She held the glass tumbler once she was out in the open. Fear was writ large on her face.

Picking up the steel tumbler near the plate she placed the glass tumbler in its place.

Salman Saheb noticed the tumbler and the plate. For a moment he was worried. Then picking up his plate he took it to the drain pipe. Finding the scrubber he began cleaning it.

The woman turned around for a moment to catch a glimpse of him and then got busy with her chores.

Mishrilal had yet to return.

—*Translated from the Hindi* 'Atithi Devo Bhav' *by M. Asaduddin*

P. SAINATH

Everybody Loves a Good Drought

Drought is, beyond question, among the more serious problems this country faces. Drought relief, almost equally beyond question, is rural India's biggest growth industry. Often, there is little relation between the two. Relief can go to regions that get lots of rainfall. Even where it goes to scarcity areas, those most in need seldom benefit from it. The poor in such regions understand this. That's why some of them call drought relief *teesra fasl* (the third crop). Only, they are not the ones who harvest it.

A great deal of drought 'relief' goes into contracts handed over to private parties. These are to lay roads, dig wells, send out water tankers, build bridges, repair tanks—the works. Think that can't total up to much? Think again. The money that goes into this industry in a single year can make the withdrawals from Bihar's animal husbandry department look like so many minor fiddles. And the Bihar scam lasted a decade and a half. The charm of *this* scam is that it is largely 'legal'. And it has soul. It's all in a good cause. The tragedy, of course, is that it rarely addresses the real problems of drought and water scarcity.

In 1994–95 alone, the rich state of Maharashtra spent over

This extract is taken from *Everybody Loves a Good Drought,* published by Penguin Books India, New Delhi, 1996.

Rs 1,170 crores on emergency measures in combating drought and on other water-related problems. This was more than the combined profits the previous year of leading companies all across the country in the organised sector of the tea and coffee, cement and automobile industries. Their profits after tax came to Rs 1,149 crores, according to a report of the Centre for Monitoring the Indian Economy. ('Corporate Finances: Industry Aggregates', CMIE, November 1994, Bombay).

In August 1995, Prime Minister Narasimha Rao inaugurated an anti-drought project in Orissa. This one will involve spending Rs 4,557 crores in six years (over Rs 750 crores a year) on just a few districts including Kalahandi, Bolangir and Koraput. Every paisa of that huge sum would be worth spending if it actually fought scarcity and built better infrastructure. That, however, is most unlikely. In part because the main causes of the problems these areas face do not even begin to get addressed.

In theory, drought-prone blocks come under a central scheme known as the Drought-Prone Areas Programme (DPAP). But bringing blocks into the DPAP is now a purely political decision. The central allocation for DPAP may be nominal. But once a block is under DPAP, a phalanx of other schemes follows bringing in huge sums of money. The same blocks then get money coming in under the employment assurance scheme (EAS), anti-desertification projects, drinking waster missions and a host of other schemes. Well, *some* people do benefit.

In several states, official data on DPAP show us many interesting things. In Maharashtra, the number of DPAP blocks was around ninety six years ago. In 1996, 147 blocks are under the DPAP. In Madhya Pradesh in the same period, the number of DPAP blocks more than doubled from roughly sixty to around 135. In Bihar, there were fifty-four DPAP blocks right through the '80s. This became fifty-five when Rameshwar Thakur became a union minister in the early '90s. His home block in Bihar came under the scheme. Today, there are 122 DPAP blocks in that state.

All this has happened during a period where there have been several successive good monsoons. There has been scarcity too for some people. But that's a different story.

Kalahandi's major problem as the reports in this section, show, does not arise from poor rainfall. Water resources experts and administrators would largely agree that, barring problems of erratic timing and spread, most Indian districts could get by on around 800 mm of rainfall annually. The lowest rainfall Kalahandi has had in the past twenty years was 978 mm. That is way above what some districts get in 'normal' years. Otherwise, Kalahandi's annual rainfall has been, on an average, 1,250 mm. That is pretty decent. In 1990–91, the district had 2,247 mm of rainfall. Besides, Kalahandi produces more food per person than both Orissa and India as a whole do. Nuapada, the worst part of old Kalahandi, and now a separate district, got 2,366 mm of rainfall in 1994.

In Palamau, too, average rainfall is not bad. The district gets 1,200–1,230 mm of rain in a normal year. In its worst year in recent history, it received 630 mm. Some districts in India get less without experiencing the same damage.

Surguja's rainfall seldom falls below 1,200 mm. In some years it gets 1,500–1,600 mm. That's roughly four times what California gets. And California grows grapes.

Yet, all these districts have problems relating to water that are quite deadly. Very different ones from those the funds address. Simply put, we have several districts in India that have an abundance of rainfall—but where one section, the poor, can suffer acute drought. That happens when available water resources are colonised by the powerful. Further, the poor are never consulted or asked to participate in designing the 'programmes' the anti-drought funds bring.

Once it was clear that drought and DPAP were linked to fund flows in a big way, it followed that everyone wanted their block under the scheme. In many cases, the powerful are not only able to bring their blocks under it, but appropriate any 'benefits' that follow.

Take Maharashtra. Around 73 per cent of sugar cane produced in the state is grown in DPAP blocks! And sugar cane is about the most water-intensive crop you can get. Secondly, the area under irrigation in Maharashtra is pathetic. Just inching towards 15 per cent of crop land. But in the DPAP blocks, in one estimate, it is 22 per cent—nearly 50 per cent higher than the state average. Annual rainfall in Lonavla near Pune seldom falls below 1,650 mm and can touch 2,000 mm. Lonavla is a DPAP block.

The many hundreds of crores spent in Maharashtra on relief and on irrigation over the years have not led to any appreciable rise in land under irrigation. In the DPAP blocks are small farmers who really feel the pressure. The water is cornered by the rich and the strong. Governments kid themselves that by throwing money at such regions, the small fish, who have big votes, can be pacified. In reality, the lion's share of funds going there is again appropriated by the powerful. And irrigation water? About two per cent of farmers in the state use around 70 per cent of it.

Drought is a complex phenomenon. You can have an agricultural drought, for instance, even when there is no meteorological drought. That is, you can have adequate rainfall and still have crop failure. Or you can have hydrological drought, with marked depletion of rivers, streams, springs and fall in groundwater levels. The reasons for these are well known but seldom addressed. It is so much nicer to just put the whole thing down to nature's vagaries. It also works this way because so many forces, at different levels, are either integrated, or get co-opted, into the drought industry. The spiral from the drought scam touches the global stage before returning.

Here's how: Take any one district. Say Surguja (it could be any other). The peasants face many water-related problems. Block-level forces—contractors and politicians—take up 'the cause'. The complaint, typically, is: Our block got far less funds than the others. The collector is ignoring us. That's why it's happening.

Well, two things are happening, really. One, the peasants of

Surguja face serious problems that are intensifying. Two, specific forces are making a pitch at the district headquarters for bringing more funds to the block.

The local stringer of a newspaper (based in, say, Bilaspur), takes up the theme: the collector is neglecting 'our block'. Most newspapers pay their stringers a pittance. Some stringers get as little as Rs 50 a month. So only those with other sources of funds can work in this capacity. In many parts of these districts, you will find that the stringer is often a small shopkeeper, a petty businessman.

If contracts for various 'public works' come to the block or district, the stringer might be among the beneficiaries. This is not true of all, but does apply to quite a few stringers. I met many intelligent, resourceful people among them. They are bright, have an ear to the ground, react quickly to situations. Quite a few of them are also small contractors. So are many block-level politicians. (So are many national politicians and newspaper owners, but that's another story.)

Reports of raging drought put pressure on a district administration strapped for resources. (Some of the stories have strong elements of truth, though death counts are often exaggerated.) The collector calls his friends: the district level correspondents. He explains that his district gets far less from the state capital than other, neighbouring ones. This could well be true. The collector is also pitching at the state capital for a better share of the resource cake. Reports of 'stepmotherly treatments' of Surguja, or whichever district it is, start appearing in newspapers in the state capital.

That embarrasses the state government. How does it respond? While doing what it can locally, it also pitches at the Centre for more funds to deal with the drought. State governments often bring down correspondents from mainline journals to the state capital. These reporters then set off on a guided tour of the 'affected areas'. Governments often have vehicles reserved for the purpose of press tours. And often, a senior official goes with the journalists to the trouble spots.

The sophisticated writers of the urban press are superior to the local press when it comes to the heart-rending stuff. The drought becomes a national issue. Copy full of phrases like 'endless stretches of parched land', accompanied by photographs, reaches urban audiences. (Now parched land is not necessarily a symbol of drought. You can have it in very wet places if you drain a pond. And you can have an acute water shortage in seemingly green areas. But parched land makes better copy and pictures.) This is more true of the English press. The language press has serious problems, but is closer to the ground.

If it is, say, mid-May when reports reach the affected region, the searing heat will impress some. With your skin and hair on fire, it is easy to believe there has been drought in the area since the dawn of time. There could be flooding here two months hence, but that doesn't matter now. Unlike the quick-on-the-uptake local stringers, the national press is seldom clued in on ground reality. There are, of course, many reporters who could handle the real stories of the place. They don't often get sent on such trips. Those are not the kind of stories their publications are looking for. Every editor knows that drought means parched land and, hopefully, pictures of emaciated people. That's what 'human interest' is about, isn't it?

The state has made its pitch at the Centre. The Centre is unfazed. It uses what it considers examples of responsible reporting (that is, reports that do not vilify the Centre) to advantage. It makes its own pitch for resources. International funding agencies, foreign donors, get into the act. UNDP, UNICEF, anyone who can throw a little money about. The global aid community is mobilised into fighting drought in a district that gets 1,500 mm of rainfall annually.

The reverse spiral begins.

Donor governments love emergency relief. It forms a negligible part of their spending, but makes for great advertising. (Emergencies of many sorts do this, not just drought. You can run television footage of the Marines kissing babies in Somalia.) There are more serious issues between rich and poor nations—like unequal trade. Settling those would be of greater help to the latter. But for that, the 'donors' would have to part with something for real. No. They prefer emergency relief.

So money comes into Delhi from several sources. The next step in the downward spiral is for central departments to fight over it. Nothing awakens the conscience like a lot of money. One department or ministry remembers it has a mission to save the forests of the suffering district. Another recalls a commitment to manage its water resources.

Then there are all the hungry, Rs 30,000-a-month consultants to be clothed and fed. Projects are drawn up with their assistance for fighting drought in the district. Or for water resource management. Or for anything at all. Studies of water problems are vital. But some of these are thought up simply because there are funds now. (The collector and a lot of peasants in the district could probably tell you a great deal about the real water problems. But they're not 'experts'.)

The money goes to the state capital where the struggle over sharing it continues. At the district level, the blocks pitch for their share. Contracts go out for various emergency works. A little money might even get spent on those affected by the water shortage. But it cannot solve their problems.

The next year the same problems will crop up all over again because the real issues were never touched.

At the end of it, many forces including well-meaning sections of the press have been co-opted into presenting a picture of natural calamity. Too often, into dramatising an event without looking at the processes behind it. The spiral works in different ways in different states. But it works.

And yet, so many people do suffer from water-related problems.

Several of India's more troublesome conflicts are linked to water. It may have taken a back seat, but the sharing of river waters was a major part of the Punjab problem. The ongoing quarrel between Tamil Nadu and Karnataka is over Cauvery waters. (Some of India's tensions with Bangladesh have their basis in water sharing disputes.) The struggle over water resources operates at the micro, village level, too, in many ways. Between villages, between hamlets within a village, between castes and classes.

Conflicts arising from man-made drought are on the rise. Deforestation does enormous damage. Villagers are increasingly losing control over common water resources. The destruction of traditional irrigation systems is gaining speed. A process of privatisation of water resources is apparent in most of the real drought areas (take the water lords of Ramnad, for instance). There are now two kinds of drought: the real and the rigged. Both can be underway at the same time, in the same place. As the reports that follow seek to show, they often are.

THE SALE OF A GIRL—1

Amlapali, Nuapada (Orissa): It was *the* human interest story of the '80s. A story about the sale of a girl in this village. A story that touched the conscience of a nation and brought Kalahandi into sharp focus. In a sense, the journalism of that period does symbolise some of the better efforts of the press. As it does some of its limitations.

It was in July 1985 that Phanas Punji, in her early thirties, shot to notoriety. She had, so the story went, 'sold' her fourteen-year-old sister-in-law, Banita Punji, to the nearly blind Bidya Podh. He paid Rs 40 to 'buy' Banita and use her as a 'domestic servant'. Phanas's husband had abandoned her two years earlier. And she was widely quoted in the press as saying: 'My own two children are starving. What could I do?'

Everyone observed that she did not deny selling the girl. The story shook the nation. It appalled Rajiv Gandhi, then prime minister. Worse, his office received confirmation of the sale. He decided to go and have a look at Kalahandi himself.

Hordes of officials descended on this part of Kalahandi. (It is now a separate district called Nuapada.) Not so much to set things right, as to prepare for the prime ministerial tour. And scores of reporters reached Nuapada, even today one of India's poorest districts. After all, the prime minister himself was going there. You couldn't miss an event like that.

The episode produced some of the most stirring journalism of the '80s. Some brilliant reporting destroyed the efforts at a cover-up by the then J.B. Patnaik government. The misery of Kalahandi stood naked. More reports followed as journalists met the myriad faces of poverty in the region. Moving stories on drought and scarcity conditions appeared in profusion. There was an almost missionary zeal to it.

Television did what print could not. It brought the actors in the drama, including J.B. Patnaik, in person before the public eye. M.J. Akbar's TV interview with Patnaik rattled the chief minister. He later denounced it in public as 'concocted'. Patnaik also damaged himself further in the state assembly. There, he implied that the sale of children was a 'tradition' in parts of western Orissa.

The press crusade had an effect. It forced two prime ministers, two chief ministers and countless ministers to visit Nuapada-Kalahandi over the years. That meant better roads, improved communications and some repairs to bridges. These receive attention only when a VIP shows up.

The crusade also brought huge funds for development. Innumerable projects were announced, mostly for Kalahandi—though poverty is hardly exclusive to this region. Voluntary agencies, many of them floating in foreign funds, descended on the district in droves—to promote development.

Those were proud moments for the media.

But nine years later, all the principal actors in that drama are in much the same state they were. Perhaps, in some ways, worse off.

Kalahandi and Nuapada remain seemingly untouched by the crores of rupees and hordes of projects thrown at them. J.B. Patnaik, too, is worse off. He is no longer chief minister.*

Last week, I met Phanas Punji at Amlapali. I also spoke to Banita and Bidya Podh at Badtunda. With me was ex-MLA Kapil Narain Tiwari. He was instrumental in breaking the original story. He has also done more than any other politician to highlight Kalahandi's plight.

Now an anganwadi worker, Phanas has lost even more of the meagre lands her husband's family once owned. All of it to moneylenders. Her husband, however, is back. 'But,' she said, 'he is unemployed most of the year as before.' Banita, now twenty-two, lives at Badtunda village in Bolangir district. That's just a few kilometres away. She is still with the 'blind old man' and they have three children to whom both seem greatly attached.

- Banita and Bidya Podh are no better off than Phanas. Banita, too, is an anganwadi worker ('I do the cooking there'). The effectiveness of the anganwadi scheme is apparent in the condition of her own three children. All are malnourished, the youngest one severely so. Both Phanas and Banita were earning Rs 100 a month in their jobs till a short while ago. Now they earn Rs 210 a month. That's about a third of what they would get if paid the official minimum wage of Rs 25 per day in Orissa. Neither is able to feed her family properly. Both look after out-of-work husbands.

- As for Bidya Podh, no one ever spoke to him. Not even when the reports on the 'sale of a girl' were being done. That might have spoilt the story. Apparently, humanising the story

---

* He has returned to that post since this report first appeared in print.

meant demonising some. Podh was a soft target. After all, he wasn't going to read the stories. He became, in some reports, the 'blind old man' who had 'bought Banita' and cruelly exploited her. One story cast him as the blind old 'landlord'. Another had him buying the girl for Rs 40 and then 'abandoning' her after satiating his lust.

Far from being the 'landlord' Banita was sold to, Podh is landless. He does not even own homestead land. The roof over their heads belongs to one of his uncles. Podh's sight is very badly impaired, indeed. Some might call him blind, yes. But he can see well enough to recognise his visitors. He certainly knew me the second time I went to his hut.

Old? The 'blind old landlord' was a young man in his twenties when the episode took place in 1985.

Kapil Tiwari hasn't changed either. It would be a great pity if he did. The man who describes himself as 'a below-the-poverty-line ex-MLA' is as angry as ever at what is happening in Kalahandi. He still relentlessly fights injustice in his role of independent political maverick.

I met and photographed all of them together: their lives ridiculously untouched by the furious national debate that raged around them.

As I write, migrants from the poverty-stricken border zone of Nuapada-Bolangir are moving, as in 1985. Only, in larger numbers. Their destinations range from Raipur, where they will pull rickshaws, to Bombay, where they will toil at construction sites. The frightening levels of joblessness propelling them are rising.

The flesh trade sending women to Raipur's brothels is thriving. The inequity of landholding patterns of old Kalahandi has not improved. The moneylenders to whom the Phanas Punjis of the world alienate their land may be less in number. They seem more powerful in scope, though. The public health system is a mess. Worse, malaria is rampant.

The development projects meant to help Kalahandi have changed. But only in name and number. In effect, they are mostly the same. Lacking popular roots, they tend to fail. Some district administrators have tried the odd positive intervention. Yet, distress sales of land, labour and produce are very much there too. In short, Nuapada, and all Kalahandi, are largely the same.

The story on the 'sale' of a girl had this positive effect: It drew attention to Kalahandi. But, the question remains. *What* in Kalahandi did it draw attention to?

MASALA MIX

VIR SANGHVI

Bhelpuri: It's All about Texture

Chaat is, for better or for worse, a North India invention. Vijay Goel, the affable Minister of State in the Prime Minister's Office, was researching the history of his Chandni Chowk constituency and his staff traced the origins of many of today's popular *chaat* dishes to the Mughal period.

No doubt the *chaatwallahs* of Lucknow claim a similar provenance for their own varieties and almost everywhere in India where you find *chaat*, there will be a North Indian (possibly a UP-ite) behind the stall, mashing the potatoes with his hands and ladling in the *dahi* while simultaneously chewing *paan*.

In Calcutta, where *phuchkas* (a cousin of the *golgappa*) are a civic obsession, the men who make them frequently speak no Bengali, have no idea who Rabindranath Tagore is and smile tolerantly as their customers address them as 'bhaiyya'. As proud as Calcutta is of the *phuchka*, the dish is as Bengali as N.D. Tiwari.

The same is true of Bombay where the *chaatwallahs* actually encourage you to call them 'bhaiyya' (not as in 'brother' or even 'milkman' but as in 'fat, sweaty person of possible North Indian origin'). The famous *chaat* stalls on Chowpatty beach now have the

This essay is taken from *Rude Food: The Collected Food Writings of Vir Sanghvi*, published by Penguin Books India, New Delhi, 2004.

owner's name emblazoned in neon lights, but as they all say 'Sharma Bhelpuri Centre', this is not much help when it comes to telling one from the other. (The easiest way to clear the beach, I've always thought, would be to stand by the water, shout 'Sharma' and then watch as all the *chaatwallahs* drop their *puris* and rush like lemmings to the sea.)

Despite the dominance of 'bhaiyyas' (their term, not mine) on the beaches of Chowpatty and Juhu, Bombay has the distinction of having invented the one item of *chaat* that does not have a North Indian origin: *bhelpuri*.

The origins of *bhelpuri* are now the subject of some dispute but legend has it that the dish was invented not on Chowpatty beach but at a restaurant called Vithal, near the Victoria Terminus railway station. (Don't bother going there now. They have a 'vegetarian Chinese' menu and offer 'Chinese *bhelpuri*'.)

The tang in the *bhelpuri*—the onion, the garlic in the chutney and the sweet-sour *khajur-imli* tastes—has nothing to do with the pious Sharmas and their time-honoured techniques of crumbling deep-fried food (samosas, *kachoris*, *tikkis* and God alone knows what else) on a *patta* before adding *dahi* and *chaat masala*. It was the contribution of the city's Gujaratis who recognized the potential for complex flavours in the sweaty simplicity of North Indian *chaat*.

While North Indian *chaat* usually had two or three basic ingredients (*papri*+*dahi*+*aloo*, for instance), *bhelpuri* had up to fifteen (*sev*, crumbled *puris*, onions, raw mango, potatoes, coriander, three kinds of chutney, etc.). Unusually, the final product did not depend on *dahi*, nor was it built around a single deep-fried dish (a *tikki*, a *kachori*, etc.), though some of the ingredients (*sev*, for instance) were deep-fried. The complexity was heightened by the mixture of textures.

Generally, Indian food is not too hot on texture; *chaat* is no exception. But *bhelpuri* is all about texture: soft but firm boiled potatoes, crunchy *sev*, crispy puffed rice and small pieces of onion that squish as you bite into them.

And because there were so many ingredients and each serving of *bhel* had to be made fresh (otherwise it got soggy), everything depended on the *chaatwallah*. If he had a generous hand with the onions, for instance, he could throw all the flavours out of gear; less potato and the dish would lack the starchy solidness that the potatoes contributed, and so on. All food (and *chaat*) depends, to some extent, on the cook; but *bhel* was the first *chaat* dish where the individual *chaatwallah* counted for so much.

Even if Vithal did invent *bhelpuri*, the restaurant soon lost any special claims to it. Gujarati housewives began making it—at home along with more typical Gujarati snacks such as *dahi-wadi* (sometimes called *khandvi*), *patra* and *dhokla*.

Because the dish lent itself to so many variations, there were soon so many different varieties that each version became known for the nice Gujarati lady who perfected it.

Not content with *bhelpuri*, Gujarati housewives then took on the rest of the *chaatwallah's* repertoire, revising, inventing and renaming his dishes. For instance, the *chaatwallah* made *pakodi puri* by stuffing a large *golgappa puri* with cooked *pakodis* and then adding *dahi* and chutney. In the hands of the housewives, *pakodi puri* came to be made without any *pakodi* at all. Instead, boiled potatoes, sprouted *moong* and *channa* (gram) became the filling. To this day Gujaratis will offer you this version of *pakodi puri* though *chaatwallahs* call their version *dahi batata puri* (usually made without gram and *moong*). But Gujaratis also surrendered any claims to their *chaat* (as they have to *paav-bhaji*).

Because *bhelpuri* consists of so many different and quite varied ingredients, it soon became a metaphor for the cosmopolitan nature of Bombay itself. Nearly every community began producing its own *bhel*.

The *chaatwallahs* included it in their repertoire—but you'll always miss home-made *bhel* if you try the Chowpatty version (unusual for a *chaat* dish).

Mangalorean owners of Udipi restaurants produced their adaptation (marked by excessive use of lemon) at restaurants with such names as Shetty's. And even Sindhis produced a hit version, perfected at the Kailash Parbat Chaat House in Colaba.

Sadly, *bhelpuri* does not travel well. You can't get a decent *bhel* in Delhi: most North Indian *chaatwallahs* are foxed by the complexity of the dish. And the only halfway decent *bhel* I've ever eaten in Calcutta was at Tit-Bits which did the home-made Gujarati version, but I've not been back for ten years.

For the real thing, I go to Bombay.

BULBUL SHARMA

The Anger of Aubergines

Mrs Kumar lifted the curtains and looked out of the window. It was still early but sometimes he arrived at 12 o'clock when he had nothing else to do. He came and sat on the brown chair which he had bought at an auction at the American Embassy fifteen years ago.

Mrs Kumar remembered every little detail of their married life though they had been separated now for seven years. She did not find her estranged life any different from their dull, wedded one. The sullen mornings, empty afternoons and silent evenings had been replaced by a different kind of quiet loneliness which she found quite soothing, like the headache balm she often used. She had this small house to look after, the garden to grow vegetables in, the mango tree to guard. Her son wrote to her once a month from New Jersey and sent her a new sweater, of the same shade, every year. The unchanging pattern of the days was broken only by Mr Kumar's weekly visit, which took place every Sunday.

Mr Kumar was a brooding, taciturn man with no expression on his face except the occasional frown which sometimes appeared to show an intense, deep-felt agitation. Otherwise there were no

This story is taken from *The Anger of Aubergines*, published by Kali for Women, New Delhi, 1998.

lines on his bland features to mark the fleeting imprint of anger, love or hatred he had ever felt.

'I am what I am,' he often said to anyone who cared to listen, and that was the truth. There was nothing more to him than the basic flesh, skin and bones, and one could see through him as if he perpetually carried an X-Ray film with him like a placard.

When he decided to separate from his wife, he did so with no emotional trauma or guilt. No reason was given and no explanation was demanded from either side. Though no papers were ever signed for a formal divorce, it was a clean, surgical cutting of ties which had never really existed. He had married her when she was 18 and he 28, because their families had long decided that they should be related through marriage so that their two businesses could merge. Mrs Kumar had brought a substantial dowry with her which had paid for his education in a prestigious university abroad, and also enabled him to buy his first suit, Rolex watch and car. They had produced one son whose conception shocked and amazed them both so much that no further attempt was made.

The son grew up in the warmth and confusion of the two joint families and did not recognise his father in the crowd of other men in the household. Till he was 18, he had been under the impression that his favourite uncle was his father. When he realised that Mr Kumar was the person who had brought him into this world, he was so stunned that he ran away from home. He was found a few days later, and before he could do anything drastic again, was married off by his grandfather to a suitable girl with a large dowry. Mrs Kumar had no say in the matter. Neither did Mr Kumar.

The day his father died Mr Kumar decided to live separately from his wife. The family, once so eager to see them united, were now indifferent since most of its members were either dead, senile or had emigrated to the U.S.A. where Mr Kumar's son had also fled when he came of age.

Mrs Kumar accepted the separation in the same calm, unruffled manner with which she had accepted her marriage to Mr Kumar, the subsequent taking over of her son, and her bleak married life.

Now only the Sundays remained to remind her that she had been married at all. She got up early on this day, bathed quickly and wore a fresh, starched saree. She finished her pooja faster than on other days and, hurriedly smearing a vermilion bindi on her forehead, went into the kitchen to marinate the meat.

The menu was more or less the same every Sunday because Mr Kumar had five or six favourite dishes which were rotated through the year. Though long separated from his wife whom he had never cared for, Mr Kumar had lunch with her regularly, once a week. The rest of the week he ate what his servant made for him, or went to his club. But come Sunday, Mr Kumar, like a murderer drawn irresistibly to the spot where he had killed his victim, headed home to lunch with his wife. He arrived at 12.30 sharp and did not have to knock or ring the bell because she always left the door open. He sat and read the newspaper while she added last minute touches to the food. Sometimes, he went into the room which had been their bedroom and checked the cupboards, but never touched anything. They never spoke to each other.

The aubergine bharta was ready and waiting to be garnished with fresh coriander leaves which she would fetch from her garden. This year she had managed to grow a bumper crop of vegetables and even the onions and garlic came from her back garden. She sliced the ginger into thin strips and dipped them in fresh lemon juice, because that is how Mr Kumar liked them. She had planted a lemon tree last year and now watched it carefully for signs of buds. Her plump, fair hands moved effortlessly as she chopped the onions, which she would then fry till they were crisp and dark brown and serve as a garnish for the pulao. Her eyes never watered when she cut onions—a virtue which had been a source of great amazement to her family.

'Let Sushma deal with the onions. She is really good at it,' her sisters would say whenever they were cooking. Mrs Kumar felt very happy when she was called to cut the onions and rushed eagerly into the kitchen, tucking her saree purposefully around her waist. The others would make room for her in the crowded kitchen and sometimes even stand around watching her as she chopped and sliced with expertise. She became so good at her craft that she could even look up and still slice layers of onions as fine as paper. Even now, sometimes, in the grey silence of the afternoons, she could hear her mother's voice echoing in the kitchen, 'Let Sushma do the onions', and it gave her a surge of happiness.

Today she had made bharta, as well as dahi meat curry, because she had found two glossy, purple aubergines in the garden this morning. She had roasted them quickly on a wood fire in the back yard and then added tomatoes and finely chopped green chillies. She did not like to over-cook the bharta like most people did, for she felt it took away the roasted flavour. The dahi meat she cooked on a slow fire till the gravy was totally absorbed in the meat, along with the flavour of cardamoms, aniseed and dry ginger. This was a Kashmiri meat curry called yakhni which she had learnt from her neighbour, but she liked adding a few touches of her own, like red chilli, to it. Sometimes after Mr Kumar left, she packed some leftover curry in a steel jar and took it across to her neighbour. She never rang the bell—just left it on her kitchen window so that she would not have to meet the husband who was a large, boisterous man with a wild look in his eyes which frightened Mrs Kumar.

She brought the bharta and placed it on the table next to the raita made with grated cucumber. Mr Kumar rustled his paper, shifted a little in his chair, but did not look up. The pulao was steaming in the cooker and she began to spoon it out carefully onto a large serving plate, the last surviving relic of the English dinner set her mother had given her in her dowry. The pink and gold pattern of the china made the cashew nuts and raisins sparkle in their bed of golden brown rice and an aroma of cardamom filled the room. Mr Kumar folded his newspaper and rose. This was his signal to come to the table. They sat opposite each other at the dining table, another find at the American Embassy auction. Mrs Kumar served her husband and then watched him eat.

'Is the salt all right?' she asked suddenly, in a low voice, startling her husband. He did not look up, just nodded, slightly unnerved by this sudden burst of chatter from his wife.

'Hope she is not going to start nattering away at meal times and ruin the food,' he thought with a stab of irritation. She did not say anything more and after serving him another helping of meat curry, went to the kitchen to fetch the mango pickle she had made with fruits from the tree in her garden. Then she, too, sat down to eat.

There was no sound except for the occasional clink of a spoon touching the plate, Mrs Kumar's bangles jangling gently and Mr Kumar's satiated burping. He continued to eat, helping himself to more meat curry. He chewed methodically on the bones, his eyes shut in deep meditation. Then he piled his plate high with pulao, which his wife had just reheated, and added another large spoonful of curry. With deft fingers he mixed the two into neat balls and threw them into his mouth one by one. Under the table, his knees shook in joyful, contented rhythm. He ended the meal by ceremoniously lifting the huge bowl of raita and drinking the entire contents in one gulp. Before he left the table he ate a slice of mango pickle. There was no dessert because he had been told to cut down his sugar intake. His doctor had also told him to keep off rich, spicy food and he did—all week. Abstention is what made this white meat curry, prepared with a fine blend of ginger and aniseed, as smooth as butter with an extra dash of red chillies burnt in pure ghee, so delicious. Yet it never failed to irritate Mr Kumar's stomach. And as he lay awake all night, tossing and turning in agony, chewing antacid tablets, he felt justified in leaving his wife.

YAKHNI (DAHI MEAT CURRY)

1½ kg mutton cubed, or lamb chops
4 tsp aniseed (saunf) powder
2 tsp saunth (dry ginger) powder
3 cups water
1 cup yogurt
2 tbsp mustard oil or any other cooking oil
red chillies to taste
salt to taste

Heat oil in a large saucepan. Add meat pieces along with water, salt, powdered aniseed and dry ginger. Cook on slow fire till meat is half cooked. Mix the yogurt with one cup of water and add to the meat. Simmer till meat is cooked. Before taking off the fire sprinkle crushed seeds of large cardamom. You can add a red chilli burnt in pure ghee if you want. Serve with plain boiled rice or pulao.

DAVID DAVIDAR

The Great Mango Yatra

'Do you really believe the Chevathar Neelam is the best mango in the world?' Daniel asked Ramdoss.

'I believe it's the best I've eaten.'

'I wonder what makes it so remarkable,' Daniel said thoughtfully.

'Could it be the soil?'

'Probably. But certainly there was some grafting done a long time ago.'

It was the summer of Daniel's second year in Doraipuram and Ramdoss and he were supervising the harvest of blue mangoes. It was four in the morning, the time at which the Chevathar Neelams were traditionally picked to ensure their sweetness was retained, and that they ripened evenly.

'I'd like to decide for myself,' Daniel said abruptly.

'Decide what?' Ramdoss asked.

'That the Chevathar Neelam is the best mango in the world.'

In his years with Daniel, Ramdoss had learned that when his brother-in-law was enthused by a new idea it was very hard to deflect him. 'What did you have in mind?' he asked.

This extract is taken from *The House of Blue Mangoes*, published by Penguin Books India, New Delhi, 2002.

Daniel didn't reply for a while, silently watching the men harvesting the mangoes flit like ghosts through the pre-dawn hush, gently picking the fruit with what looked like giant butterfly nets and depositing them in cane baskets filled with straw.

'I'd like to taste the finest mangoes available to satisfy myself that the Chevathar Neelam is the best!'

Ramdoss's heart sank. The time, the cost, the travel! 'But, anna, Doraipuram needs your guiding hand, we can't wander the world tasting mangoes.'

'India has the world's greatest mangoes, there's no need to leave its shores. I've always wanted to eat Alphonsos, Langdas, Chausas and Maldas. There's no point trying to make me change my mind, Ramdoss, it's made up and we're going.'

He was as good as his word. The great mango yatra began in Kerala, where Daniel, Ramdoss and the four gardeners who made up the party tasted the Ollour, a fruit with thick yellow skin and flesh and a faintly resinous after-taste. It was a fruit they were all familiar with, as it was found in the bazaars of Nagercoil and Meenakshikoil.

As summer progressed, dozens of varieties of mangoes began to ripen. The group from Doraipuram trailed through the fruit markets of the south, making the acquaintance of many well-known mangoes such as the regal Jehangiri, named for an emperor, the Banganapalli with its sweet, pale, whitish-yellow pulp, and the rare and delicious Himayuddin with a taste in the upper registers of the palate. In the fruit markets of Madura, they ate Rumanis round as cricket balls and so thin-skinned a baby could peel them, Mulgoas so enormous that they often tipped the scales at three kilograms and the highly prized Cherukurasam.

Then they had to hurry west, for the fruiting season of the Alphonso was at its peak. Deciding that it was not practical to journey to Ratnagiri, Bulsad and Belgaum, where the celebrated Alphonso orchards perfumed the air, even infusing the rice paddies, they headed instead for Bombay. Straight off the train, they made for Crawford Market. Long before they caught sight of the country's most famous mango, they could smell it, its scent rising above the odours of rotting cabbage and corn, sweat and kerosene. They turned a corner and suddenly there they were—row upon row of gilded Alphonsos arranged in tiers behind gesticulating, yelling mango traders and their equally vociferous customers. Daniel ate his first Alphonso, and as the taste—a touch of tartness, a spill of honey, a profusion of fresh, light notes on a deep bass foundation—sank into his palate he understood why it was so coveted. He would have liked to have lingered longer in the west, but there was still much ground to cover during the short season, and they were soon on a train heading east, their last memory of the great western mangoes being a glass of juice, thick and sweet and clarified sunlight, made from that other classic, the Pairi.

As they made their journeys, Daniel steeped himself in mango lore. He discovered that the mango grew nearly everywhere on the subcontinent and that there were over a thousand recognized varieties. Ramdoss successfully dissuaded his friend from even thinking about sampling them all, suggesting instead that for practical reasons they limit themselves to the most renowned. He learned that *Mangifera indica*, to give it its proper name, had evolved somewhere in the mysterious northeastern corner of the country over two thousand years before, and had been spread by travellers and other carriers throughout Southeast Asia, China and the Malay archipelago. Greedy Portuguese traders and adventurers were the first pale skins to encounter it in the early years of the sixteenth century. Immediately falling under its spell, they had introduced the fruit to Africa and South America. About the same time, it had travelled by another route to the West Indies, the Philippines and thence to Mexico. In the nineteenth century, it had appeared in the orchards of California, Florida and Hawaii.

Everywhere they travelled, there were fascinating stories about the fruit, a delicacy so prized among connoisseurs that it drove its admirers to all sorts of excess. The Mughal emperor Akbar's romance with the mango made even the Dorais' obsession with it pale in comparison. Never one to do things by halves, he had ordered an army of malis to raise an orchard of a hundred thousand trees in Darbhanga. Even more dedicated to the cause of the fruit was the Nawab Wajid Ali Shah of Lucknow who was fêted throughout the land for the excellence of his mango orchards where nearly thirteen hundred varieties were raised; the prince's mango marriages were famous, as were his mango parties where, to the sound of tabla and santoor, the nobility gathered in pavilions constructed in the orchards, and tasted mangoes plucked from trees by women specially selected for their long tapering fingers, the better to grasp the fruit.

They spent a week in the east acquainting themselves with the finer points of the Malda, also called the Bombay Green, which had a subtle taste that seemed almost anaemic until it expanded to fill the senses. They sampled the exceedingly sweet, thin-skinned Himsagar and the Bombai, not to be confused with the Bombay Green. And Daniel was thrilled to be invited to a mango-tasting festival by an ageing Murshidabad nawab. Graciously inviting his guests to take their places at the head table, the Nawab showed Daniel how he ate the fruit. He first munched on a spicy, coarsely ground kabab so that his palate was completely fresh and then delicately picked at a little of the heart flesh of the Gulabkhas, a mango that tasted of roses. 'Truly, an unusual way to eat the fruit,' Daniel remarked to Ramdoss. 'Why didn't we think of something like that?'

They had one other major mango-growing region to visit before the long journey home. Daniel had heard a lot about the Malihabadi Dussehri, and when he tasted it, he was quick to accept its claims to greatness. But he discovered that its claim to being the finest mango in the country was by no means secure, for there were those who would bestow that honour on the Langda, which according to legend was first grown by a lame fakir from the holy city of Benares. When Daniel encountered it, he was overwhelmed by its qualities—the pale green skin, the orange-yellow flesh and above all the taste: a distinctive sweetness balanced by a slight tartness. They decided not to wait for the late-fruiting Chausa to arrive in the markets: Ramdoss managed to persuade Daniel to abandon his plans to visit Lahore and Rangoon and they took the train home. On the way back, Daniel discussed the dozens of varieties they had tasted. He referred to the notes he'd made, he recalled their distinctive qualities, and he tried as fairly as he could to determine the greatest mango he had encountered in the course of his yatra.

A week after he'd returned to Doraipuram, Daniel still couldn't pick the winner. That evening, when he and Ramdoss took their daily walk, he said, 'You know, Ramu, we've spent months trying to find out whether the Chevathar Neelam is finer than any other mango.'

'Yes,' Ramdoss said cautiously. But Daniel didn't pick up the conversation for he was lost in a reverie. He saw himself reach up to pick a Chevathar Neelam from his father's orchard, the fruit invested with the golden light of the sun. He tore at the warm fragrant skin with his teeth, then bit down into the flesh, the nectar running in yellow rivulets down his face, neck, even his arms, its unmatched flavour overwhelming him. 'Ramu,' Daniel said slowly, 'we went a long way to know what I've always known. There's no question that the Chevathar Neelam is the greatest mango in the world.' Then, to Ramdoss's disquiet, he added, 'Now that we know that, we need to proclaim its glories far and wide.'

As always when in the grip of an obsession, Dr Dorai worked single-mindedly in pursuit of his objective. He lavished money and attention on the mango topes, enriching the soil, guarding against common diseases and infestations. Startled stem-borers and mango hoppers, shoot-borers and blossom midges died by the thousand as an army of gardeners attacked them, with their bare hands if necessary.

By the time the next fruiting season came round, Daniel was ready to inaugurate Doraipuram's first Blue Mango Festival. The finest mangoes had already been carefully harvested and left to ripen in enormous storerooms at the rear of Neelam Illum. On the appointed day they were taken from the densely scented rooms and carried to the pandal that had been erected on the banks of the Chevathar. For the celebrations, Daniel had copied many details from the mango-tasting ceremony he had attended in Murshidabad, but there were some touches that were unique.

He had commissioned the legendary weavers of the region to weave a hundred mats with a special mango pattern, and these covered the red earth of the river bank. The Collector, who was the chief guest (the Murshidabad nawab had been unable to make the journey), sat at the head table along with Daniel, Ramdoss, Narasimhan, other local dignitaries and the heads of the founding families. A band played soft music and lamps lit the mango groves. As the heart flesh of the Neelam was ceremoniously served on small plates, each guest munched first on a hot vadai (a variant that Daniel was rather proud of) before tasting the fruit. Once the formal tasting of the Neelam was over, other varieties were presented, seventy-seven in all. The Collector gave up after tasting twenty-two types of mango, Narasimhan managed twelve more, and only Daniel and Ramdoss tasted them all.

The formal tasting was only a part of the festivities. The mango groves echoed with laughter and excitement as the settlers and hundreds of visitors participated in mango-eating competitions and other feats of skill, endurance and frolic.

When the party finally concluded at two in the morning, queasy stomachs notwithstanding, it was declared a great success. 'We must do this every year,' Dr Dorai said to Ramdoss and Lily as he bid goodbye to the last guests. They received the news in silence, which Daniel chose to interpret positively.

Chitra Banerjee Divakaruni

The Secrets of Spices

At the store each day has a colour, a smell. And if you know to listen, a melody. And Friday, Friday when I am closest to restlessness, hums like a car getting ready. Humming and vibrating, all set to disappear down that neon freeway beyond which surely lie open fields coloured like indigo. You breathe it in all the way because who knows when you will breathe next. And then you find the brake is jammed.

So perhaps it's fitting that the lonely American comes into the store on a Friday evening, the full moon already floating above the shoulder of the woman on the cut-out billboard by the freeway, and she in a black evening gown holding up a glass of Chivas. The headlights of oncoming cars hit the rhinestone straps of her gown so they shine like anticipation. Her eyes are like smoke, her mouth like pomegranates. They hurt me. And when I listen, the speeding cars sound mournful as wind in island bamboo.

I start to say I'm closing, but then I look at him and I can't.

It's not as if I haven't seen Americans. They come in here all the time, the professor types in tweed with patches on jacket elbows or in long skirts in earnest earth colours, Hare Krishnas

This extract is taken from *The Mistress of Spices*, published by Doubleday, London, 1997.

in wrinkled white kurtas with shaved heads, backpack-toting students in seldom-laundered jeans, leftover hippies lankhaired and beaded. They want fresh coriander seed, organic of course, or pure ghee for a Karma-free diet, or yesterday's *burfis* at half price. They lower hoarse voices *Hey lady got any hashish*.

I give them what they want. I forget them.

Sometimes I am tempted. For instance. When Kwesi comes in, with his wine-dark skin, his hair the tight-curled tendrils of night clouds. Kwesi who walks like a warrior, without sound, who holds his body in grace and without fear so I long to ask what he does.

And that scar like lightning on his forehead, that bump of knuckle broken and mended on his left hand.

But I do not. It is not permitted.

'Remember why you are going,' the Old One said. 'To help your own kind, and them only. The others, they must go elsewhere for their need.'

And so I let the clamour of the store drown out Kwesi's heart beating its story. I look away from his desires, which are coloured simple as childhood meadows. I weigh and pack what he has bought, powder of garbanzo, ground cumin, two bunches of cilantro. 'Very nice,' I say when he tells me he's going to make *pakoras* for a special friend, and without more talk wave him good-bye. And all the while I keep the door of my mind firmly shut.

But the lonely American feels different, feels like I might have trouble doing the same with him. It isn't what he's wearing. Black tailored pants, black shoes, a plain black leather jacket—but even I so little experienced in this can tell their expensiveness. Nor how he stands, slim and easy-hipped, a casual hand slipped into a pocket, rocking back a little on his heels. Nor his face, though it is arresting enough with its sharp jawline, its high tilted cheekbones hinting stubbornness, his thick blueblack hair falling onto his forehead in careless elegance. And his eyes, very dark, with little points of light flickering deep within. There's nothing in him to show lonely except a spiderweb thought in the corner of my mind, nothing to account for why I'm drawn so.

Then it comes to me. With the others I have always known what they wanted. At once.

'Oh, just looking,' he says when I ask in my oldwoman voice that I suddenly wish were not so quavery.

Just looking, and gives a surprisingly lopsided smile and gazes at me from under straight brows, as though he's really seeing me, *me* underneath this body, and likes what he sees. Though how can that be.

He keeps on gazing straight into my eyes as no one except the Old One has ever done.

There's a lurching inside me, like something stitched up tearing loose.

O danger.

And now I can't read him at all. I go inside him to search and am wound around in a silk cloud. So all I have for knowledge is the quirk of his eyebrow as though he finds it amusing, all of it, but surely I'm silly to think he knows what I'm doing.

I want it, though. I want him to know. And I want him, knowing, to be amused. How long it has been since someone looked at me except in ignorance. Or awe. As I think this, loneliness fills my chest, a new dull aching weight, like drowning water. It is a surprise. I did not know that Mistresses could feel so lonely.

American I too am looking. I thought all my looking was done when I found the spices but then I saw you and now I no longer know.

I want to tell him this. I want to believe he'll understand.

In my head an echo like a song of stone. *A Mistress must carve her own wanting out of her chest, must fill the hollow left behind with the needs of those she serves.*

It is my own voice, out of a time and place that seems so distant I want to call it not-real. To turn my back on it. But.

'You are welcome to look,' I tell the American, my tone all business. 'I must be getting ready to close the shop.' To give myself something to do I restack packets of *papads*, pour *rawa* into paper sacks and label them carefully, push a bin of *atta* to the other side of the doorway.

'Here, let me help you.'

And before I have stopped thinking that his voice is like gold-roasted *besan* all mixed with sugar, his hand is on the rim of the bin, touching mine.

What words can I choose to describe it, this touch that goes through me like a blade of fire, yet so sweet that I want the hurting to never stop. I snatch my hand away obedient to the Mistress laws, but the sensation stays.

And this thought: no one ever wanted to help me before.

'A great place you have here. I love the feel of it,' says my American.

Yes I know it is a liberty I take, to call him mine. To smile my response when I should be saying *Please go, it is much too late, good-bye good night.*

Instead I pick up a packet. 'This is *dhania*,' I say. 'Coriander seed, sphere-shaped like the earth, for clearing your sight. When you soak it and drink, the water purges you of old guilts.'

Why am I telling him this. Tilo stop.

But that silk cloud pulls my words out of me. And into him.

He nods and touches the tiny globes through the plastic covering, courteous and unsurprised, as though what I am saying is most natural.

'And this'—I open a lid and sift the fine powder through my fingers—'is *amchur*. Made from black salt and mangoes dried and pounded, to heal the taste buds, to bring back love of life.'

Tilo don't babble like a girl.

'Ah.' He bends his head to sniff, lifts his eyes to smile approval. 'It's like nothing I've ever smelled before—but I like it.'

Then he moves away.

And says in a voice grown formal, 'I've kept you too long already. You should be closing up.'

Tilottama. Fool who should know better. To think he'd be interested.

At the door he raises his hand, in salute or good-bye or maybe just to wave away the hovering moths. I feel a great sorrow because he is leaving empty-handed, because I couldn't find what he was looking for. Because something is twisting inside, telling me I am losing him, the one man whose heart I could not read.

And then.

'I'll be seeing you,' says the lonely American, and smiles a rhinestone smile. As though he really means it. As though he too will be waiting.

After the lonely American leaves, I wander the store, aimless-sad. Dissatisfaction, that old poison I thought I'd been cured of, bubbles up thick and viscous in me. I cannot bear to lock up. Barring the door would be to admit that he is really gone. Outside, streetlights blink on. Men and women turn up the collars of their coats and disappear underground into the dim clank and clatter of the subway. A yellow fog fills the deserted streets, and in the distance sirens begin to wail, reminding us how fugitive happiness is. But of course no one listens.

I am looking for a spice for him.

'Different spices may help us with different troubles,' the Old One told us after she had taught us the common cures. 'But for each person there is one special spice. No, not for you—the Mistresses must never use the spices for their own ends—but for all who come to you it exists. It is called *mahamul*, the root spice, and for each person it is different. *Mahamul* to enhance fortune, to bring success or joy, to avert ill luck. When you do not know how else to help someone, you must go deep into your being and search out the *mahamul*.'

Lonely American, how shall I begin, I who have always prided myself on the quick remedy?

I roam the shelves. *Kalo jire*? *Ajwain*? Powder of mango-gingerroot? *Choon*, the burning white lime that is wrapped in betel leaves? Nothing seems suitable. Nothing feels right. Perhaps the fault is in me, in my distracted soul. I Tilo who cannot stop thinking about those eyes dark as a tropical night, as deep, as filled with peril.

And why do I persist in calling him lonely? Perhaps even now, even as I stalk discontented down the aisle of lentils, as I plunge restive arms elbow-deep in a bin of *rajma* and let the cool red pods roll over my skin, he is turning a key. The door opens, and a woman with hair like gold mist rises from the couch to take him in her—

No. It isn't so. I will not let it be so.

He enters and turns on a light, flips a switch, and the sound of a *sarod* fills the empty room. He leans back against a Jaipuri cushion—for he loves all things Indian— and thinks about what he has seen today, a store smelling of all the world, a woman whose ageless eyes pull at him like—

Idle wishing. Idle, riskful wishing.

'When you begin to weave your own desires into your vision,' the Old One told us, 'the true seeing is taken from you. You grow confused, and the spices no longer obey you.'

Back Tilo, before it's too late. I force my mind to emptiness. I will trust only my hands, my hands with their singing bones to know what the lonely American needs.

The store stands unbarred, lucent crystal vial under the poised boot-heel of night. The doorway swarms grey with mothwings. But I cannot tend to it now.

I enter the inner room and close my eyes. In the dark my hands glow like lanterns. I trail my fingers along the dusty shelves.

Phosphorous fingers coral fingers, I wait for you to tell me, what I must do.

In his bedroom the lonely American kicks off his shoes, turns down the silk covers of his bed. He shrugs off his shirt and lets it fall to the floor. Candlelight plays liquid on his shoulders, his back, the hard, muscled swell of his buttocks as he lets his pants fall too and stands straight, lithe, made of ivory. In a moment he will turn—

Fluid fills my mouth in a hot sweet rush. In all my lives before, fortune-teller and pirate queen and apprentice of spices, I have never seen a naked man, never desired to see it.

Then my hands shudder to a stop.

Not now, hands, not now. Give me just a moment more.

But they are immovable, adamantine. Mine and not mine. Fisted around something hard and grainy, a pulsing lump whose acrid smell cuts through my vision.

The images crumble, dust or dreaming, and are gone.

Sighing, I open unwilling eyes.

In my hand, a nugget of asafoetida.

A crash in the other room, like something breaking. Or is it the night throwing itself against the store's windowpanes?

Spark-hard rock of Mars, urging the receiver to glory and fame, away from Venus's seductions. Baleful yellow asafoetida to leach away softness and leave a man all sinew and bone.

A gust of wind blows in the smell of wet overcoats. The floor is a floe of ice under my stumbling. I force myself to the door. In my hands the bar feels deadly heavy. Almost I cannot lift it. I must use all my strength to push it shaking into place before it is too late.

Asafoetida *hing*, which is the antidote to love.

I lean against the door, spent, knowing what is expected of me, Mistress of Spices, but also their handmaid.

I feel them watching, like a held breath.

Even the air is like iron.

When I can move again, I go to the handicrafts case. I push aside batik scarves and mirrored cushion covers and brass paper knives and terracotta goddesses, let them all tumble to the floor until I find it, a small smooth ebony box lined with velvet like a blackbird's wing. I open it and drop in the asafoetida, and in the precise, angled island script the Old One taught us I write, *For the lonely American.*

Around me arises a soft relieved humming. A breeze caresses my cheek, a gentle exhalation, moist with approval. Or is it tears—I who have never cried before?

I avert my face from the store, from the million spice eyes, tiny, bright, everywhere. Steel points like nails for me to step on. For the first time since I became a Mistress, I pull a covering around my inmost thoughts.

I am not sure it will work, my deception.

But it seems to. Or is it only the spices humouring me? I slide the box to the back of the shelf under the cash register, to wait in the dust until he comes. I lie down. Around me the spices calm, settle into the rhythms of the night. Their love winds around me heavy as the sevenfold gold Benarasi that women must wear at their wedding.

So much love, how will I breathe?

When the store is lulled into sleep, I uncover the secret chamber of my being and look in. And am not surprised at what I find.

I will not give it to him, heart-hardening asafoetida to my lonely American.

No matter what the spices want.

Not yet, or never?

I do not know the answer to that.

But deep inside I feel the first tremor, warning of earthquakes to come.

The rich Indians descend from hills that twinkle brighter than stars, so bright that it is easy to forget it is only electricity. Their cars gleam like waxed apples, glide like swans over the potholes outside my store.

The car stops, the uniformed chauffeur jumps out to hold open the gold-handled door, and a foot in a gold sandal steps down. Soft and arched and almost white. Rosepetal toes curling in disdain away from what lines the street, wadded paper, rotting peels, dog shit, shucked-off condoms thrown from the back windows of cars.

The rich Indians rarely speak, as if too much money has clogged their throats. Inside the store which they have entered only because friends said, 'O it's so quaint, you *must* go see at least once,' they point. And the chauffeur springs to fetch. Basmati rice, extra-long grain, aged in jute sacking to make it sweet. The finest flour, genuine Elephant brand. Mustard oil in a costly glass bottle, even though sitting right beside are the economy tins. The chauffeur staggers beneath the load. But there's more. Fresh *lauki* flown in from the Philippines, and emerald leafed *methi saag* that I have grown in a box on the back windowsill. A whole box of saffron like shavings of flame and, by the pound, tiny shelled pistas—the most expensive kind—green as mango buds.

'If you wait one week,' I say, 'they will go on sale.' The rich Indians look at me with heavy eyes that are almost no colour at all. They nod at the chauffeur and he picks up another two pounds.

I hide my smile.

The rich Indians crane their necks and lift their chins high because they have to be more always than other people, taller, handsomer, better dressed. Or at least richer. They heave their bodies like moneybags out the door and into their satin cars, leaving the crumbly odour of old banknotes behind.

Other rich people send lists instead, because being a rich person is a busy job. Golf cruises charity luncheons in the Cornelian Room shopping for new Lamborghinis and cigar cases inlaid with lapis lazuli.

Still others have forgotten to be Indian and eat caviar only.

For all of them in the evening I burn *tulsi*, basil which is the plant of humility, curber of ego. The sweet smoke of basil whose taste I know on my own tongue, for many times the Old One has burned it for me too. Basil sacred to Sri Ram, which slakes the craving for power, which turns the thoughts inward, away from worldliness.

Because inward even rich people are people only.

I must tell this to myself over and over. And also what the Old One taught us: 'Not for you to pick and choose your compassion. The ones who anger you most, you must bend most to help.'

There is something else that I must tell you.

When I look deep into the lives of rich people, sometimes I am forced to humility, to say Who would have thought. For instance. Anant Soni who at the end of a day of corporate video conferences sits by his mother's bedside to rub her arthritic hands. And Dr Lalchandani's wife who stares unseeing out the bedroom window of her designer home because across town her husband is in bed with another woman. And Prameela Vijh who sells million-dollar houses and sends money to her sister in a battered women's shelter. And Rajesh whose company went public the same day the doctor pushed the biopsy report across the table at him and said *chemo*.

And right now in front of me a woman in oversize Bill Blass jeans and Gucci shoes is buying stacks and stacks of naans for a party tonight, is drumming rubyflash fingers on the counter as I ring up the flat brown bread, is saying shrill as tin 'Come *on* I'm in a hurry.' But inside she is thinking of her teenage son. He's been acting so strange lately, hanging out with boys who frighten her with their razor earrings and biker jackets and heavy boots as though for war, their cold, cold eyes and slits of mouths that are becoming *his* eyes, *his* mouth. Could he be taking— Her mind shudders away from the word she cannot say even inside her clamped lips, and under the layers, foundation and concealer and rouge and thick fuchsia eyeshadow, her face grows bruised with love.

Rich woman I thank you for reminding me. Beneath the shiniest armour, gold-plated or diamond, the beat of the vulnerable flesh.

Into a corner of her matching Gucci purse I place *hartuki*, shrivelled seed in the shape of a womb, which has no American name. *Hartuki* to help mothers bear the pain that starts with the birthing and continues for ever, the pain and joy both, tangled dark and blue as an umbilical cord around an infant's throat.

Saturday comes upon me like the unexpected flash of rainbow under a bird's black wing, like the swirl-spread skirt of a *kathak* dancer, fast and then faster. Saturday is drums bursting from the stereos of the young men who drive by dangerous-slow, and what are they looking for. Saturday takes my breath. For Saturday I put up signs: FRESH-FRESH METHI HOME GROWN, DIWALI SALE LOWEST PRICES; LATEST MOVIES BEST ACTORS, JUHI CHAWLA-AMIR KHAN, RENT 2 DAYS FOR COST OF ONE. And even, daringly, ASK IF YOU CANNOT FIND.

So many people on Saturday, it seems the walls must take a deep breath just to hold them in. All those voices, Hindi Oriya Assamese Urdu Tamil English, layered one on the other like notes from a *tanpura,* all those voices asking for more than their words, asking for happiness except no one seems to know where. And so I must listen to the spaces between, must weigh them in my coral-boned hands. Must whisper chants over packets and sacks even as I weigh and measure and ring up, even as I call out in my pretend-strict voice, 'Please no touching *mithais*' and, 'If bottle breaks you must pay.'

All who come to my store on Saturday, I love them.

You must not think that only the unhappy visit my store. The others come too, and they are many. A father carrying his daughter on his shoulders, picking up *laddus* on the way to the zoo. A retired couple, she holding his elbow as he leans on his cane. Two wives out for an afternoon of shopping and talk. A young computer scientist planning to impress his visiting parents with his new cooking skills. They step through my doors lightly, and as they move from aisle to aisle, choosing, the faintest of radiances flickers around them.

See, bunches of podina *leaves green as the forests of our childhood. Hold them up and smell how fresh and pungent, isn't this cause enough for gladness. Tear open a packet of chilli-cashews and cram a handful into the mouth. Chew. That hot taste, that crumble and crunch against your cheeks, the delicious tears that rise to your eyes. Here's* kumkum *powder red as the heart of a hibiscus flower to put on our foreheads for married luck. And look, look, Mysore sandalwood soap with its calm bright fragrance, the same brand you used to buy me in India so many years ago when we were newlyweds. Ah life, how fine it is.*

I send a blessing behind them as they leave, a whisper of thanks that they have let me share their joy. But already they are fading from my mind, already I am turning from them to the others. The ones whom I need because they need me.

Manu who is seventeen, in a 49ers jacket so shiny red it's like a yell, running in impatient to pick up a sack of *bajra atta* for his mother before he goes to shoot some hoops at school. Angry Manu who is a senior at Ridgefield High, thinking Not fair not fair. Because when he said 'prom' his father shouted, 'All that drinking whisky-beer and dancing pressed up against cheap American girls in miniskirts, what are you thinking of.' Manu poised tip-toe inside furious fluorescent Nike shoes that he bought with money saved up cleaning bathrooms in his uncle's motel, ready to take off if only he knew where he would land.

Manu I give you a slab of sesame candy made with sweet molasses, *gur* to slow you down just enough to hear the frightened love in your father's voice losing you to America.

And Daksha who comes in with her white nurse's uniform starched and shiny, even her shoes even her smile.

'Daksha what do you need today?'

'Aunty today is *ekadasi* you know, eleventh day of the moon, and my mother-in-law being a widow must not eat rice. So I thought maybe some cracked wheat to make a *dalia* pudding for her and as long as I was here, might as well pick up some of your *methi*, my husband is so fond of *methi parathas*.'

As she sifts through the bittergreen leaves I watch her face. Under the edges where the shine has rubbed off, the smile pulls down. Every night coming home from the hospital to cook, rolling out *chapatis* hot hot with ghee because her mother-in-law says old food from the fridge is good only for servants or dogs. Boiling frying seasoning ladling serving wiping up while everyone sits saying, 'Good,' saying, 'Yes, more,' even her husband, because after all isn't the kitchen the woman's place.

In answer to my asking she says, 'Yes Aunty it's hard but what to do. After all we must take care of our old. It makes too much trouble in the house if I say I can't do all this work. But sometimes I wish—'

She stops. Daksha to whom no one listens so she has forgotten how to say. And inside her, pushing up against her palate enormous and silent, the horror of what she sees all day. In the AIDS ward those young, young men grown light as children in their eroding bones. Their fragile bruised skin, their enormous waiting eyes.

Daksha here is seed of black pepper to be boiled whole and drunk to loosen your throat so you can learn to say No, that word so hard for Indian women. *No* and *Hear me now*.

And Daksha before you go, here is *amla* for a different resistance. *Amla* which I too would like to take some days to help bear the pain that cannot be changed, pain growing slow and huge like a monsoon cloud which if you let it will blot out the sun.

Now Vinod sidles in, Vinod who owns India Market on the other side of the bay and comes sometimes to check out the competition, who hefts a five-pound packet of *dal* with practised hands to see if it's just a little less, like in his store. Who thinks *fool* when it isn't. Vinod who jumps when I say, 'How's business Vinod-*bhai*' because he has always thought I don't know who he is. I give him a packet filled with green-brown-black and say, 'Compliments of management' and hide my laugh behind my hand while he sniffs at it suspiciously.

'Ah *kari patti*,' he says finally. Inside he is thinking *Crazy woman*, is thinking $2.49 *profit*, as he slips it into his pocket, astringent leaf dried dark on the stem to reduce mistrust and avarice.

I. Allan Sealy

Just Desserts

This was a formative period in the Great Trotter's career. He gathered around him cooks, Muslim cooks from Nakhlau, Hindu cooks from Benares, Parsi cooks from Bombay, Christian cooks from Goa, Daman, and Diu, Jewish cooks from Cochin, cooks from Assam to Gujarat, from Kashmir to Kerala, cooks from Trans-oxiana and those parts, free Brahmin cooks, bound Pariyah cooks, bellicose Jat cooks, egg-brahmins from Rohilkhand, fish-brahmins from Bengal, non-garlic Jains, chapati Punjabis, rice Madrasis, Gujaratis who use sugar in their curries (*Admirable Race*), Goans who use vinegar, Pahadis who use fruit, Burmans who use coconut, turmeric-grinders from Malaya, Cambodian gingermen, Javanese peppermen, Bangkok onionmen, Cuttack macemen, drifters from the Cardamom Hills, curry-powder miners from the Sagarpaysans, muscle-bound masalchis, footloose spice-tasters, shapely oilmen, good-looking deep-fryers, dashing rice-factors, jobbing boners, stringy kneaders, rakish stokers, brawny strainers, tetchy peelers, stodgy griddlemen, suave rolling-pin artistes, smarmy pot-stirrers, avid tasters, Tibetan marrow-men, Szechuan noodle-winders, Kazhaki pemmican-traders, Georgian goulash-

This extract is taken from *The Trotter-Nama,* published by IndiaInk, New Delhi, 1990.

turners, Armenian cinnamon-shakers, and a half-Turkish baker's apprentice with eyes like living coals.

A man who sits on a saltpetre hill can command much.

As Sans Souci took shape around him, Justin grew into his house, a dome appearing there, a belly here; there a turret, here a fold; here a palpitating buttock, there a gibbous barbican. And as his appetite for curries deepened, his tastes widened to take in mint chutneys, cauliflower pickles, cucumber salads, green mango achars, tomato kasaundis, lotus-root, tamarind, pepper-water, pastes, purees, preserves, curds, raitas, and a thousand accompaniments of rich and satisfying food.

There was one lack (*Ignoble Deficiency, National Scandal*). Justin longed for dessert. But the Indian cooks, who held sway in the kitchens, one and all looked at him askance: sweets, certainly, they allowed, but in their place, not with meals. Justin was not appeased. How to shake off a habit instilled in him by a stepmother who having failed in song found succour in desserts? And to the horror of the young baker's apprentice-and-waiter who regularly brought him a saucer of digestive anise seed to conclude a meal, the First Trotter sent for and broke a pomegranate of crystal sugar and mixed its kernels in with the aromatic seed. In this modest way, soon to be refined, was born the first true Indian dessert: a sweet eaten directly following the other courses and not at some casual remove (*Path-Breaker, Sweet Outrider*).

Having perfected his menu, the Great Trotter looked about him and found a banquetting hall risen at no great distance from the unfinished North Tower. Down the length of the hall, between pillars of aqua marble, ran a long table, varnished and buffed to a gloss that concealed the many leaves by which its length could be increased depending on the number of guests expected. High-backed chairs upholstered with maroon leather stood along the walls, ready to be drawn up should the occasion arise. Chandeliers cut and worked by Bohemian craftsmen hung in festoons waiting for the brilliant dinner parties that would last far into the night. The walls beyond the colonnades were lined with tapestries depicting revels of bygone ages in far countries; the pictures in between showed wedding scenes with wine and food in plenty and riotous guests convivially entwined. But Justin ate alone.

The First Trotter dined in solitude. His gigantic meals took up a fraction of the table, being carried to him in relays of ascending complexity, the covers shifted nearer the Nakhlau end as he progressed, sinking ever deeper into his upright chair. At length the First Trotter would sigh and call for his finger-bowl, indicating that he was done with preliminaries. The sigh would twine about the marble columns, creep down the corridor, and slip in at the kitchen door. At once another and louder sigh would come back out. Puri fryers would get up and stretch, curry-factors mop their armpits; a few hours' rest was theirs, for now the sweetmeat brigade were busying themselves with trays of halva, hefting bowls of laddus on their shoulders, unfurling sheets of beaten silver for the jalebis. When Justin saw out of the corner of his eye a dozen bearers making for him along the corridor in Indian file, his heart would leap up and go out to meet them and he would count himself the most fortunate of men. I will call this place Sans Souci, he breathed; and he did.

The last sweet gone (*Evening Raga, Dark Pavan*) Justin was yet conscious of an unnamed anxiety that roamed the table, hovering like some disconsolate wasp. A knowledge he had been dimly aware of all along began to coat his tongue and for a moment cleft it to the roof of his mouth. Justin was bored. He was tired, not of life, not of eating (*Hair-Splitting Narrator, Quibbling School-man*), but of eating alone. Justin was lonely. Not that he was ignorant of the pleasures of secret food-hoards, solitary feasts, private rumination. Nor were the giant banquetting hall meals devoid of charm, and their advantage over communal meals did not escape one who had known the privations of a regimental mess. It was simply that he could not, he knew, always and forever eat alone. On such occasions Justin would have liked to lift his head and see at the far end of the table a face, soft and contemplative, regarding him with, if not motherly devotion, wifely love.

DEPRIVATION

BIBHUTIBHUSHAN BANDOPADHYAYA

Apu's Trials

Apu had always been poor, but never before had he faced such enormous hardships. His parents had indulged him, and even when things had seemed very difficult indeed after his father's death, he had not had to starve. Sarbajaya had protected him from the harsh realities of life as only a mother can protect her young. Diwanpur had been difficult, but even so, it had been possible to indulge in a few luxuries occasionally. But then, things were that much cheaper then.

Calcutta was a different story. Besides, a war had started in Europe. Clothes had become impossibly expensive. He had only one good shirt—made of tulle—which he had to wash every other day. He could not go out until it was dry. Sometimes he was forced to put it on even before it had dried properly. The effort of washing it in the morning made him doubly hungry. A plate of muri did nothing to help. There were days when Apu felt strange while attending his classes, an empty stomach made his head feel so light that he could not concentrate.

There was an additional problem of accommodation. Sureshwar had finished his final exams and gone home. His room in the mess

This extract is taken from *Aparajito*, published by HarperCollins *Publishers* India Limited, New Delhi, 1999.

had gone to someone else. But before leaving, Sureshwar had spoken to someone he knew in a medicine factory. His acquaintance had agreed to share his room with Apu, at least temporarily. The room was small and directly over the factory. Half of it was crammed with empty cartons and packing boxes. Behind these, endless rubbish had been stashed over a long period of time. There was a faint stench that refused to go away. There were mice, too. Already, Apu had discovered two tiny holes in his only good shirt. Cockroaches abounded, but what Apu found most objectionable was his roommate. He was grateful to him, but the other man seemed to have absolutely no notion of cleanliness. Fond of his hookah, he got up several times during the night and left heaps of used tobacco on the floor. Apu got tired of cleaning up after him.

Walking aimlessly, one day he found himself near a tram stop. A hawker was selling newspapers, shouting out the headlines. There was fresh news about the war. Apu paid no attention. He looked idly at the people standing at the tram stop. Suddenly, his eyes fell on a young man wearing glasses. His face seemed familiar. Where had he seen him before? The young man glanced in Apu's direction and caught his eye. Now Apu could recognise him. It was Suresh. His father used to own the property next to Apu's house in Nischindipur. They had once been neighbours, although Suresh and his family had moved out of Nischindipur long before Apu. Their property had stood abandoned for years. Suresh happened to recognize Apu as he moved forward eagerly. 'Why, Suresh da, it's you!' he said.

'Yes. Apurbo, isn't it? Do you work here?' Suresh spoke lightly. He had clearly become a city lad. There was a certain polish and sophistication in his appearance and speech, which suddenly made Apu feel a little unsure of himself.

'N-no. I am a student. First year, Ripon College,' he replied.

'I see. So where are you off to now?'

Apu did not answer his question. 'Where is Jethima?' he asked instead. He had always called Suresh's mother Jethima. They had not been particularly close to Apu's family, but now he felt as though Suresh and his mother were people he had known all his life. In his own excitement, he failed to notice the very casual tone Suresh was using. It was true that he had recognised Apu, but that had made no great difference. Suresh was not overcome with joy.

'Ma? Ma is in Shyambajar. That's where we live now. We bought a new house there.'

'And your sister? Atashi di? Is she there? Sunil? What's Sunil doing?'

'Sunil's still in school. All right then, I must catch this tram.'

'What are you doing these days, Suresh da?'

'I am a medical student. I'm in my third year.'

'I will go and visit you one day.'

'Very well. Goodbye.'

Suresh jumped into a tram. Apu ran alongside and asked hurriedly, 'Your address? Suresh da you didn't tell me . . .'

'24/2C Vishwakosh Lane, Shyambajar,' Suresh shouted. The tram disappeared.

The following Sunday, Apu wore his tulle shirt (having washed it the previous evening) and borrowed some polish for his shoes. He would meet Suresh's mother and sister. He had to dress as well as he could.

It proved fairly easy to find the house. It wasn't very large, but built according to the latest design. A maid opened the door and showed him into the drawing room. Apu noticed electric switches on the wall and felt very pleased. It was nice to think someone he knew lived in this house. But Suresh was not at home. He would have to wait. Apu did not mind. He sat admiring the furniture, the clock on the wall, the calendar, the paintings, the old roll-top desk in a corner. To think he knew the people who owned these lovely things! He felt a little proud.

It was quite late by the time Suresh arrived. Apu rose to his feet and greeted him with a smile. 'Why, it's Apurbo!' exclaimed Suresh, 'When did you get here?'

'A long time ago,' Apu replied, 'What a nice house this is, Suresh da!'

'Yes . . . my uncle bought it . . . . Could you excuse me for a moment?'

Suresh went into the house. 'He's gone to tell his mother I'm here,' Apu said to himself. 'Now he's going to come back and take me in to meet her. Then she'll ask me to stay for lunch.'

Suresh returned an hour later. He sat down, leant back lazily and said, 'So . . . what have you been doing with yourself?' Then, without waiting for a reply, he picked up a newspaper and began reading it. Apu noted with some surprise that he was chewing a paan. How could he have a paan before lunch? Or had he eaten already?

Another hour passed. It was now one o'clock. Suresh went on reading his paper, just occasionally throwing a few casual questions at Apu. Then he put the paper aside, rose and said, 'Why don't you read the paper, Apurbo? I must go and lie-down. I say, would you like a daab?'

A daab? Why would he wish to have the water of a green coconut before lunch? Taken aback, Apu stammered, 'Why, n-no, I don't think. . . .'

'Very well,' said Suresh indifferently and went inside again.

Apu continued to wait patiently. It was now half past two. When did these people have their lunch? Or was lunch delayed today because it was a Sunday? Ah, that must be it. But when another thirty minutes passed, it finally dawned upon Apu that there was something wrong somewhere. There had been a mistake, but who had made it? Was it he, or was it they? The pangs of hunger had grown so strong that he could no longer sit still. He half rose to his feet, but at this moment he saw Suresh's younger brother, Sunil, come out of the house; before Apu could call out to him, he picked up a bicycle and went out. This sight of the young boy made him feel both pleased and surprised. Was it really the same Sunil? He remembered going to a dinner with him in Nischindipur. The host had given them packets of food to take back home. For this reason, Sunil's mother had called Apu 'the son of a greedy Brahmin'.

He felt no rancour to think about it. These people belonged to the most cherished part of his life. He had not come here for any selfish gain, but simply to meet old friends. It did not occur to him even once that his sudden arrival might be seen as an imposition, or an attempt to worm his way into their house. It was only his inherent sense of wonder that had brought him here. Who knew that, one day, he would meet here in Calcutta the people who owned the house next to his own, back in Nischindipur? This simple fact was enough to enchant him. It was as if, walking down the long and weary road of life, he had suddenly turned an unexpected corner, and found a green wood full of fragrant flowers.

Not everyone possesses such a sense of wonder. Only a mind that is alive, alert, generous and capable of accepting new thoughts and new images, can experience wonder. Those who have called wonder the 'Mother of Philosophy' have not been able to capture its true meaning. Wonder itself is the 'philosophy', the rest merely defines it.

Suresh re-emerged after three o'clock. 'I had night duty, you see,' he said, yawning, 'I didn't get any sleep last night. So I had to lie down . . . I believe there's a hockey match this evening. Would you like to come with me?'

Apu felt a little contrite for having blamed Suresh earlier for going to sleep. If he had not slept the night before, naturally he was tired. But clearly it was time to go. 'No, thank you,' he said, rising, 'I have an exam tomorrow, I must go back and study for it. Only . . . er . . . can I just see Jethima before I go?'

'Of course. Come with me.'

Apu followed Suresh with hesitant steps into an inner room,

where his mother was sitting. 'Ma, Apu here would like a word,' Suresh said. 'Remember Apu? From Nischindipur?'

Apu quickly touched her feet. Now he knew that Suresh had simply kept him sitting outside, he had not found it necessary to tell his mother, or anyone else, about his visit. Jethima said, 'Oh yes, I see. What do you do here, Apu?'

Apu had hardly ever spoken to this lady. Her grave face and arrogant behaviour (which, as a child, he had not been able to grasp fully) used to frighten him. Now, he swallowed and stuttered a little: 'I . . . I . . . study in Calcutta . . . in a college, that is.'

Jethima seemed surprised. 'In a college? When did you finish school? Didn't you go to Kashi?'

Apu explained. 'I see,' said Jethima briefly. Almost immediately, a young woman in her early twenties came in, accompanied by a girl of about sixteen. Apu recognised the older woman. It was Atashi, Suresh's sister. 'Atashi di! I am Apu,' he said. Atashi behaved with greater warmth than her mother. She recognised him, and seemed quite willing to spend a few minutes chatting. Jethima left the room in a few seconds. Apu was not introduced to the other girl, but he caught her staring at him. Then she and Atashi left together.

What was Apu going to do now? Should he simply get up and leave? Wouldn't that be rude? He no longer felt hungry, but strangely dizzy. Slowly, he rose to his feet and stepped out. The young girl was crossing the passage outside. Apu called her, 'I am going now. Will you please tell Jethima? Er . . . I have some work, you see . . .'

The girl stopped and looked at him. 'But you didn't even have a cup of tea!' she exclaimed. 'Wait, let me go and tell my aunt.'

'N-no, no,' Apu said hastily, 'please don't bother. I don't really want any tea.'

'It's no bother.' The girl disappeared, and returned a little later with a cup of tea and a plate of halwa. Apu pounced upon the plate and gobbled what was on it. The hot tea burnt his mouth; then he poured some into a saucer to cool it.

'Are you a cousin or something?' the girl asked. 'No, it's all right, you may leave the plate here. Would you like some more halwa?'

'No, thank you. I . . . I am not very hungry. And yes, I am a distant cousin.'

When he returned to his room quite late that night after his dinner at the temple, he discovered that another man had turned up for the night. This was nothing unusual. The workers in the factory downstairs received visitors occasionally, who were offered the same room. Normally, Apu wouldn't mind, but this room was so small and cramped that it became impossible to move with three people in it, let alone sit and read in peace.

Apu had met the new arrival once before. He was in the business of supplying potatoes to wholesale dealers, and was given to talking nonstop. Apu was forced to come out almost as soon as he returned.

'Where are you off to again?' the man called.

'Just outside. It's so hot today.'

A few moments later, the man spoke again: 'Whose bed is this? Sir, is it yours? Look, look, I spilt water near your bed, please remove it . . . damn!'

Apu came back and moved his mattress as far as he could from a pool of water in the middle of the floor. What could he say? He had been allowed to stay here only because his roommate had felt sorry for him. How could he protest if things were not to his liking? To tell the truth, today he was too preoccupied to notice or feel anything, even anger. He stood on the little balcony outside, staring at the old wooden railing and its peeling paint, and thought of Suresh's house. What a lovely house he lived in! They had electric lights and fans, such beautiful furniture, their women had so much style. They had tea and snacks on the dot of four . . . Lakshmi smiled on them, they lacked nothing.

It was only he and his family that seemed cursed. Why was his mother forced to live alone in a village? Why was he floating around in the city like this, on a half-empty stomach, without a penny in his pocket, wearing an old shirt? What had he done to deserve this?

Three days later, there was a special puja, called Jagaddhatri Puja. Apu had no idea the people of Calcutta celebrated it with such fanfare. He had never seen such a thing in the village. Shehnais were being played in every lane, and garlands of deodar leaves were strung on doorways.

In the next lane, a puja was being held in the house of a rich man. When darkness fell, Apu could see a large number of guests going into the house to have dinner. What if . . . what if he slipped in with them? It was such a long time since he had been to a big dinner. Could he do it? Who would recognise him, anyway?

Apu stood in his balcony, swinging between temptation and fear.

—*Translated from the Bengali* Aparajito *by Gopa Majumdar*

R.K. Narayan

Fasting

A wandering newspaper correspondent who had come to the village picked the news. The government had sent a commission to inquire into the drought conditions and suggest remedies, and with it came a press correspondent. While wandering around he heard about the Swamiji, went to the temple across the river, and sent off a wire to his paper at Madras, which circulated in all the towns of India. 'Holy man's penance to end drought', said the heading, and then a brief description followed.

This was the starting point.

Public interest was roused. The newspaper office was besieged for more news. They ordered the reporter to go back. He sent a second telegram to say 'Fifth day of fast'. He described the scene: how the Swami came to the river's edge, faced its source, stood knee-deep in the water from six to eight in the morning, muttering something between his lips, his eyes shut, his palms pressed together in a salute to the gods, presumably. It had been difficult enough to find knee-deep water, but the villagers had made an artificial basin in sand and, when it didn't fill, fetched water from distant wells and filled it, so that the man had always knee-deep

This extract is taken from *The Guide*, published by Penguin Books India, New Delhi, 1993.

water to stand in. The holy man stood there for two hours, then walked up the steps slowly and lay down on a mat in the pillared hall of the temple, while his devotees kept fanning him continuously. He took notice of hardly anyone, though there was a big crowd around. He fasted totally. He lay down and shut his eyes in order that his penance might be successful. For that he conserved all his energy. When he was not standing in the water, he was in deep meditation. The villagers had set aside all their normal avocations in order to be near this great soul all the time. When the slept they remained there, guarding him, and though there was a fair-sized crowd, it remained totally silent.

But each day the crowd increased. In a week there was a permanent hum pervading the place. Children shouted and played about, women came carrying caskets filled with pots, firewood, and foodstuffs, and cooked the food for their men and children. There were small curls of smoke going up all along the river bank, on the opposite slope and on this bank also. It was studded with picnic groups, with the women's bright-coloured sarees shining in the sun; men too had festive dress. Bullocks unyoked from their carts jingled their bells as they ate the straw under the trees. People swarmed around little water-holes.

Raju saw them across his pillared hall whenever he opened his eyes. He knew what that smoke meant; he knew that they were eating and enjoying themselves. He wondered what they might be eating—rice boiled with a pinch of saffron, melted *ghee*—and what were the vegetables? Probably none in this drought. The sight tormented him.

This was actually the fourth day of his fast. Fortunately on the first day he had concealed a little stale food, left over from the previous day, in an aluminium vessel behind a stone pillar in the innermost sanctum—some rice mixed with buttermilk, and a piece of vegetable thrown in. Fortunately, too, he was able on the first day to snatch a little privacy at the end of the day's prayer and penance, late at night. The crowd had not been so heavy then. Velan had business at home and had gone, leaving two others to attend on the Swami. The Swami had been lying on the mat in the pillared hall, with the two villagers looking on and waving a huge palmyra fan at his face. He had felt weakened by his day's fasting. He had suddenly told them, 'Sleep, if you like; I'll be back,' and he rose in a businesslike manner and passed into his inner sanctum.

'I don't have to tell the fellows where I am going or why or how long I shall be gone out of sight.' He felt indignant. He had lost all privacy. People all the time watching and staring, lynx-eyed, as if he were a thief! In the inner sanctum he briskly thrust his hand into a niche and pulled out his aluminium pot. He sat down behind the pedestal, swallowed his food in three or four large mouthfuls, making as little noise as possible. It was stale rice, dry and stiff and two days old; it tasted awful, but it appeased his hunger. He washed it down with water. He went to the back yard and rinsed his mouth noiselessly—he didn't want to smell of food when he went back to his mat.

Lying on his mat, he brooded. He felt sick of the whole thing. When the assembly was at its thickest, could he not stand up on a high pedestal and cry, 'Get out, all of you, and leave me alone, I am not the man to save you. No power on earth can save you if you are doomed. Why do you bother me with all this fasting and austerity?'

It would not help. They might enjoy it as a joke. He had his back to the wall, there was no further retreat. This realization helped him to get through the trial with a little more resignation on the second day of his penance. Once again he stood up in water, muttering with his face to the hills, and watching the picnic groups enjoying themselves all over the place. At night he left Velan for a while and sneaked in to look for leftover food in his aluminium vessel—it was really an act of desperation. He knew full well that he had finished off the vessel the previous night. Still he hoped, childishly, for a miracle. 'When they want me to perform all sorts of miracles, why not make a start with my own aluminium vessel?' he reflected caustically. He felt weak. He was enraged at the emptiness of his larder. He wondered for a moment if he could make a last desperate appeal to Velan to let him eat— and if only he minded, how he could save him! Velan ought to know, yet the fool would not stop thinking that he was a saviour. He banged the aluminium vessel in irritation and went back to his mat. What if the vessel did get shattered? It was not going to be of any use. What was the point of pampering an empty vessel? When he was seated, Velan asked respectfully, 'What was that noise, master?'

'An empty vessel. Have you not heard the saying, "An empty vessel makes much noise"?'

Velan permitted himself a polite laugh and declared with admiration, 'How many good sentiments and philosophies you have gathered in that head of yours, sir!' . . .

Velan, fanning him, had fallen asleep—he had just doubled up in his seat with the fan in his hand. Raju, who lay awake, had let his mind roam and touch the depths of morbid and fantastic thought. He was now touched by the sight of this man hunched in his seat. The poor fellow was tremendously excited and straining himself in order to make this penance a success, providing the great man concerned with every comfort—except, of course, food. Why not give the poor devil a chance, Raju said to himself, instead of hankering after food which one could not get anyway. He felt enraged at the persistence of food-thoughts. With a sort of vindictive resolution he told himself, 'I'll chase away all thought of food. For the next ten days I shall eradicate all thoughts of tongue and stomach from my mind.'

This resolution gave him a peculiar strength. He developed on those lines: 'If by avoiding food I should help the trees bloom, and the grass grow, why not do it thoroughly?' For the first time in his life he was making an earnest effort: for the first time he was learning the thrill of full application, outside money and love; for the first time he was doing a thing in which he was not personally interested. He felt suddenly so enthusiastic that it gave him a new strength to go through with the ordeal. The fourth day of his fast found him quite sprightly. He went down to the river, stood facing upstream with his eyes shut, and repeated the litany. It was no more than a supplication to the heavens to send down rain and save humanity. It was set in a certain rhythmic chant, which lulled his senses and awareness, so that as he went on saying it over and over again the world around became bland. He nearly lost all sensation, except the numbness at his knees, through constant contact with cold water. Lack of food gave him a peculiar floating feeling, which he rather enjoyed, with the thought in the background, 'This enjoyment is something Velan cannot take away from me.'

The hum of humanity around was increasing. His awareness of his surroundings was gradually lessening in a sort of inverse proportion. He was not aware of it, but the world was beginning to press around. The pen of the wandering journalist had done the trick. Its repercussions were far and wide. The railways were the first to feel the pressure. They had to run special trains for the crowds that were going to Malgudi. People travelled on footboards and on the roofs of coaches. The little Malgudi station was choked with passengers. Outside, the station buses stood, the conductors crying, 'Special for Mangala leaving. Hurry up. Hurry up.' People rushed up from the station into the buses and almost sat on top of one another. Gaffur's taxi drove up and down a dozen times a day. And the crowd congregated around the river at Mangala. People sat in groups along its sandbank, down its stones and steps, all the way up the opposite bank, wherever they could squeeze themselves in . . .

A large crowd always stood around and watched the saint with profound awe. They touched the water at his feet and sprinkled it over their heads. They stood indefinitely around, until the master of ceremonies, Velan, begged them to move. 'Please go away. The Swami must have fresh air. If you have had your *darshan*, move on and let others have theirs. Don't be selfish.' And then the people moved on and enjoyed themselves in various ways.

When the Swami went in to lie on his mat in the hall, they came again to look at him and stood about until Velan once again told them to keep moving. A few were specially privileged to sit on the edge of the mat very close to the great man . . .

The pink visitor stooped low to ask the schoolmaster, sitting beside the Swami, 'Can I speak to him in English?'

'Yes. He knows English.'

The man lowered himself on to the edge of the mat and with difficulty sat down on the floor, Indian fashion, crossing his legs. He bent close to the Swami to say, 'I'm James J. Malone. I'm from California. My business is production of films and TV shows. I have come to shoot this subject, take it back to our country, and show it to our people there, I have in my pocket the sanction from New Delhi for this project. May I have yours?'

Raju thought over it and nodded serenely.

'Okay. Thanks a lot. I won't disturb you—but will you let me shoot pictures of you ? I wouldn't disturb you. Will it bother you if I move a few things up and fix the cable and lights?'

'No, you may do your work,' said the sage.

The man became extremely busy. He sprang to his feet, pulled the trailer into position, and started his generator. Its throbbing filled the place, overwhelming all other noises. It brought in a huge crowd of men, women, and children to watch the fun. All the other attractions in the camp became secondary. As Malone drew the cables about, a big crowd followed him. He grinned at them affably and went about his business, Velan and one or two others ran through the crowd, crying, 'Is this a fish market? Get away, all of you who have no work here!' But nobody was affected by his orders. They climbed pillars and pedestals and clung to all sorts of places to reach positions of vantage. Malone went on with his job without noticing anything. Finally, when he had the lights ready, he brought in his camera and took pictures of the people and the temple, and of the Swami from various angles and distances.

'I'm sorry, Swami, if the light is too strong.' When he had finished with the pictures, he brought in a microphone, put it near the Swami's face, and said, 'Let us chat. Okay? Tell me, how do you like it here?'

'I am only doing what I have to do; that's all. My likes and dislikes do not count.'

'How long have you been without food now?'

'Ten days.'

'Do you feel weak?'

'Yes.'

'When will you break your fast?'

'Twelfth day.'

'Do you expect to have the rains by then?'

'Why not?'

'Can fasting abolish all wars and bring world peace?'

'Yes.'

'Do you champion fasting for everyone?'

'Yes.'

'What about the caste system? Is it going?'

'Yes.'

'Will you tell us something about your early life?'

'What do you want me to say?'

'Er—for instance, have you always been a yogi?'

'Yes; more or less.'

It was very hard for the Swami to keep up a continuous flow of talk. He felt exhausted and lay back. Velan and others looked on with concern. The schoolmaster said, 'He is fatigued.'

'Well, I guess we will let him rest for a while. I'm sorry to bother you.'

The Swami lay back with his eyes closed. A couple of doctors, deputed by the government to watch and report, went to the Swami, felt his pulse and heart. They helped him to stretch himself on a mat. A big hush fell upon the crowd. Velan plied his fan more vigorously than ever. He looked distraught and unhappy. In fact, keeping a sympathetic fast, he was now eating on alternate days, confining his diet to saltless boiled greens. He looked worn out. He said to the master, 'One more day. I don't know how he is going to bear it. I dread to think how he can pull through another day.'

Malone resigned himself to waiting. He looked at the doctor and asked, 'How do you find him?'

'Not very satisfactory; blood pressure is two hundred systolic. We suspect one of the kidneys is affected. Uremia is setting in. We are trying to give him small doses of saline and glucose. His life is valuable to the country.'

'Would you say a few words about his health?' Malone asked, thrusting his microphone forward. He was sitting on the head of a carved elephant decorating the steps to the pillared hall.

The doctors looked at each other in panic and said, 'Sorry. We are government servants—we cannot do it without permission. Our reports are released only from headquarters. We cannot give them direct. Sorry.'

'Okay. I wouldn't hurt your customs.' He looked at his watch and said, 'I guess that's all for the day.' . . .

The eleventh day, morning. The crowd, pouring in all night, had nearly trebled itself because it was the last day of the fast. All night one could hear the voices of people and the sound of vehicles rattling over the roads and pathways. Velan and a band of his assistants formed a cordon and kept the crowd out of the pillared hall. They said, 'The Swami must have fresh air to breathe. It's the only thing he takes now. Don't choke the air. Everyone can have his *darshan* at the river, I promise. Go away now. He is resting.' It was an all-night vigil. The numerous lanterns and lamps created a criss-cross of bewildering shadows on all hedges, trees, and walls.

At five-thirty in the morning the doctors examined the Swami. They wrote and signed a bulletin saying: 'Swami's condition grave. Declines glucose and saline. Should break the fast immediately. Advise procedure.' They sent a man running to send off this telegram to their headquarters.

It was a top-priority government telegram, and it fetched a reply within an hour: 'Imperative that Swami should be saved. Persuade best to cooperate. Should not risk life. Try give glucose and saline. Persuade Swami resume fast later.'

They sat beside the Swami and read the message to him. He smiled at it. He beckoned Velan to come nearer.

The doctors appealed, 'Tell him he should save himself. Please, do your best. He is very weak.'

Velan bent close to the Swami and said, 'The doctors say—'

In answer Raju asked the man to bend nearer, and whispered, 'Help me to my feet,' and clung to his arm and lifted himself. He got to his feet. He had to be held by Velan and another on each side. Many in the camp were still sleeping. Raju could not walk, but he insisted upon pulling himself along all the same. He panted with the effort. He went down the steps of the river, halting for breath on each step, and finally reached his basin of water. He stepped into it, shut his eyes, and turned towards the mountain, his lips muttering the prayer. Velan and another held him each by an arm. The morning sun was out by now; a great shaft of light illuminated the surroundings. It was difficult to hold Raju on his feet, as he had a tendency to flop down. They held him as if he were a baby. Raju opened his eyes, looked about, and said, 'Velan, it's raining in the hills. I can feel it coming up under my feet, up my legs—' He sagged down.

MANJULA PADMANABHAN

The Diet

Ten days before the arrival of the Dutch guests, I had been to see a doctor about losing weight. His name was Dr Shiva Prasad. He had recently opened a diet clinic highly recommended to me by a friend.

When I called to make the initial appointment, the doctor asked if I was married. I said 'no'. He asked if I had any friends or relatives in whose company I regularly ate my meals. I said I had a boyfriend called Prashant with whom I spent most of my spare time, including dinner every day. He was copy chief at an ad agency and his workday usually ended around 6.30 p.m. He would collect me from Palm View on his motorbike and we would spend the rest of the evening either at my married brother's house or at a movie. If we didn't eat at my brother's house we ate at a restaurant. The doctor advised me to bring my friend along for the first 'briefing'. According to him, the cooperation of regular eating companions was essential to the success of a diet.

So I invited Prashant to accompany me. We spent an hour with the doctor. He was a marvellous advertisement for his clinic: slender as a whip and surrounded by framed portraits of the forty

This extract is taken from *Getting There*, published by Picador India, New Delhi, 2002.

racehorses he owned at his stables in Bangalore. The impression he gave was that if his 'patients' followed his instructions, they might succeed not only in losing weight but in gaining racehorses too. As he put it, 'It's not about becoming thin or fat: it's about becoming successful.'

He showed us progress slides of his prize patient, a woman who, at the start of the diet, looked like a wrestler dressed in a printed silk sari. 'The first time she came in here, she couldn't walk on her own! She had to be supported by her husband!' She lost 60 kilos in eleven months. The slides, taken from the front, back and sides, were like a time-lapse film of the Michelin Tyre Man being deflated very gradually. Even Prashant, who had come with the intention of scoffing, was impressed. So I signed up.

One day later, when I went back to the clinic for the introductory session, the doctor showed me more slides of his former patients. This time, because Prashant was not with us, I saw them unclothed.

They looked terrible. We are so used to seeing pictures of female nudes who look like articulated dolls that when we see the more typical sort of woman without her clothes on, she looks diseased. One girl had a 16-inch waist and 40-inch hips. Her body was like a cartoon, wildly out of proportion. She must have wanted to reduce her hips, but the record showed that she had lost weight uniformly, including on her waist. The last slide revealed her with her middle dwindled to nothingness and her hips more prominent than ever before. She resembled a giant ant masquerading as a woman.

The prize patient, whose success had seemed so spectacular when she was clothed, looked like a sack of loose brown skin standing to attention when she was naked. Her breasts were like used tea bags. As the weight loss progressed, the sachets deflated gradually, becoming little more than flaps of skin. There seemed to be no nipples, just two tired points aimed at the floor. The huge mound of her abdomen collapsed slowly across the months, but only the mass of it. The skin remained, hanging from her waist down, covering her pubic area. When she posed for the frontal view, the folded skin covered that area like an apron. When she posed for the slides in profile, she held up the lower edge of this fold so that you could see the extent of it.

It wasn't easy to guess her thoughts. Her face was expressionless. Her appearance suggested that she came from a deeply conservative, traditional background, yet here she was, posing naked for a doctor's unsympathetic camera. Was the lack of expression a sign of diffidence or confidence? Had she agreed out of her own volition or had her husband forced her? Was he in the room with her when these pictures were taken? Had she agreed because she imagined she was making a valuable contribution to a study of weight loss amongst obese Third World women? Had she been convinced on the grounds that she represented that rarest of breeds, a Third World woman who was yet rich enough to have weight to lose? Did she herself want to lose weight or had she done it, all of it, out of deference to her husband's wish for a slender wife?

She held her head stiffly, her expression opaque, offering no answers.

The flap bothered me. How did she relate to it, I wondered. Did she despise it? Did she pinch and prod it when she had a bath? Did she wash underneath it with revulsion? Did she sigh when she tucked it away under the waistband of her sari-petticoat? Or did she regard it with a certain horrified fondness, the way, I imagined, some people regarded extra digits on their hands? I remember meeting a woman who had a second thumb on her right hand. Its nail was as perfectly manicured as the other nails on the hand. I remember thinking well of her for having accepted her own irregularity, for celebrating it rather than slicing it off.

Some of the other patients whose slides I saw that day had resorted to plastic surgery to excise the unwanted folds of skin. But they had been left with scars like livid pink zippers, running across their abdomens.

I felt disturbed. I didn't want to look like a limp balloon or a surgeon's embroidery sampler. I couldn't understand why none of the patients actually looked attractive at the end of their ordeal. But I had already committed myself to being a patient. I paid my non-refundable introductory fee of 500 rupees and meekly produced a urine sample after submitting to having my blood pressure taken and my weight recorded in a clear plastic folder with my name printed smartly on its cover. The initial entry read: 65.8 kg. Height: 5' 5". I wanted to add, Self-image: 0.00—but didn't. The doctor was not easily amused, I noticed. Gaining racehorses was a serious business.

The slides were followed by a two-hour 'psychometric test'. It began with an interview with Dr Prasad's wife, Mrs Prasad. She told me that she was a practising analyst and that the purpose of the session was to determine my fitness for a course of dieting. 'Few people realize to what extent their lives can be affected by a change in eating habits,' she said. 'We have to know a little about your personality in order to adjust our method to suit your individual type.'

It sounded reasonable. She had pepper-and-salt hair and half-shut eyes which gazed at me with an expression that reduced me to a case number on a shiny plastic folder, cabinet 7b, drawer II.

We began with a résumé of family history. Yes, both my parents were alive. My father had retired from the Foreign Service as Ambassador. He and my mother lived in their own house in Calicut, surrounded by all our extended family of relatives. I had one brother, one sister, both married. Both had children.

She paused in her tracks. 'How do you feel about that?' she asked. Her expression was carefully neutral.

'About what?' I asked in return.

She may have sighed. 'It's quite normal, you know. Two elder siblings, both married, both with children. You're twenty-four, so it's not too late, of course, for you to follow their path but … it happens. Feelings of inadequacy, a desire to compensate—it could explain your overeating for example . . .'

As I understood the drift of the enquiry, I started to smile in anticipation. 'Oh, no!' I exclaimed. 'I don't feel inadequate—I've *never* wanted to marry—'

She cut me at once. 'You mean, you've never had an *opportunity* to marry—'

'No.' I was very accustomed to arguing this point. It always surprised me that I faced so much resistance. 'I am opposed to marriage—as an institution. I don't believe that it's the best way for men and women to, you know, live together and . . .' I shrugged, 'raise children, whatever.' I believed that most people had children because they didn't realize that they could choose not to. If they knew, I believed, hardly any would bother having them. 'Marriage is too restrictive—it's an instrument of patriarchy, after all, a method of ensuring that property is passed from one generation to the next through the paternal line. I mean, obviously that's important, but it's only a system, not a law of nature—and it's used to control women's sexuality—to define it . . .'

She allowed me to carry on for a few moments in this vein. When I paused for breath, she nodded, then asked, 'Would you call yourself a feminist?'

I said, relieved to be given a chance to reveal my orientation, 'Oh, yes. Absolutely . . .'

She nodded again and said, 'Then why don't you want children? If you feel so strongly about being a feminist shouldn't that mean you want to explore your feminine nature by having children?'

I said, 'Ah—but I don't like children. I've never wanted to have any.'

I kept looking for some sign that the statements I made were having an impact on her but she didn't so much as raise her eyebrows. She said, 'I see. For how long, would you say, you've not liked children? Can you think of a specific period when these feelings began?'

I said, 'I can't remember ever liking small children. When I was small, I didn't like children younger than myself. I thought they were sort of . . . *squirmy*. And wet. Little children always seemed to be sort of *damp*.' She listened without comment. 'I never wanted to pick them up or have anything to do with them. I don't understand why other people like them so much. I assume that it's a survival tactic—protecting the young—raw instinct, whatever. To keep the species alive. That sort of thing—'

'Ok,' she said. 'So you don't want to get married and you don't like children. What would you say you like?'

I said, 'My work. I'm an artist, you know.' I thought it so strange that she hadn't asked me any questions about my professional life. 'An illustrator, actually. And a cartoonist—though not all the time. I mean, I'd like to be a cartoonist, but I don't get commissions to draw the sort of cartoons that interest me. I'm a freelancer, so I get paid for each piece of work I complete. No salary, and no one pays on time. It's quite difficult to keep ahead of my expenses. I stopped accepting money from my parents when I was twenty-one. I've been living away from home since then and . . . I'm not very practical. But if I could do what I really wanted, then I would just spend all day drawing and painting.'

I was gabbling, wanting her to show a response. Once more, however, she listened as if what I said was random noise. 'I also like to write. I don't get the opportunity to do the kind of work I'd like . . .' I faltered to a stop. I felt she wasn't listening.

She asked, 'What about boyfriends?' I said I had one. At this, she made a small notation in a notepad open in front of her. I felt I had to hammer home my point, so I volunteered, '. . . Though, of course, I don't plan to marry him.'

She looked, for an instant, straight at me instead of through me and said, 'Meaning, you don't love him.' It wasn't a question, but a statement. It left me speechless. I believed the reason I didn't want to marry him was that I didn't believe in the patriarchal establishment. I tried to explain this, but she cut me short.

She asked me what I liked about food, whether it was the type of food or the quantity that I preferred. Whether I ate the same amount when I was alone or when I was in company. Whether I liked particular types of food more than others or whether I was indifferent to tastes and flavours. I said I just liked to eat, I wasn't especially concerned about rare and unusual foods, that I was quite happy with, for instance, fried eggs every morning for months on end. Hot toast and butter were what I liked best. Ice cream was good too. I had a sweet tooth.

'What about cooking?' she asked. 'What types of food do you like to cook?'

'I don't cook,' I said. 'Never go near the kitchen.'

'All right,' she said, 'Do you have any feminine interests?'

And I said, 'Oh—yes! I like jewellery and perfume!' The moment the words were out of my mouth, I knew I had failed the encounter.

The correct answer, following the feminist canon, would have been that 'masculine' and 'feminine' were outmoded concepts. As a woman, whatever I did should be considered adequately 'feminine' without requiring external reference points. But I had blundered full-tilt into the trap of sex-defined preference. It was a rout.

For the remainder of my time with Mrs Prasad, the only thing I was conscious of was the sound, in my head, of my feminist self popping and crackling on a spit of chagrin. By the time I had slunk out of that office I was emotionally gutted. I felt like a frog that has been pegged out on a dissection board with all its vital organs on display but no gentle chloroform to spare it the awareness of this humiliating and spreadeagled fate.

Mrs Prasad was followed by Dr Nalini, a psychiatrist researching the link between food habits and psychological disorders. After making a careful list of what foods I liked and the history of my 'eating disorder', she brought out her set of Rorschach blots.

It surprised me that they were coloured. I had always assumed that, being 'ink blots', they would be black. Instead, they resembled nothing more than the shape of menstrual blood stains on panties. The pinkish-red colour of many of them heightened that impression. In card after card, that's all I could see. I understood how frustrating it must be to be the needle of a gramophone stuck in a groove, as I heard myself say yet again, 'Uhhh … menstrual stain.' There was only one in which I felt I saw something different: little fox faces and a couple of bats hovering overhead.

The final hurdle for the day, after the blots, was to draw a picture, one each, of a man and of a woman.

I had read about such exercises. I knew that they were not meant to be tests of skill, but as a tool for digging out unconscious messages embedded in the mind of the test-subject. The success of the exercise depended upon the subject's spontaneous rendering of a man and a woman. But I am an artist. As an artist, I do not draw spontaneously. I labour over my work. How could I short-circuit my natural approach to drawing in order to produce a sketch in the style of someone who doesn't draw for a living? I was completely paralysed.

I started one drawing, scratched it out , then stared at the blank page helplessly for at least fifteen minutes before finally producing two featureless silhouettes of the type used in physical fitness handbooks. I was painfully conscious that whatever I drew would be picked up for interpretation. Every line would be heavy with meaning, however much I might desire to draw something neutral. Just the desire to draw something neutral had a meaning.

If I drew the man in the centre of the page it could mean that I gave men pride of place. If I drew the man and the woman as a couple, it could mean that I believed in monogamy. Did I in fact believe in monogamy? Did I wish to be typecast as one who believed in monogamy? Did I care either way?

Should I draw the couple facing one another? Clothed? If unclothed then to what extent should I detail their sexual features? Should the woman-silhouette have long hair? And wouldn't that mean that deep in my subconscious I believed that a True Woman was long-haired and traditional? And, my own being short, did that mean that I had symbolically castrated my femininity by cutting off my hair?

Should I draw both figures the same height, even though I knew that going by averages men are taller than women? And was it honest, anyway, for me to be assessing the significance of what I drew in this manner? Was it morally right to want to influence the results of the test by trying to assess what was expected of me and doing the opposite on purpose? And what exactly was that purpose?

I apologized twice to Dr Nalini for taking so long. I explained that I was an artist by profession and that therefore I couldn't perform unselfconsciously. I don't know whether she understood the nature of my dilemma. I think she was tired and wanted to go home.

In the end, I scribbled my two pathetic silhouettes in the slapdash manner I believed non-artists approached the task. I wondered what Rembrandt would have done, what Picasso would have done. And van Gogh? He would have refused the test altogether, perhaps. Or drawn a perfectly detailed ear. Truly great artists do not agonize, they just draw, paying no attention to the petty concerns of researchers.

My woman figure was on the left, facing left, with only the barest minimum of an outline. The man was spaced a decent distance away from her, also facing left. Neither of them had any discernible hair, they were both the same height. The woman had a small breast-bump and the man an equally modest crotch-bump.

I left the clinic feeling profoundly diminished. It was eight o'clock, and the city's night was alive with the harsh glitter of neon signs, chrome-plated cars, blinding headlights, windscreens flashing hypnotically as they passed under the corner street lamp. There was a relentless drizzle. Umbrellas, slick with rain, were being borne along by a procession of weary commuters.

I saw a taxi stop 10 yards from where I stood. I willed it to remain in place till I could reach it. I willed the driver to be compliant, to be eager to please, to be agreeable to take me in any direction I wished to go. I willed the shadowy figure hurrying towards the vehicle to be stricken with doubts about the validity of his claim to the cab.

And my will prevailed on all counts.

I leaned back on the plastic covers of the taxi's seat. The despair of a few moments ago had been wiped clear, like water from a car's windscreen. Outside, the night, the puddles, the damp trouser cuffs and the muddy sari hems. Inside, the warm dry cab and the knowledge that I would be home soon.

Anjana Appachana

Leftovers

Why were children born to the same parents so different? Anirudh. With what ease she had carried him, with what ease he has been born. Madhu had predicted that she would have a boy, but Mataji had had her qualms. 'All my daughters-in-law have had sons,' she said to Anu, 'but with you, who knows.' But Anu too had obliged and Mataji's joy had been boundless. When Anu went back to Delhi with Him and Prabha and the baby, her parents sent silk sarees for all the women in His family—his sisters, and his brothers' wives—and many boxes of sweets. There had been a huge hawan for the baby a few weeks later, three times as big as the one they had for Prabha. And from the time he was born Anirudh was a happy, bubbly baby.

And Prabha? At the age of three she had asked Mataji at the dining table, 'Dadima, why are you eating?'

Mataji had pinched her cheek and said, 'Because it is time to eat food now.'

'But, Dadima,' Prabha had asked, puzzled, 'you were saying Mumma's food is very bad?'

'That it is,' Mataji had said, her smile disappearing.

This extract is from *Listening Now*, published by IndiaInk, New Delhi, 1998.

'But everything you have eaten three times,' Prabha said.

Later when Anu had told Madhu about this, Madhu had laughed heartily and said, 'Very sharp your Prabha is, that I must say.'

'No, Madhu,' Anu had said, disturbed, 'there is an innocence in her, a great simplicity.'

Madhu had looked amused. 'What you cannot say to Mataji, that Prabha says. What is so innocent about that?'

'She is very young, Madhu.'

Madhu smiled meaningfully. 'She is learning early, what else.'

The conversation had disturbed Anu more than she could understand. But when she told Padma, Padma went into peals of laughter. 'Anu,' Padma said, 'she is an innocent child, she is only saying what she's observing. Tell me, how many children are there like her?'

None, Anu thought later, but it would do her no good. Even now Prabha was so unequivocal about her feelings, about her convictions of what was right and what was wrong. Like Him she was, but He was a man.

It was very well feeling that way, nothing was wrong with that. What was wrong was acting on it, and Prabha acted on what she felt. What was wrong was telling people what you thought and Prabha told people what she thought. What was wrong was questioning the way things were and Prabha questioned the way things were. How would Prabha survive her nature in a world where women just shouldn't act on their beliefs, where to do so was certain disaster? A sense of fairness was no quality to bring into a marriage. That was a quality that stood you in good stead only in the relationships outside marriage and in the Other World, the world outside the domestic one, and how many women knew that world anyway? To stand by one's beliefs and speak one's mind was necessary in the professional world, good men did that, He did that, it was not the most practical thing as she had seen, after all He didn't get his promotions as fast as his colleagues did, but she understood, she respected him for it.

But His beliefs and His principles were no good at home because they did not apply there. He didn't know the world she inhabited, where words like *fairness* and *justice* rang hollow. On the homefront it had as much worth as the onion skins which she couldn't even feed to the cows who came mooing to the back of the kitchen door every afternoon. She gave the cows potato skins and mango skins, she gave them the bananas that were too black and overripe even for her to eat. They loved her for it, they nuzzled in the palm of her hand and when they saw her standing at the kitchen door which opened into the back lawn they came to her, mooing joyfully. That was the way to be, like a cow, grateful for the leftovers, that was the way to be, placid, unruffled, peaceful.

Once Mataji had tried to feed the onion skins to her cow. 'The less that is wasted, the better it is,' Mataji had intoned. But the cows refused to touch them, turned away and ambled back to the road. 'Much they think of themselves,' Mataji had said, affronted, 'you have spoiled them too much.' Then she had looked at Anu and snapped, 'What is there to laugh about, Bahurani?'

Arre, Mataji, Anu had wanted to tell her, you think that I too have been spoilt with a diet of leftovers; if you could feed me onion skins you would. She had laughed so much that Mataji had been meaner to her than ever that day. Honesty, Principles, Integrity. How high-sounding, how nice. At home it only applied to His mother and His sisters and brothers, to His nieces and nephews and to His own children. It was she who had to bear the brunt of His principles and His integrity and His honesty.

She, Anu, did have faith in Prabha, but what was the use. She had had faith in Him too and in principle, she still had it. The reality was what mattered, and Prabha was too young to know the consequences of fighting for truth and justice. Acceptance, that was the truth. Justice, there was none. Truth meant violence, assault. On the surface it was what had happened to her and Madhu and Padma that day at the mela, but that was just its outward manifestation. The everyday violations did as much damage.

Prabha would have to learn to accept both.

Like the fool that she was she had told Him about the mela incident the same night. Why? Her need for comfort, for understanding? Once, long ago, he had given her both. Then too he had never spoken of his feelings for her, but she had known how he felt and the knowledge had sufficed. Perhaps it was this then that made her speak—her need to know if he too would suffer for her as he had suffered when she began to bleed when she was pregnant with Prabha, perhaps she hoped that the old, never-forgotten tenderness would surface again, would allow her tears to come. She began to tell him and warning bells began to ring; she ignored them. He didn't say anything as she told him, there was nothing in his expression, no anger, no shock, nothing. After she finished He said, 'I thought you were going to the jewellers at Chandni Chowk.'

She looked at him blankly. She saw the beginnings of something like distaste on his face. 'What was the need to lie to Mataji?' he asked.

She had forgotten. Completely forgotten. She continued looking at his face, her own full of panic. He closed his eyes. She said, 'Mataji doesn't like me to go anywhere.'

He didn't open his eyes as he replied, 'I can't force you to like my mother. But what foolish things you imagine, do not attribute those things to her.'

After some time Anu said, 'Your mother says I put water in the milk that I give her.' He turned his back to her and didn't reply. 'Did you hear me?' she asked.

'What has that to do with all of this?' he asked. She tried to speak but couldn't. There was too much to say so she said nothing. 'You take two and two and you make five,' he said. 'Mataji must have said the milkman put water in the milk. You hear it as her saying you have done it.'

'Mataji used to say I denied Kamala milk at night. She used to say I drank up the milk secretly in the kitchen and didn't give Kamala her milk.'

She heard him sigh. 'I don't know from where you drag up things.'

'Nothing makes a difference to you,' she said. She turned her back to him, the tears coming. It was as though those hands were on her again, she could smell those men, she could feel her hair being pulled and the fingers under her saree blouse. The bath hadn't helped, even though her body was red after scrubbing with the pumice stone. She found that she was making a noise as she cried, a horrible noise, trying to stifle it made the sound even worse.

'If Mataji doesn't want you to go anywhere it is because she knows what can happen to you,' he said. 'You may not believe it, but it is of great concern to her, your safety, your well-being. If you want to lie to her and go out on your own, then you must be prepared to take the consequences.' She moved away from him till she was lying at the edge of the bed. 'Why do these things happen only to you?' he said, sounding tired.

She should never have told him. Not just this, but the other things which she had told him over the years, about the man who followed her all the way to the vegetable shop and back, about the man who had felt her thigh in the D.T.C. bus. She hadn't been able to help herself—out it came.

'You *told* your husband all these things?' Madhu had asked her, shocked, when she once mentioned it to Madhu.

'Why not, what fault was it of mine?' Anu retorted.

'So what did He say?'

'I don't remember,' Anu said vaguely.

'*I* can't tell my husband about these things.' Madhu shuddered. '*He* would get so angry that he would kill those men—he is so protective about me, see.'

If only He would get angry about these things. But if he got angry at all it was at her, nor at the fact that it had happened to her. 'These things can always be avoided,' he said, 'do not travel by bus, take a scooter.'

'Where is the money for a scooter?'

'If you want money for a scooter, ask me for it, when you want something for yourself have I ever refused?'

'Have I ever asked for any money to buy something for myself?'

'Keep to the issue we are talking about.'

'You always tell me to cut down, cut down, where is the money for scooters?'

'About things like this if money has to be spent, it has to be spent,' he said, 'use the housekeeping money and I will give you more.'

'I am not eating fruits, I am not drinking milk, and you ask me to take scooters.'

'If you are not eating fruits and not drinking milk do not blame me, did I ask you not to?'

'No, but you asked me to cut down.'

'So cut down on other things.'

'What things?'

'The problem with you is that you can never keep to the issue at hand.'

'No scooter will go to the vegetable shop—what can I do if some man decides to follow me?'

'Don't walk alone, take one of your friends—Mrs Nanda, Mrs Rao.'

'Every day I should ask them to come with me vegetable shopping because I am scared that some man will follow me? They have better things to do, I have better things to ask them.'

'If that is the case then don't complain.'

Silence.

'You just don't understand.'

'I understand very well. The problem with you is that all your problems are self-inflicted.'

'Much you know about my problems.'

'All right, all right.'

'When I came back from Lucknow, you had given Mataji money for the house and asked her to give it to me.'

'You have started again.'

'She never gave me the money. She said to me that she had no money.'

'Why must you bring my mother into everything?'

'One day before I came back from Lucknow you gave her all the household money. You said, Take it from her. She said, I don't have any money. What was I to spend for the house?'

'She must have forgotten. Ask her again.'

'Where do you think I spent from? I spent the money my father gave me to buy a silk saree for myself.'

'For your faults you are always blaming others. Remember this. I did not ask you to spend your father's money. Nor did my mother.'

'You ask her for the money. She will never give me.'

'I do not ask you to do my office work for me. You do not ask me to do your work. If you have a quarrel with her, sort it out with her. Do not drag me into it.'

Anu turned over in her bed, her eyes dry. Outside she could hear the crickets chirping, and the light of the full moon streamed in from the window. In the distance she heard a dog barking. He was fast asleep as usual. No difference it had made. No difference that his wife had been violated. When their children were hurt or upset he acted as if the world were collapsing. When Prabha fell and bruised her knee he coddled her as if she had broken her leg. When Prabha bashed up the boys who threatened her and Mallika he said, It is all right, never let anyone do an injustice to you. From the darkness Anu heard his voice saying, 'The people in the outside world will not change. Accept that and try and behave accordingly.'

Once she had gone to the dentist to have a cavity attended to.

She had sat on the chair, her mouth open, wincing slightly as he began the drilling. Half an hour it had taken, she looked up at the ceiling and the spots over there, she let her mind drift, let the tiredness fill her body, felt the tension ooze away, felt her body relax. Her eyes grew heavy.

She awoke to see the dentist peering worriedly at her. 'Are you all right?'

She nodded, shook her head, smiled. 'I'm sorry, I fell asleep,' she said.

He looked at her as if she were some creature from another planet. 'I saw,' he said. 'You did not feel any pain?'

She shook her head again, stepping down from the chair. 'It was a deep sleep,' she said and began to laugh.

'Do you drink milk, take vitamins?' he asked.

She shook her head.

'You start, then. This is a sign of weakness.'

Holding her lips tight to suppress her laughter, she nodded.

But now there was no waking up, most of the time she didn't even feel any pain. Better this way. She tried not to think about the early days, it made her feel ashamed, embarrassed, as though she were a voyeur peeping into the lives of two other people. Now, the nearest He came to her was when He wanted sex, and she never felt so distant from Him as she did then. Two minutes it took, as quick as her single early morning cup of tea, and the tea was infinitely more satisfying. No, not more satisfying. *More* implied that the other was also satisfying in a lesser way, and the word *satisfying* didn't apply to something in which she didn't participate. There was a great deal she didn't participate in; how could this need be alive, dependent as it was on the others?

Some things could never be uttered; there was shame in uttering them. And humiliation. Once, when things had begun to change she had wanted to say to him, Will you hold me at times other than when you are on top of me? After all, she had known it once. Once she had known her love for him to be fiercest at such moments. Now, in a process unknown even to her the quality of her love had changed. It could not be asked for, what he had once given her. But the sadness of it was, he did not even know it had stopped. Did he remember it had once been there? The sadness of it was, she did.

It was strange, how in marriage one had to find time to do everything, most of it not related at all to the man one had married. And for talk and for love there was no time at all, no attempt, no thought. The leftovers—that was what lovemaking and conversations with one's husband were, like the sides of bread that Anirudh left on his plate, like the yellow, sticky remains of dal and rice on the plate.

It was true, what her mother always said: 'A woman's fulfillment is her children. Without children what is there?' For your children, and only for them were you Everything. Once on a rare occasion when she had burnt the potatoes a little, Mataji had grumbled loudly at the lunch table. 'It *isn't* burnt, it *isn't* burnt,' Prabha had said equally loudly and scraped the bowl of potatoes and eaten every one. Then she took the burnt potatoes from Anirudh's plate which he hadn't eaten, and ate those too. 'Tomorrow also you make the same, Mumma,' Prabha said, looking at her with love.

'Yes, yes, make,' Mataji had said, pushing her thali away in disgust, '*I* cannot eat such food.'

'Dadima,' Prabha said indignantly, 'Cinderella's stepmother talks like you.'

'Who, who?' Mataji asked.

Anu put her fingers around Prabha's arm so tightly that Prabha cried out. Anu dragged her to her room and smacked her hard. Prabha burst into tears. 'Stay there till you learn to keep your mouth shut,' she said.

'Teach her to say more, Bahurani, teach her more,' Mataji said as Anu came out of Prabha's room, 'everything I understand, everything.'

It was impossible to remain tender with Prabha, impossible.

The day after the mela incident was Anu's fast—nothing to eat all day until after the puja in the late evening, Mataji kept the same fast. His sister, her husband and children were expected for two weeks the next day, so she had to prepare for that too. In the evening, finally, after she and Mataji bathed and did their puja, she made the puris and heated the rest of the food and fed everyone. She wanted to sit by herself and eat, let everyone finish, then she would sit in peace without having to get up a hundred times to get this and get that. Kamala was also with them for a week, which was all the time her mother-in-law was willing to spare.

'What is your fast and puja for, Mumma?' Prabha asked, eating her third puri with enjoyment.

'This is a fast for sons,' she replied, serving Anirudh another hot puri. 'Why, Mumma?' Prabha looked puzzled.

'For their long life and for them to live in good health and happily,' she said going into the kitchen to turn the puris.

'Mumma,' Prabha said when she came back and served Him and Mataji, 'this fast is for Anirudh?'

'Yes.' She nodded and went back to the kitchen to fry the rest of the puris.

When she came back, Prabha said, 'Mumma, when do you keep a fast for me?'

Anu paused in the act of spooning some dahi into Mataji's bowl. She served Mataji, then served Him and Anirudh some aloo. She put another puri onto Prabha's plate.

'Mumma.'

She went back to the kitchen and finished frying the puris. After they had all finished eating, she cleared the thalis and other dishes, put them in the sink and came back and began serving the khir.

'Mumma, tell me.'

She went back to the kitchen. An hour later, after washing the dishes and cleaning the kitchen, she went back to the dining room and began to serve herself. She felt the tiredness seep into her body.

She looked up. Prabha was sitting opposite her, and her eyes were full of unshed tears. 'Arre, what happened?' she asked, startled.

'Mumma, when do you keep a fast for me?' One tear rolled slowly down Prabha's cheek. She wiped her nose with the back of her hand, then burst into tears, trying to hold back the sounds that racked her body, but unable to.

'Prabha, beti.' Her father put down his paper and came to her. He dragged a chair and, sitting next to her, put one arm around her and with his other hand wiped the tears from her cheek. 'What need is there to cry, my child?' he said over and over again. He smoothed her forehead, took out a handkerchief from his pocket, wiped her cheek again. He put his hand on her cheek and drew her head into his neck, murmuring comfortingly. Anu finished her puri, forced herself to finish the rest on her plate. Her appetite had gone.

She got up and cleared the dishes, washed them, cleaned the table again. Tomorrow she would have to get the vegetables and rations first thing after breakfast, His sister and family were coming in the evening. She changed into her old saree and went to the children's room. He was sitting next to Prabha, stroking her forehead. Her eyes were closed, her hand, limp in sleep, was lying in his. Anu went to Anirudh and brushed her finger against his cheek. His cheeks were red, his hair rumpled, his plump hands against the pillow. He was smiling even in his sleep, she found herself smiling too, she wanted to pick him up and hold him the way she used to when he was a baby.

She was fast asleep when He spoke to her, she opened her eyes and looked dazedly at him. 'Already you are asleep?' he asked.

She saw his face and suddenly she was wide awake. 'What is the matter?'

'Prabha wasn't answering my question as to why she was crying. After a long time she told me. Is it true?'

'Is what true?' she asked wearily.

'That you keep a fast for Anirudh and not for her?'

She took a deep breath and said, 'What do you think.'

'What can I think. I told her, That is not true at all, if your mother keeps a fast it is for both of you, not for one of you. She just would not believe me, she kept crying.' He paused, then said, 'When I'm talking to you try and look in my direction,' he said.

'When I talk to you, you don't.'

She heard him expel a noisy breath.

She said, 'Yes it is true, I keep a fast for Anirudh, I have been keeping it all these years ever since he was born, what do you know of it.'

He said, disbelievingly, 'For one child you keep and not for the other?'

'What your mother told me to do, that I do.'

'She told you to exclude Prabha?'

'No. When Anirudh was born, she said, Now you have a son, now you must keep a fast for him once a year. So I kept a fast once a year. That's all.' He didn't answer. She said, 'Your mother also, she also keeps a fast for you and your brothers. She doesn't keep it for your sisters.' She stretched her legs and closed her eyes.

'Do not bring my mother into this. She is of another generation. You, you need not do things blindly.'

'That is the only way to do it.'

'In answering back you are very quick. Perhaps you should be as quick in thinking.'

'Tell your mother that.'

There was a silence, then he said, 'From now onwards your fast will include Prabha. Tomorrow you tell Prabha that you fast for both of them.'

'I won't tell her that. I don't want to lie to Prabha. She knows what the truth is.'

'You won't lie to Prabha, but you will lie to Mataji when you want to go wandering about with your friends. Suddenly truth has become very meaningful to you.'

'You understand nothing.'

'I understand everything. I understand how twisted your mind has become. Your simplicity, your innocence, your softness, everything that I first knew you for, nothing remains.' He turned his back to her. 'I know how your mind works,' and now it was he who sounded tired, the anger all gone, 'I know the thoughts you have about me these days. Because I say nothing do not think I don't know. If I am no longer what I was, then remember, you also are not the person I married.'

MAHASWETA DEVI

Salt

Not by hand, or by bread, *nimak se marega*—I'll kill you by salt, Uttamchand Bania had said. He was the *bania*, the trader—he was also the *mahajan*, the moneylender; and for many generations, his family had ruled the Jhujhar *belt*. That the local Oraon and Kol peoples would say 'no' to him was unimaginable.

But the unimaginable did occur. In the reign of this *sarkar*. Before this, *sarkars* had come and *sarkars* had gone, but nothing like this had ever happened.

Jhujhar is an adivasi village in the lap of the Palamau Reserve Forest. The villagers are allowed to graze cattle and goats in the forest, and pick sticks and twigs off the forest floor for firewood. They can also take leaves to thatch their huts. Apart from this, they steal bamboo, tubers and tamarind leaves. The Forest Department turns a blind eye. They kill the odd porcupine, rabbit or bird. The census of these forest creatures and birds is not totally accurate. Hence, the Forest Department keeps its eyes shut about this as well. But they rarely manage to snare any meat. Because the animals are now too alert. They can't be trapped easily.

The village is in the lap of the Reserve Forest. A strip of land

---

This extract is taken from *Bitter Soil*, published by Seagull Books Pvt. Ltd, Kolkata, 1998.

crowding the bank of the Koel river. The land, however, belongs to Uttamchand. After the Kol rebellion of 1831, the Hindu traders who re-entered this area were Uttamchand's forefathers. One of them bought up the adivasis' fertile jungle land hand over fist. In those days, like today, it was very easy to buy land and drive out the adivasis. Adivasis then were as wary as they are today of accounts–documents–deeds–laws. Hence the adivasis of Jhujhar don't even know when they once owned their own land. When they could bring the harvest of their own labour home.

The village is bound in the shackles of *betbegari* to Uttamchand. For the past few generations. To repay the unrecorded debts of their forefathers, year after year, at harvesting time, they trudge twelve miles to Uttamchand's village, Tahar, and, in return for a meal and a handful of crop, offer *begar* or wageless labour. The crop-share that they get is added to the debit side of the accounts ledger. They didn't even know that *betbegari* was illegal. They found out courtesy the Inspector of the Adivasi Office. But they did not stop giving *betbegari*. Because they knew that it was impossible for them to take Uttamchand, who extracted *betbegari*, to court. Is it feasible to go all the way to Daltonganj just for this? What about a lawyer? Someone to advise and counsel them? The Adivasi Welfare Office is beyond their reach, too. The office is in town. They are in the village. This is not a large village situated on the rail or bus routes. This village consists of seventy-six people belonging to seventeen families. Until the third election after independence, the government did not even know of their existence. They have been voting since the fourth election. Election times are good times. Uttamchand says—Why go all that way to cast your vote? Take a rupee each, my fathers and mothers. I'll vote on your behalf.

From the fourth election onwards, this was the prevailing

Editor's note: English words used in the original Bengali text have been italicized by the translator.

arrangement. But everything changed in '77. The teacher at the closest primary school, Balkishan Singh, began to frequent Jhujhar village. He wheedled and coaxed them into sending three boys from the village to school. He explained that the sixth election was an important affair. They must cast their own votes. Money per head? Balkishan's efforts had brought them projects worth much more. A panchayati well in Jhujhar village. Huge well, lots of water. Till now, water had been carried from the river, and in summer one almost died fetching water.

Uttamchand first took offence over this matter of the vote.

A new ministry after the vote. The old offices and old officers reborn in new roles. The only road to Jhujhar village is a footpath. The youth-team came down that path, and noted down the particulars of those families who were doing *betbegari* to repay debts. Purti Munda was the most *vocal* personality of the village. He was the only person in the entire village who had been to Ranchi and Daltonganj, and worked as a coolie in Dhanbad. Since his financial condition remained unchanged, he spat upon the outside world and returned to Jhujhar.

He said—What's the use of asking us? Everything's written in Uttamchand's book. You're the ones who write things down.

—Do you know that *betbegari* is illegal?

—What's the good of our knowing that? If we don't do it, the *mahajan* won't give us loans.

—The *mahajan* will be dealt with now.

—See what you can do.

—Come with us.

—Let's go.

In front of Purti Munda, the youths tell Uttamchand, From this year onwards, no adivasi in this area will give wageless labour. If anyone is forced, we'll make sure he gets legal redress.

—As you say, Uttamchand answers, and is forced to abide by this order in practice, too. He couldn't even prevent the Jhujhar dwellers from farming his land. The youth-team told him—These people have been cultivating the land for more than twelve years. They have a right to half the crop.

—Half is mine.

—When the crop is harvested, our *samiti* will divide it in your presence.

—As you say.

Purti Munda said, all at once—Give us two bucks. Let's drink some toddy before we go home. What kind of a day is this, anyway? Whose was the first face we saw on waking up?

The youngsters said—No. Give up drinking. This addiction is what destroys the adivasi.

On the way home Purti Munda spent the eight annas he had tucked into his waistcloth on toddy, and stroking the earthen *bhand* said—Destroys! What do the babus know? How else would we forget the burning hunger in our bellies?

Uttamchand accepted the defeat, but vowed to avenge himself. He said—I'll kill them by salt.

Only he can make such an arrogant proclamation. Because the people of Jhujhar buy their necessities from the markets at Palani or Muru. And all the grocery shops in these markets belong to Uttamchand.

Uttamchand said—Let them find out what *ghato* tastes like without salt. What *nimak haraami*—after being fed and clothed by me for so long, how dare they bite the hand that feeds them!

At first, Purti and the others didn't give much importance to the unavailability of salt in the market. When it hit them, they rushed to Daltonganj. To the youth-team office. One of the boys sat in the office, listening to the transistor. He heard them out and said—This isn't within our jurisdiction. If the shopowner won't sell to you, what can we do? We're having to rush off in all directions now. With much bigger problems.

There was not, never has been, any give and take between the ideas of the babus and those of Purti. Purti just could not explain that their lives were impossible without salt. That their *ghato* was flavoured with salt alone.

Fearing the worst, they pooled their bus fare and bought ten kilos of salt. And walked eighteen miles to the village. Then they distributed the salt to all the households in the village and said, 'Use it sparingly.'

But ten kilos of salt are neither infinite nor eternal. This time Purti caught hold of the *thikadar* of the Forest Department—Give us work. Pay us in salt, not cash.

—Salt?

Despite many steep price hikes, salt is still the cheapest commodity in India, so this proposal to work for salt makes the contractor blink. He feels the need to find out more about these people. Since they farm Uttamchand's land, he goes to Uttamchand. What he learns convinces him that they are nothing but trouble-makers. Get the militant urban youth on their side and then negotiate revolutionary contracts with the merchant they've dealt with for years! If he gives them work, he'll certainly be in hot water. Hence, the contractor shoos away Purti and the rest; and, heads hanging, the black-skinned people walk away across the white sands.

After this, in the harvesting season, they try to get salt in exchange for crops. Result—the crop is bartered away for a few handfuls of salt. Now, everyone accuses Purti—They told you to go to the *mahajan* and you trotted off obediently? How will you arrange salt for us? Trying to prove your manhood! Become a *leader*!

—If I hadn't, would *betbegari* have ended?

—So? We'd have carried on the way we were.

—Would you have won rights to the crop?

—We'd have started fasting!

To the villagers of Jhujhar, those days of wageless labour, with no rights to the crop, seem happier by comparison. They mentally weigh the losses and gains.

Dark, dirty lumps of salt prove much heavier in the balance;

while an end to wageless labour, and the right to a share of the crop, come out lighter.

The village elder says—So, okay, we eat our *ghato* without salt. But why do we feel so breathless? So listless?

Everyone feels that salt is not the cause; actually, the reason for all this is that the gods are angry. The village elder sighs deeply and says—It's happening to everyone. We'll have to do *puja* at Haramdeo's shrine. Take my two pet chickens, sell them to the Forest Guard, and get some salt, Purti. Let's taste salt for a day, at least.

The Forest Guard is delighted at this amazing proposal. Says— I'll get salt from the *store*, wait.

—Even if you buy the hens cheap, you won't get them for less than eight rupees.

—Okay.

—How much salt can we get for eight rupees?

—Sixteen kilos.

—Get it, then.

Very dark, lumpy salt.

—Black salt?

—It's for the elephants and deer—what do they care about black or white?

—They eat salt? Salt?

—Yes, man. We have to give them salt-earth.

—What happens if you don't?

—They wilt.

—Where do you put it?

—There are certain spots.

Lost in thought, Purti returns to the village with the salt. Elephants and deer eat salt from *salt licks*. He is completely preoccupied with this piece of news, and does not realize that the sack of salt on his shoulder cannot possibly weigh sixteen kilos. On the day of the puja, a goat is killed and there's much feasting. Later, Purti comes and sits by the river, alone. As he drinks, he stares at the forest. Elephants graze at dawn and in the evening. They aren't seen during the day. Where do they go to eat the salt-earth, and when? It's a huge forest. Purti will comb the jungle to find the salt.

The market stalls don't sell them salt these days. The youth-teams don't completely ignore this news. It's there in some corner of their minds. One of them gets hold of a Medical Representative and asks him how *omnipotent* salt is for the human body. The Medical Representative has just started practising and has had no chance yet to display all his learning. What he says makes the youth's head reel.

His explanation: Salt and water are the *inorganic* and *mineral* constituents of the body. They are indispensable for life and have an important role to play in bodily *functions*. The main salts are *chloride*, *carbonates*, *bicarbonates*, *sulphates* and *phosphates*. These occur as compounds along with *sodium*, *potassium*, *calcium*, *magnesium*, *chloride* and *iron*, CO_2, *sulphur* and *phosphorus*. In general, one can say that salt performs the following functions within all living bodies:

1. Protects and maintains the internal physiological balance.

2. Keeps the water content of the body balanced and maintains the *volume* of blood.

3. Maintains the *acid-base* balance of the body.

4. Provides vital components to the skeletal system and teeth. Salt is also essential for preserving the *proper irritability* of the *nerve cells* and muscles. It is essential for blood *coagulation*.

5. Salt is the necessary constituent of some *enzyme systems*, *respiratory pigments* and *hormones*.

6. Salt regulates and controls the *cell membranes* and *capillary permeability* in a living body.

So many complicated facts further baffle the youth and he says—What the hell, *yaar*, did I ask you to coach me for an exam?

—Why d'you want to know, then?

—What can go wrong if one doesn't eat salt?

—What can go wrong? If you eat *high calorie* foods instead, you'll be able to make do with a minimum salt intake.

—*Arrey*, there are people who have no connection with *calories*.

—Yes, yes, Indian people don't have proper *food habits*.

—*Arrey*, the people I'm talking about . . .

The youth realizes that all this boxing with shadows will end in his getting a headache. The Daltonganj tea shop is not a million *jojans* away from Jhujhar village. But the two places are situated in two constellations in the universe and no matter how many songs and poems are written about the stars in the sky, who doesn't know that they are hotter than billions of suns, and that the dark sky between them holds these fiery, circling stars many billions of miles distant from one another? Daltonganj is hot with the timber trade. Jhujhar is hot with the deprivation endured by a few wretched adivasis exiled from modern Bharat. To make this *terrycloth*-and-*powder*-bedecked glamorous young man comprehend the problems of Purti Munda is akin to conjuring in thin air, an effort doomed to failure.

—Who're you talking about, then?

—They only eat *ghato*, or *maroa* or boiled *bhutta* and vegetables or fruits or meat and fish.

—They don't eat salt? Why?

—They don't get it.

—That's a tall tale. Salt is the cheapest commodity going.

—Salt isn't being sold to them . . .

—Lies!

—What happens if those who eat only *low-calorie cereals* don't get salt?

—Who are these people? Have you seen the new *fillum*?

—No. Come on, tell me!

—*Arrey*, how can I explain to an ignoramus!

—Why else did you become a pundit?

—Salt *controls* the *fluids* in the body and in the blood. If there's no salt the blood *coagulation* will increase and the blood will become thick. The *heart* will have trouble *pumping* this thickened blood, putting a pressure on the respiratory processes. *Muscles* will develop *cramps*. Moving about will become a *strain*. The bones and teeth will definitely rot. There'll be a *general decay* of the *body*. Forget all this silly stuff! Come, let's go see the *fillum*.

The film had mighty *gunmen*, gunfights, a voluptuous *tongawalli* and Amitabh Bachchan. But after Amjad Khan was duly punished by the process of law, the youth, on returning home, his mouth stuffed with Benarasi *paan*, still couldn't sweep the problems of Jhujhar out of his mind. The next day, he went to Uttamchand's house in Tahar.

At his accusation, Uttamchand said—Earlier, the adivasis never used to lie. Now they've become real mischief-makers.

—Why?

—So I'm not selling salt to Purti and his people?

—No.

—*Arrey*, I'm not selling salt to anyone. There's no profit in salt. I haven't supplied salt since the last market. Weren't they sold salt before that? How strange! Not even a little salt? Amazing! Perhaps there's no salt left in the shops.

—You aren't selling salt? Why?

—No profit.

—Is this correct?

—Since I'm Uttamchand, a *bania* who helped the Congress in earlier times, everything I say or do has to be wrong!

—You don't understand!

—No, babusaab. Sure I helped the Congress—if I don't help the ruling party, a poor rural merchant like me can't survive. When you people told me to, I stopped *betbegari* and gave up rights to the crop. The Congress boys never told me to do all this. If they had, I would have done it. Now, how can I do what you're asking? If you tell me to sell something that makes no profit, it's coercion.

—Are they coming to borrow money?

—No, no, why should they? They're getting grain. All I got

were the few crumbs that were left over.

—You know how little that land yields.

—What can I do? If the land is low-yielding, is it my fault? And you know what? Even if they want to borrow, I shan't lend.

—Why?

—Now look! When you lend money, you must realize the debt, and that's illegal, according to your *sarkar*. Look, lots of dancing isn't all there is to Ganesh *puja*. Such laws existed earlier, too. The Congressi *sarkar* kept its eyes shut. Because they understood the people's problems. They knew that if the *mahajan* didn't lend them money, the *junglee* adivasis would die of starvation. You people don't understand that. Good! You must be doing whatever you're doing for the best. If the results are good, everything's fine. I'm not going to lend them money.

The youth concedes defeat and comes away with the good intention of arranging to start a people's shop in the Jhujhar belt at the first opportunity. The intention stays with him for a few days. Then he goes off elsewhere to settle a dispute over an illicit liquor shop, and forgets all about Jhujhar.

Despite all the youths' good intentions, Purti and his people are consigned to a saltless darkness. Purti, however, doesn't abandon his efforts. Every day he silently *combs* the jungle. The deers' *salt lick* is close to the Forest Office. Then, one day, chasing a rabbit, he comes upon the elephants' *salt lick*. It is a symbolic scene. Purti at the top of a tree, in fear of his life. Not far off, a herd of elephants, eating salt-earth. Stony salt. Scattered on the stones, mixed with a handful of earth.

—They've made a field of salt! Purti says to himself.

Then, as the sky darkens, the elephants leave. The elephants of Betla understand '*show business*'. As dusk falls, the *tourists* climb into jeeps and come to the jungle to see the animals. They are used to watching herds of elephants feasting on bamboo stalks. The elephants wend their way towards the bamboo.

After all the elephants have left, an old tusker arrives. With due warning. He shows no sign of domesticity, though elephants, as a rule, are family-minded animals. *Ekoa*! Purti says to himself, and clings to the tree in fear. Some young elephant has driven him away and taken over as leader of the herd. Such elephants are called *ekoa*, and the *ekoa* is highly *avoidable*. There's no knowing what the *ekoa* will do. Exiled from leadership and from the herd, his behaviour turns *irresponsible*.

The *ekoa* sprays the *salt lick* with urine and goes off. Purti realizes that this is his way of doing whatever harm he can.

Avoiding elephant piss, he collects some salt-earth, ties it in his waistcloth and returns home. He heats water and drops the salt-earth into it. Tells his wife—Tomorrow we'll check how much salt remains once the earth settles as sediment.

—Salt in water?

—Yes.

In the morning they find both salt and soil mixed together at the bottom. Purti sighs and says—Well, it's still salt! The bastards sell no salt at all in the market . . .

He strains the dirty, salty water through a cloth and eats it, tells the others, and warns everybody about the *ekoa*. The village elder says—Be very careful! Remember what happened that time?

Everyone remembers. Every year, a herd of elephants from Saranda Forest would come to Betla, and then go back. Some years ago, some irresponsible adivasi lad shot an arrow and killed an elephant calf. The elephants, furious, encircled the dead calf, walking around him as if taking an oath incomprehensible to man.

Then they began their war of revenge. The residents of Jhujhar and Kolna villages fled. The first year, they ransacked the two villages and left.

The next year, they came from Saranda and killed two coolies working in the jungle.

The third year, they returned and smashed a bus and car parked below the Betla Forest Bungalow.

Sating their desire for vengeance on man after three years, they calm down. It was not possible to proclaim them *rogues* and kill them. Because they would always move as a herd, and the older elephants would undertake *retribution*. At present, the whole of Betla is surrounded by barbed wire. Elephants are very intelligent animals; they understand the barrier of barbed wire, and respect it.

The village elder said—Whatever else you do, don't anger the elephants. Especially not the *ekoa*. They don't forget.

Their wasted bodies had worn down the youth. They said, with ashen faces—We'll be careful. Even doing puja hasn't helped. We can't breathe easily, and bearing loads makes our limbs ache.

They were careful. They stole the salt-earth carefully. Don't climb down from the trees before making sure that all the elephants have gone—They kept Purti's instructions in mind.

Then, possibly because of the *ekoa,* the *salt lick* is *shifted*. Salt licks are located in two or three spots. Much later, when the equation of *ekoa* + Jhujhar adivasis + *salt lick* came in for investigation, the Forest Department had a very logical explanation.

Whether *ekoa* or herd, the responsibility for the *elephant population* rests with the Forest Department. This *ekoa* is a rascal. He pisses on the *salt lick*. He licks up the salt-earth. The Forest Department hoped that if they built *salt licks* at different places, and the *ekoa* visited one, the elephant herd could use another.

The *ekoa* was upsetting all calculations. He wandered here and there. Because he was not with the herd, his sense of time was changing, too. He'd turn up at the *salt lick* at odd hours, not just at dawn or dusk. His nature was changing. Possibly he sensed that salt-earth was being stolen. Sometimes he'd come and stand in the middle of the road, unmoving even in the face of jeep headlights. The jeep had to be turned round. Was he becoming suspicious of human beings? Was he trying to pick up human smells with the radar of his trunk?

A kind of tension was created in the Forest Department and slowly began to increase, centred around this elephant. Such an *ekoa* can suddenly begin to cause trouble. The problem was that, until designated and proved a *man-killer* or *rogue*, no protected elephant can be destroyed.

Everyone was secretly waiting for this tension to explode. Forest Department coolies began to say that they were scared to go to work as long as the *ekoa* was there. Spotting the *ekoa* at a distance, standing and marking their movements, they dropped their work and fled. The *ekoa* had grown suspicious. So had those who came to replenish the *salt licks*. Handfuls of salt-earth seemed to have been grabbed and snatched, nothing left, they had never seen such a thing. Who'd steal something like salt-earth? No. They didn't report it. It didn't seem important enough to report. There's so much salt in *store*.

The *elephant population* was also puzzled and disturbed. There were *salt licks*, but no salt. They, too, couldn't quite understand it. Everything seemed topsy-turvy.

The reason for all this was Purti and two other lads.

At first they were careful, very careful. From evening on, they'd remain wrapped around the topmost branches, unmoving, as if dead. Once the herd and the *ekoa* had gone, they'd steal the salt-earth. Possibly, now that they were eating salt again, their muscles were once again capable of swift and natural action, the body's *osmosis* returning to normal, the heart able to pump blood at a normal pressure with the liquid content of blood increased, and the *electrolyte* balance of the body reinstated.

Possibly. And immediately, all the slippery human cunning returns to their brains. They forget about caution. They begin to lift salt-earth before the elephants come each evening. They have no idea that the *ekoa* has seen them.

Suddenly, the *ekoa* is seen less often in the forest. It is learnt that at dusk the *ekoa* stands amid the white sands of the river and carefully watches something in the distance.

—What's he watching?

—The adivasis going off across the river.

This information is not comforting. But the *ekoa* has changed the *target* of his attentions, and this news *relaxes* the Forest Department's *tension*. However, it is announced that if anyone finds out what the elephant is up to, the office must be informed.

After a few days, work on the *khair* trees has to be abandoned once again. Because the *khair* forests lie in the heart of the jungle, on the way to the ancient Palamau fort. It is learnt that the *ekoa* is roaming around this ancient fort.

This is the fort of the once-independent kings of Palamau. The sight of this huge, mountainous, ruined stone and brick fortress in the dense Betla forest is really terrifying. In this natural forest of towering trees it is much taller than the highest *sal*. The eye is not prepared for such a massive man-made *structure*. And because of this, the fort is a frightening sight.

The jungle coolies spot the *ekoa* close to the fort walls, prowling even more soundlessly than the tiger, avoiding dry leaves, its trunk extended as if in search of something. As soon as they see this, they flee.

Purti Munda and the others naturally had no way of knowing all this, because the moment they sensed the approach of anyone connected with the Forest Department they'd scatter and hide in the forest. To the Forest Department people, a few grains of salt are nothing. But it was because of that salt that Purti and the others had decided not to show themselves. If the Forest Department people saw them, they'd nab them as salt-thieves. While these misunderstandings were rife, the *ekoa*, deprived of salt to lick and piss on, had embarked on a hunt for the guilty—he had understood correctly: there was some kind of link between the *salt lick* and Jhujhar. That's why he would stand and wait on the white sand, in the dark, staring towards Jhujhar. The scene is symbolic. River, sands, sky, night, Palamau fort in the background, a lonely elephant. An immortal and peaceful picture. But, the only difference is that the schemes that were twisting about in the above elephant's brain did not leave much scope for releasing white doves.

A few days pass thus. Then, one night, without a single witness, the elephant tramps across sand and water and, reaching Jhujhar village, stands still by the well. Morning comes, everyone opens his door and comes out as per habit to perform the morning task, and, seeing the sun rising from behind the stationary *ekoa* beside the well, promptly closes his door and sits inside in silence, turned to stone with fear. Eyeing him through the slit in the window, Purti Munda silently prays—*Hei* aba! Let no one shoot an arrow! *Hei* aba! Let no one shoot an arrow!

No one shoots, and the elephant, seeming to have his suspicions confirmed, leaves the village, crosses the river and goes away. Only when he disappears into the jungle does everyone come out, and the village elder says—What I feared has happened. You must have been careless, he's seen you. Why else would he come?

—He hasn't seen us. If he had, wouldn't we have known, wouldn't we have seen him? Is an elephant a rabbit?

—An elephant is an ant—an elephant is a butterfly—an elephant is the breeze! Such a huge body, but when it wants, it can creep up unnoticed and squash your head with its foot, and you won't even know. You fool! You shit-eating insect! You didn't see him, he saw you. Why else would he come?

—What's done is done, now show us a way out.

—Purti! I really don't know how to punish you to my satisfaction. The adivasi who goes off to work in the coal mines or as a coolie in the town, stays away. You didn't. You were kicked out, you came back thinking yourself a know-all. And you got into a dispute with Uttamchand. A tiger. Then you led the elephant into the village.

—What's the solution?

—No one will go to fetch salt. Each of you prepare escape holes in your thatch roofs. If you catch sight of the elephant, run!

Purti says—Shall we cut down thorny bushes and build a fence? They do it in the jungle. Elephants are scared of them.

—Yes, yes, in a village on stony ground! Where'll you build the fence? Which side will you protect?

—Then?

—Don't steal salt. Maybe that'll make him forget.

Purti and the rest obeyed the village elder. They didn't go to steal salt any more. Strangely, the elephant didn't come back, either. One day Purti said to the Forest Beat Officer—That *ekoa* had come to the village the other day. We were very scared.

—So were we. I don't see the fellow any more. Maybe he's gone.

Everyone felt that he really had gone. As if the dusky animal had melted into the green forest. An animal census is taken by counting pug-marks on the banks of water bodies. Without bothering to check the water bodies or ponds, the Forest Department declared that the *ekoa* had disappeared.

From the bend in the river, where the bamboos swept the ground, the *ekoa* watched everything and tried to comprehend the situation. No hands touch the *salt lick* anymore, no longer does the impure scent of man cling to the air. Is this a new strategy of attack? It was as if he was realizing that man is *basically* an *irrational* being. It is an *irrational* act to anger the *ekoa* and take salt-earth. It's *rational* not to do this. But man can't do logical things for a sustained period. It was as if the *ekoa* knew that Purti and the others wouldn't be able to, either.

Purti and the rest ultimately did act *irrationally*. And the most amazing thing is that a week before they did, Uttamchand had decided 'Enough is enough' and had begun to sell salt wholesale in the market. No one knows whether Purti and the others knew of this. Perhaps they didn't know. Perhaps they'd heard, but didn't believe that Uttamchand would sell them salt. Perhaps they were enticed by the idea of stealing salt-earth from under the *ekoa's* nose or by fooling him. Perhaps they thought this an act of great courage, one that would establish their virility and their status as achievers. Perhaps. Or maybe they felt like *outwitting* the Forest Department. No one knows what was in the minds of Purti and the rest. But after prolonged interrogation it is learnt that before dawn broke, Purti and two other youths left with sacks. They left saying—Watch it, watch it, wife, don't raise your voice. We'll go and come carefully. The elephants leave at sunrise, we'll go then.

They go, and the *ekoa* makes its move. The elephant is the largest animal that walks the earth. But when a rogue elephant starts a battle of wits with man, then, if he so desires, he can make less noise than an ant. He carefully side-steps each dried leaf. With unbelievable caution. So, when Purti turned around, it seemed to him as if the ancient Palamau fort itself was coming towards them. From very close, an elephant looks even larger than it really is.

The elephant attacked in silence, but the three men shrieked and shrieked. At their screams, the distant elephant herds grow restless, the deer start and plunge off. The human shrieks are swiftly felled into total silence. Then, the elephant rends the sky, trumpeting in almost human glee, and stamps off, trampling the forest underfoot.

What Purti and the others had to say about why this happened will never be known. Smashed, trampled human bodies cannot give evidence or bear witness.

—They died trying to steal salt-earth? Salt-earth?

Everyone thinks the same thing, and the behaviour of Purti and the rest seems completely incomprehensible. Finally, the *daroga* says—They must have been drunk.

No one complicates matters by wondering aloud whether it is usual for adivasis to be drunk early in the morning. This matter of stealing salt-earth is so incomprehensible! A thing as cheap as salt! Why would Purti and the others do such an *irrational* thing unless they were drunk?

—They died trying to steal the elephant's salt-earth! These few words uttered by the *daroga* becomes their *epitaph*, and it is proved finally that the inhabitants of Jhujhar can by no means be trusted. The herbivorous animal needs salt, and now man steals even that! This unnatural act reminds them once more of how difficult it is to protect wild animals from the greed of humans.

Without his knowing it, the *ekoa* is *declared* a '*rogue*', and because his death will not anger the herd, as he is a loner, a *commissioned* hunter shoots him dead. The event makes a short item in the newspapers, and even the Jhujhar villagers turn up to see the dead *ekoa*. Looking at the elephant, the village elder is dimly aware of the fact that none of this is quite right. The apparent truth is that the elephant died because it killed Purti and the others. But the underlying truth seems to be something else. All this because of mere salt! They couldn't get salt. If they could buy salt, three men and one elephant would still be alive. Someone else was responsible, someone else. The person who would not sell the salt? Or some other law? Some other system? The law and the system under whose aegis Uttamchand's refusal to sell salt is not counted as a crime? Because his thought process is hazy and because his stock of words is limited, he cannot explain anything to anyone.

—This is not right. He tosses just these few words in the direction of the babus, and then leaves with the other villagers, and, walking single file across the white sands, returns to Jhujhar, shaking his head. He knows that the babus will never understand how salt can become something to risk one's life for, that this business will always remain unreal to them. And because he knows this, he doesn't look back, not once. Across the breast of the sands, their figures gradually grow smaller. They walk fast. They will feel at ease only when they return to their own life, a life in which there is no disbelief, no easy explanation for the deaths of Purti and the others, no attempt to deny the reality of their *existence* with simple explanations. That life.

—Translated from the Bengali 'Noon' by Ipsita Chanda

ACROSS THE SEVEN SEAS

Jhumpa Lahiri

Mrs Sen's

Eliot had been going to Mrs Sen's for nearly a month, ever since school started in September. The year before he was looked after by a university student named Abby, a slim, freckled girl who read books without pictures on their covers, and refused to prepare any food for Eliot containing meat. Before that an older woman, Mrs Linden, greeted him when he came home each afternoon, sipping coffee from a thermos and working on crossword puzzles while Eliot played on his own. Abby received her degree and moved off to another university, while Mrs Linden was, in the end, fired when Eliot's mother discovered that Mrs Linden's thermos contained more whiskey than coffee. Mrs Sen came to them in tidy ballpoint script, posted on an index card outside the supermarket: 'Professor's wife, responsible and kind, I will care for your child in my home.' On the telephone Eliot's mother told Mrs Sen that the previous baby-sitters had come to their house. 'Eliot is eleven. He can feed and entertain himself; I just want an adult in the house, in case of an emergency.' But Mrs Sen did not know how to drive.

This story is taken from *The Interpreter of Maladies*, published by Flamingo, London, 2000.

'As you can see, our home is quite clean, quite safe for a child,' Mrs Sen had said at their first meeting. It was a university apartment located on the fringes of the campus. The lobby was tiled in unattractive squares of tan, with a row of mailboxes marked with masking tape or white labels. Inside, intersecting shadows left by a vacuum cleaner were frozen on the surface of a plush pear-colored carpet. Mismatched remnants of other carpets were positioned in front of the sofa and chairs, like individual welcome mats anticipating where a person's feet would contact the floor. White drum-shaped lampshades flanking the sofa were still wrapped in the manufacturer's plastic. The TV and the telephone were covered by pieces of yellow fabric with scalloped edges. There was tea in a tall gray pot, along with mugs, and butter biscuits on a tray. Mr Sen, a short, stocky man with slightly protuberant eyes and glasses with black rectangular frames, had been there, too. He crossed his legs with some effort, and held his mug with both hands very close to his mouth, even when he wasn't drinking. Neither Mr nor Mrs Sen wore shoes; Eliot noticed several pairs lined on the shelves of a small bookcase by the front door. They wore flip-flops. 'Mr Sen teaches mathematics at the university,' Mrs Sen had said by way of introduction, as if they were only distantly acquainted.

She was about thirty. She had a small gap between her teeth and faded pockmarks on her chin, yet her eyes were beautiful, with thick, flaring brows and liquid flourishes that extended beyond the natural width of the lids. She wore a shimmering white sari patterned with orange paisleys, more suitable for an evening affair than for that quiet, faintly drizzling August afternoon. Her lips were coated in a complementary coral gloss, and a bit of the color had strayed beyond the borders.

Yet it was his mother, Eliot had thought, in her cuffed, beige shorts and her rope-soled shoes, who looked odd. Her cropped hair, a shade similar to her shorts, seemed too lank and sensible, and in that room where all things were so carefully covered, her shaved knees and thighs too exposed. She refused a biscuit each time Mrs Sen extended the plate in her direction, and asked a long series of questions, the answers to which she recorded on a steno pad. Would there be other children in the apartment? Had Mrs Sen cared for children before? How long had she lived in this country? Most of all she was concerned that Mrs Sen did not know how to drive. Eliot's mother worked in an office fifty miles north, and his father, the last she had heard, lived two thousand miles west.

'I have been giving her lessons, actually,' Mr Sen said, setting his mug on the coffee table. It was the first time he had spoken. 'By my estimate Mrs Sen should have her driver's license by December.'

'Is that so?' Eliot's mother noted the information on her pad.

'Yes, I am learning,' Mrs Sen said. 'But I am a slow student. At home, you know, we have a driver.'

'You mean a chauffeur?'

Mrs Sen glanced at Mr Sen, who nodded.

Eliot's mother nodded, too, looking around the room. 'And that's all . . . in India?'

'Yes,' Mrs Sen replied. The mention of the word seemed to release something in her. She neatened the border of her sari where it rose diagonally across her chest. She, too, looked around the room, as if she noticed in the lampshades, in the teapot, in the shadows frozen on the carpet, something the rest of them could not. 'Everything is there.'

Eliot didn't mind going to Mrs Sen's after school. By September the tiny beach house where he and his mother lived year-round was already cold; Eliot and his mother had to bring a portable heater along whenever they moved from one room to another, and to seal the windows with plastic sheets and a hair drier. The beach was barren and dull to play on alone; the only neighbors who stayed on past Labor Day, a young married couple, had no children, and Eliot no longer found it interesting to gather broken mussel shells in his bucket, or to stroke the seaweed, strewn like strips of emerald lasagna on the sand. Mrs Sen's apartment was warm, sometimes too warm; the radiators continuously hissed like a pressure cooker. Eliot learned to remove his sneakers first thing in Mrs Sen's doorway, and to place them on the bookcase next to a row of Mrs Sen's slippers, each a different color, with soles as flat as cardboard and a ring of leather to hold her big toe.

He especially enjoyed watching Mrs Sen as she chopped things, seated on newspapers on the living room floor. Instead of a knife she used a blade that curved like the prow of a Viking ship, sailing to battle in distant seas. The blade was hinged at one end to a narrow wooden base. The steel, more black than silver, lacked a uniform polish, and had a serrated crest, she told Eliot, for grating. Each afternoon Mrs Sen lifted the blade and locked it into place, so that it met the base at an angle. Facing the sharp edge without ever touching it, she took whole vegetables between her hands and hacked them apart: cauliflower, cabbage, butternut squash. She split things in half, then quarters, speedily producing florets, cubes, slices, and shreds. She could peel a potato in seconds. At times she sat cross-legged, at times with legs splayed, surrounded by an array of colanders and shallow bowls of water in which she immersed her chopped ingredients.

While she worked she kept an eye on the television and an eye on Eliot, but she never seemed to keep an eye on the blade. Nevertheless she refused to let Eliot walk around when she was chopping. 'Just sit, sit please, it will take just two more minutes,' she said, pointing to the sofa, which was draped at all times with a green and black bedcover printed with rows of elephants bearing palanquins on their backs. The daily procedure took about an hour. In order to occupy Eliot she supplied him with the comics section of the newspaper, and crackers spread with peanut butter, and sometimes a Popsicle, or carrot sticks sculpted with her blade. She would have roped off the area if she could. Once, though, she broke her own rule; in need of additional supplies, and reluctant to rise from the catastrophic mess that barricaded her, she asked Eliot to fetch something from the kitchen. 'If you don't mind, there is a plastic bowl, large enough to hold this spinach, in the cabinet next to the fridge. Careful, oh dear, be careful,' she cautioned as he approached. 'Just leave it, thank you, on the coffee table, I can reach.'

She had brought the blade from India, where apparently there was at least one in every household. 'Whenever there is a wedding in the family,' she told Eliot one day, 'or a large celebration of any kind, my mother sends out word in the evening for all the neighborhood women to bring blades just like this one, and then they sit in an enormous circle on the roof of our building, laughing and gossiping and slicing fifty kilos of vegetables through the night.' Her profile hovered protectively over her work, a confetti of cucumber, eggplant, and onion skins heaped around her. 'It is impossible to fall asleep those nights, listening to their chatter.' She paused to look at a pine tree framed by the living room window. 'Here, in this place where Mr Sen has brought me, I cannot sometimes sleep in so much silence.'

Another day she sat prying the pimpled yellow fat off chicken parts, then dividing them between thigh and leg. As the bones cracked apart over the blade her golden bangles jostled, her forearms glowed, and she exhaled audibly through her nose. At one point she paused, gripping the chicken with both hands, and stared out the window. Fat and sinew clung to her fingers.

'Eliot, if I began to scream right now at the top of my lungs, would someone come?'

'Mrs Sen, what's wrong?'

'Nothing. I am only asking if someone would come.'

Eliot shrugged. 'Maybe.'

'At home that is all you have to do. Not everybody has a

telephone. But just raise your voice a bit, or express grief or joy of any kind, and one whole neighborhood and half of another has come to share the news, to help with arrangements.'

By then Eliot understood that when Mrs Sen said home, she meant India, not the apartment where she sat chopping vegetables. He thought of his own home, just five miles away, and the young married couple who waved from time to time as they jogged at sunset along the shore. On Labor Day they'd had a party. People were piled on the deck, eating, drinking, the sound of their laughter rising above the weary sigh of the waves. Eliot and his mother weren't invited. It was one of the rare days his mother had off, but they didn't go anywhere. She did the laundry, and balanced the checkbook, and, with Eliot's help, vacuumed the inside of the car. Eliot had suggested that they go through the car wash a few miles down the road as they did every now and then, so that they could sit inside, safe and dry, as soap and water and a circle of giant canvas ribbons slapped the windshield, but his mother said she was too tired, and sprayed the car with a hose. When, by evening, the crowd on the neighbors' deck began dancing, she looked up their number in the phone book and asked them to keep it down.

'They might call you,' Eliot said eventually to Mrs Sen. 'But they might complain that you were making too much noise.'

From where Eliot sat on the sofa he could detect her curious scent of mothballs and cumin, and he could see the perfectly centered part in her braided hair, which was shaded with crushed vermilion and therefore appeared to be blushing. At first Eliot had wondered if she had cut her scalp, or if something had bitten her there. But then one day he saw her standing before the bathroom mirror, solemnly applying, with the head of a thumbtack, a fresh stroke of scarlet powder, which she stored in a small jam jar. A few grains of the powder fell on the bridge of her nose as she used the thumbtack to stamp a dot above her eyebrows. 'I must wear the powder every day,' she explained when Eliot asked her what it was for, 'for the rest of the days that I am married.'

'Like a wedding ring, you mean?'

'Exactly, Eliot, exactly like a wedding ring. Only with no fear of losing it in the dishwater.'

By the time Eliot's mother arrived at twenty past six, Mrs Sen always made sure all evidence of her chopping was disposed of. The blade was scrubbed, rinsed, dried, folded, and stowed away in a cupboard with the aid of a stepladder. With Eliot's help the newspapers were crushed with all the peels and seeds and skins inside them. Brimming bowls and colanders lined the countertop, spices and pastes were measured and blended, and eventually a collection of broths simmered over periwinkle flames on the stove. It was never a special occasion, nor was she ever expecting company. It was merely dinner for herself and Mr Sen, as indicated by the two plates and two glasses she set, without napkins or silverware, on the square Formica table at one end of the living room.

As he pressed the newspapers deeper into the garbage pail, Eliot felt that he and Mrs Sen were disobeying some unspoken rule. Perhaps it was because of the urgency with which Mrs Sen accomplished everything, pinching salt and sugar between her fingernails, running water through lentils, sponging all imaginable surfaces, shutting cupboard doors with a series of successive clicks. It gave him a little shock to see his mother all of a sudden, in the transparent stockings and shoulder-padded suit she wore to her job, peering into the corners of Mrs Sen's apartment. She tended to hover on the far side of the door frame, calling to Eliot to put on his sneakers and gather his things, but Mrs Sen would not allow it. Each evening she insisted that his mother sit on the sofa, where she was served something to eat: a glass of bright pink yogurt with rose syrup, breaded mincemeat with raisins, a bowl of semolina halva.

'Really, Mrs Sen. I take a late lunch. You shouldn't go to so much trouble.'

'It is no trouble. Just like Eliot. No trouble at all.'

His mother nibbled Mrs Sen's concoctions with eyes cast upward, in search of an opinion. She kept her knees pressed together, the high heels she never removed pressed into the pear-colored carpet. 'It's delicious,' she would conclude, setting down the plate after a bite or two. Eliot knew she didn't like the tastes; she'd told him so once in the car. He also knew she didn't eat lunch at work, because the first thing she did when they were back at the beach house was pour herself a glass of wine and eat bread and cheese, sometimes so much of it that she wasn't hungry for the pizza they normally ordered for dinner. She sat at the table as he ate, drinking more wine and asking how his day was, but eventually she went to the deck to smoke a cigarette, leaving Eliot to wrap up the leftovers.

Each afternoon Mrs Sen stood in a grove of pine trees by the main road where the school bus dropped off Eliot along with two or three other children who lived nearby. Eliot always sensed that Mrs Sen had been waiting for some time, as if eager to greet a person she hadn't seen in years. The hair at her temples blew about in the breeze, the column of vermilion fresh in her part. She wore navy blue sunglasses a little too big for her face. Her sari, a different pattern each day, fluttered below the hem of a checkered all-weather coat. Acorns and caterpillars dotted the asphalt loop that framed the complex of about a dozen brick buildings, all identical, embedded in a communal expanse of log chips. As they walked back from the bus stop she produced a sandwich bag from her pocket, and offered Eliot the peeled wedges of an orange, or lightly salted peanuts, which she had already shelled.

They proceeded directly to the car, and for twenty minutes Mrs Sen practiced driving. It was a toffee colored sedan with vinyl seats. There was an AM radio with chrome buttons, and on the ledge over the back seat, a box of Kleenex and an ice scraper. Mrs Sen told Eliot she didn't feel right leaving him alone in the apartment, but Eliot knew she wanted him sitting beside her because she was afraid. She dreaded the roar of the ignition, and placed her hands over her ears to block out the sound as she pressed her slippered feet to the gas, revving the engine.

'Mr Sen says that once I receive my license, everything will improve. What do you think, Eliot? Will things improve?'

'You could go places,' Eliot suggested. 'You could go anywhere.'

'Could I drive all the way to Calcutta? How long would that take, Eliot? Ten thousand miles, at fifty miles per hour?'

Eliot could not do the math in his head. He watched Mrs Sen adjust the driver's seat, the rearview mirror, the sunglasses on top of her head. She tuned the radio to a station that played symphonies. 'Is it Beethoven?' she asked once, pronouncing the first part of the composer's name not 'bay,' but 'bee,' like the insect. She rolled down the window on her side, and asked Eliot to do the same. Eventually she pressed her foot to the brake pedal, manipulated the automatic gear shift as if it were an enormous, leaky pen and backed inch by inch out of the parking space. She circled the apartment complex once, then once again.

'How am I doing, Eliot? Am I going to pass?'

She was continuously distracted. She stopped the car without warning to listen to something on the radio, or to stare at something, anything, in the road. If she passed a person, she waved. If she saw a bird twenty feet in front of her, she beeped the horn with her index finger and waited for it to fly away. In India, she said, the driver sat on the right side, not the left. Slowly they crept past the swing set, the laundry building, the dark green trash bins, the rows of parked cars. Each time they approached the grove of pine trees where the asphalt loop met the main road, she leaned forward, pinning all her weight against the brake as cars hurtled past. It was a narrow road painted with a solid yellow stripe, with one lane of traffic in either direction.

'Impossible, Eliot. How can I go there?'

'You need to wait until no one's coming.'

'Why will not any body slow down?'

'No one's coming now.'

'But what about the car from the right, do you see? And look, a truck is behind it. Anyway, I am not allowed on the main road without Mr Sen.'

'You have to turn and speed up fast,' Eliot said. That was the way his mother did it, as if without thinking. It seemed so simple when he sat beside his mother, gliding in the evenings back to the beach house. Then the road was just a road, the other cars merely part of the scenery. But when he sat with Mrs Sen, under an autumn sun that glowed without warmth through the trees, he saw how that same stream of cars made her knuckles pale, her wrists tremble, and her English falter.

'Everyone, this people, too much in their world.'

Two things, Eliot learned, made Mrs Sen happy. One was the arrival of a letter from her family. It was her custom to check the mailbox after driving practice. She would unlock the box, but she would ask Eliot to reach inside, telling him what to look for, and then she would shut her eyes and shield them with her hands while he shuffled through the bills and magazines that came in Mr Sen's name. At first Eliot found Mrs Sen's anxiety incomprehensible; his mother had a p.o. box in town, and she collected mail so infrequently that once their electricity was cut off for three days. Weeks passed at Mrs Sen's before he found a blue aerogram, grainy to the touch, crammed with stamps showing a bald man at a spinning wheel, and blackened by postmarks.

'Is this it, Mrs Sen?'

For the first time she embraced him, clasping his face to her sari, surrounding him with her odor of mothballs and cumin. She seized the letter from his hands.

As soon as they were inside the apartment she kicked off her slippers this way and that, drew a wire pin from her hair, and slit the top and sides of the aerogram in three strokes. Her eyes darted back and forth as she read. As soon as she was finished, she cast aside the embroidery that covered the telephone, dialed, and asked, 'Yes, is Mr Sen there, please? It is Mrs Sen and it is very important.'

Subsequently she spoke in her own language, rapid and riotous to Eliot's ears; it was clear that she was reading the contents of the letter, word by word. As she read her voice was louder and seemed to shift in key. Though she stood plainly before him, Eliot had the sensation that Mrs Sen was no longer present in the room with the pear-colored carpet.

Afterward the apartment was suddenly too small to contain her. They crossed the main road and walked a short distance to the university quadrangle, where bells in a stone tower chimed on the hour. They wandered through the student union, and dragged a tray together along the cafeteria ledge, and ate french fries heaped in a cardboard boat among students chatting at circular tables. Eliot drank soda from a paper cup, Mrs Sen steeped a tea bag with sugar and cream. After eating they explored the art building, looking at sculptures and silk screens in cool corridors thick with the fragrance of wet paint and clay. They walked past the mathematics building, where Mr Sen taught his classes.

They ended up in the noisy, chlorine-scented wing of the athletic building where, through a wide window on the fourth floor, they watched swimmers crossing from end to end in glaring turquoise pools. Mrs Sen took the aerogram from India out of her purse and studied the front and back. She unfolded it and reread to herself, sighing every now and then. When she had finished she gazed for some time at the swimmers.

'My sister has had a baby girl. By the time I see her, depending if Mr Sen gets his tenure, she will be three years old. Her own aunt will be a stranger. If we sit side by side on a train she will not know my face.' She put away the letter, then placed a hand on Eliot's head. 'Do you miss your mother, Eliot, these afternoons with me?'

The thought had never occurred to him.

'You must miss her. When I think of you, only a boy, separated from your mother for so much of the day, I am ashamed.'

'I see her at night.'

'When I was your age I was growing up without knowing that one day I would be so far. You are wiser than that, Eliot. You already taste the way things must be.'

The other thing that made Mrs Sen happy was fish from the seaside. It was always a whole fish she desired, not shellfish, or the fillets Eliot's mother had broiled one night a few months ago when she'd invited a man from her office to dinner—a man who'd spent the night in his mother's bedroom, but whom Eliot never saw again. One evening when Eliot's mother came to pick him up, Mrs Sen served her a tuna croquette, explaining that it was really supposed to be made with a fish called bhetki. 'It is very frustrating,' Mrs Sen apologized with an emphasis on the second syllable of the word. 'To live so close to the ocean and not to have so much fish.' In the summer, she said, she liked to go to a market by the beach. She added that while the fish there tasted nothing like the fish in India, at least it was fresh. Now that it was getting colder, the boats were no longer going out regularly, and sometimes there was no whole fish available for weeks at a time.

'Try the supermarket,' his mother suggested.

Mrs Sen shook her head. 'In the supermarket I can feed a cat thirty-two dinners from one of thirty-two tins, but I can never find a single fish I like, never a single.' Mrs Sen said she had grown up eating fish twice a day. She added that in Calcutta people ate fish first thing in the morning, last thing before bed, as a snack after school if they were lucky. They ate the tail, the eggs, even the head. It was available in any market, at any hour, from dawn until midnight. 'All you have to do is leave the house and walk a bit, and there you are.'

Every few days Mrs Sen would open up the yellow pages, dial a number that she had ticked in the margin, and ask if there was any whole fish available. If so, she would ask the market to hold it. 'Under Sen, yes, S as in Sam, N as in New York. Mr Sen will be there to pick it up.' Then she would call Mr Sen at the university. A few minutes later Mr Sen would arrive, patting Eliot on the head but not kissing Mrs Sen. He read his mail at the Formica table and drank a cup of tea before heading out; half an hour later he would return, carrying a paper bag with a smiling lobster drawn on the front of it, and hand it to Mrs Sen, and head back to the university to teach his evening class. One day, when he handed Mrs Sen the paper bag, he said, 'No more fish for a while. Cook the chicken in the freezer. I need to start holding office hours.'

For the next few days, instead of calling the fish market, Mrs Sen thawed chicken legs in the kitchen sink and chopped them with her blade. One day she made a stew with green beans and tinned sardines. But the following week the man who ran the fish market called Mrs Sen; he assumed she wanted the fish, and said he would hold it until the end of the day under her name. She was flattered. 'Isn't that nice of him, Eliot? The man said he looked up my name in the telephone book. He said there is only one Sen. Do you know how many Sens are in the Calcutta telephone book?'

She told Eliot to put on his shoes and his jacket, and then she called Mr Sen at the university. Eliot tied his sneakers by the bookcase and waited for her to join him, to choose from her row of slippers. After a few minutes he called out her name. When Mrs Sen did not reply, he untied his sneakers and returned to the living room, where he found her on the sofa, weeping. Her face was in her hands and tears dripped through her fingers. Through them she murmured something about a meeting Mr Sen was required to attend. Slowly she stood up and rearranged the cloth over the telephone. Eliot followed her, walking for the first time in his sneakers across the pear-colored carpet. She stared at him. Her lower eyelids were swollen into thin pink crests. 'Tell me, Eliot. Is it too much to ask?'

Before he could answer, she took him by the hand and led him to the bedroom, whose door was normally kept shut. Apart from the bed, which lacked a headboard, the only other things in the room were a side table with a telephone on it, an ironing board, and a bureau. She flung open the drawers of the bureau and the door of the closet, filled with saris of every imaginable texture and shade, brocaded with gold and silver threads. Some were transparent, tissue thin, others as thick as drapes, with tassels knotted along the edges. In the closet they were on hangers; in the drawers they were folded flat, or wound tightly like thick scrolls. She sifted through the drawers, letting saris spill over the edges. 'When have I ever worn this one? And this? And this?' She tossed the saris one by one from the drawers, then pried several from their hangers. They landed like a pile of tangled sheets on the bed. The room was filled with an intense smell of mothballs.

'"Send pictures," they write. "Send pictures of your new life." What picture can I send?' She sat, exhausted, on the edge of the bed, where there was now barely room for her. 'They think I live the life of a queen, Eliot.' She looked around the blank walls of the room. 'They think I press buttons and the house is clean. They think I live in a palace.'

The phone rang. Mrs Sen let it ring several times before picking up the extension by the bed. During the conversation she seemed only to be replying to things, and wiping her face with the ends of one of the saris. When she got off the phone she stuffed the saris without folding them back into the drawers, and then she and Eliot put on their shoes and went to the car, where they waited for Mr Sen to meet them.

'Why don't you drive today?' Mr Sen asked when he appeared,

rapping on the hood of the car with his knuckles. They always spoke to each other in English when Eliot was present.

'Not today. Another day.'

'How do you expect to pass the test if you refuse to drive on a road with other cars?'

'Eliot is here today.'

'He is here every day. It's for your own good. Eliot, tell Mrs Sen it's for her own good.'

She refused.

They drove in silence, along the same roads that Eliot and his mother took back to the beach house each evening. But in the back seat of Mr and Mrs Sen's car the ride seemed unfamiliar, and took longer than usual. The gulls whose tedious cries woke him each morning now thrilled him as they dipped and flapped across the sky. They passed one beach after another, and the shacks, now locked up, that sold frozen lemonade and quahogs in summer. Only one of the shacks was open. It was the fish market.

Mrs Sen unlocked her door and turned toward Mr Sen, who had not yet unfastened his seat belt. 'Are you coming?'

Mr Sen handed her some bills from his wallet. 'I have a meeting in twenty minutes,' he said, staring at the dashboard as he spoke. 'Please don't waste time.'

Eliot accompanied her into the dank little shop, whose walls were festooned with nets and starfish and buoys. A group of tourists with cameras around their necks huddled by the counter, some sampling stuffed clams, others pointing to a large chart illustrating fifty different varieties of North Atlantic fish. Mrs Sen took a ticket from the machine at the counter and waited in line. Eliot stood by the lobsters, which stirred one on top of another in their murky tank, their claws bound by yellow rubber bands. He watched as Mrs Sen laughed and chatted, when it was her turn in line, with a man with a bright red face and yellow teeth, dressed in a black rubber apron. In either hand he held a mackerel by the tail.

'You are sure what you sell me is very fresh?'

'Any fresher and they'd answer that question themselves.'

The dial shivered toward its verdict on the scale.

'You want this cleaned, Mrs Sen?'

She nodded. 'Leave the heads on, please.'

'You got cats at home?'

'No cats. Only a husband.'

Later, in the apartment, she pulled the blade out of the cupboard, spread newspapers across the carpet, and inspected her treasures. One by one she drew them from the paper wrapping, wrinkled and tinged with blood. She stroked the tails, prodded the bellies, pried apart the gutted flesh. With a pair of scissors she clipped the fins. She tucked a finger under the gills, a red so bright they made her vermilion seem pale. She grasped the body, lined with inky streaks, at either end, and notched it at intervals against the blade.

'Why do you do that?' Eliot asked.

'To see how many pieces. If I cut properly, from this fish I will get three meals.' She sawed off the head and set it on a pie plate.

In November came a series of days when Mrs Sen refused to practice driving. The blade never emerged from the cupboard, newspapers were not spread on the floor. She did not call the fish store, nor did she thaw chicken. In silence she prepared crackers with peanut butter for Eliot, then sat reading old aerograms from a shoebox. When it was time for Eliot to leave she gathered together his things without inviting his mother to sit on the sofa and eat something first. When, eventually, his mother asked him in the car if he'd noticed a change in Mrs Sen's behavior, he said he hadn't. He didn't tell her that Mrs Sen paced the apartment, staring at the plastic-covered lampshades as if noticing them for the first time. He didn't tell her she switched on the television but never watched it, or that she made herself tea but let it grow cold on the coffee table. One day she played a tape of something she called a raga; it sounded a little bit like someone plucking very slowly and then very quickly on a violin, and Mrs Sen said it was supposed to be heard only in the late afternoon, as the sun was setting. As the music played, for nearly an hour, she sat on the sofa with her eyes closed. Afterward she said, 'It is more sad even than your Beethoven, isn't it?' Another day she played a cassette of people talking in her language—a farewell present, she told Eliot, that her family had made for her. As the succession of voices laughed and said their bit, Mrs Sen identified each speaker. 'My third uncle, my cousin, my father, my grandfather.' One speaker sang a song. Another recited a poem. The final voice on the tape belonged to Mrs Sen's mother. It was quieter and sounded more serious than the others. There was a pause between each sentence, and during this pause Mrs Sen translated for Eliot: 'The price of goat rose two rupees. The mangoes at the market are not very sweet. College Street is flooded.' She turned off the tape. 'These are things that happened the day I left India.' The next day she played the same cassette all over again. This time, when her grandfather was speaking, she stopped the tape. She told Eliot she'd received a letter over the weekend. Her grandfather was dead.

A week later Mrs Sen began cooking again. One day as she sat slicing cabbage on the living room floor, Mr Sen called. He wanted to take Eliot and Mrs Sen to the seaside. For the occasion Mrs Sen put on a red sari and red lipstick; she freshened the vermilion in her part and rebraided her hair. She knotted a scarf under her chin, arranged her sunglasses on top of her head, and put a pocket camera in her purse. As Mr Sen backed out of the parking lot, he put his arm across the top of the front seat, so that it looked as if he had his arm around Mrs Sen. 'It's getting too cold for that top coat,' he said to her at one point. 'We should get you something warmer.' At the shop they bought mackerel, and butterfish, and sea bass. This time Mr Sen came into the shop with them. It was Mr Sen who asked whether the fish was fresh and to cut it this way or that way. They bought so much fish that Eliot had to hold one of the bags. After they put the bags in the trunk, Mr Sen announced that he was hungry, and Mrs Sen agreed, so they crossed the street to a restaurant where the take-out window was still open. They sat at a picnic table and ate two baskets of clam cakes. Mrs Sen put a good deal of Tabasco sauce and black pepper on hers. 'Like pakoras, no?' Her face was flushed, her lipstick faded, and she laughed at everything Mr Sen said.

Behind the restaurant was a small beach, and when they were done eating they walked for a while along the shore, into a wind so strong that they had to walk backward. Mrs Sen pointed to the water, and said that at a certain moment, each wave resembled a sari drying on a clothesline. 'Impossible!' she shouted eventually, laughing as she turned back, her eyes teary. 'I cannot move.' Instead she took a picture of Eliot and Mr Sen standing on the sand. 'Now one of us,' she said, pressing Eliot against her checkered coat and giving the camera to Mr Sen. Finally the camera was given to Eliot. 'Hold it steady,' said Mr Sen. Eliot looked through the tiny window in the camera and waited for Mr and Mrs Sen to move closer together, but they didn't. They didn't hold hands or put their arms around each other's waists. Both smiled with their mouths closed, squinting into the wind, Mrs Sen's red sari leaping like flames under her coat.

In the car, warm at last and exhausted from the wind and the clam cakes, they admired the dunes, the ships they could see in the distance, the view of the lighthouse, the peach and purple sky. After a while Mr Sen slowed down and stopped by the side of the road.

'What's wrong?' Mrs Sen asked.

'You are going to drive home today.'

'Not today.'

'Yes, today.' Mr Sen stepped out of the car and opened the door on Mrs Sen's side. A fierce wind blew into the car, accompanied by the sound of waves crashing on the shore. Finally she slid over to the driver's side, but spent a long time adjusting her sari and her sunglasses. Eliot turned and looked through the back window. The road was empty. Mrs Sen turned on the radio, filling up the car with violin music.

'It helps me to concentrate,' Mrs Sen said, and turned the radio on again.

'Put on your signal,' Mr Sen directed.

'I know what to do.'

For about a mile she was fine, though far slower than the other cars that passed her. But when the town approached, and traffic lights loomed on wires in the distance, she went even slower.

'Switch lanes,' Mr Sen said. 'You will have to bear left at the rotary.'

Mrs Sen did not.

'Switch lanes, I tell you.' He shut off the radio. 'Are you listening to me?'

A car beeped its horn, then another. She beeped defiantly in response, stopped, then pulled without signaling to the side of the road. 'No more,' she said, her forehead resting against the top of the steering wheel. 'I hate it. I hate driving. I won't go on.'

She stopped driving after that. The next time the fish store called she did not call Mr Sen at his office. She had decided to try something new. There was a town bus that ran on an hourly schedule between the university and the seaside. After the university it made two stops, first at a nursing home, then at a shopping plaza without a name, which consisted of a bookstore, a shoe store, a drugstore, a pet store, and a record store. On benches under the portico, elderly women from the nursing home sat in pairs, in knee-length overcoats with oversized buttons, eating lozenges.

'Eliot,' Mrs Sen asked him while they were sitting on the bus, 'will you put your mother in a nursing home when she is old?'

'Maybe,' he said. 'But I would visit every day.'

'You say that now, but you will see, when you are a man your life will be in places you cannot know now.' She counted on her fingers: 'You will have a wife, and children of your own, and they will want to be driven to different places at the same time. No matter how kind they are, one day they will complain about visiting your mother, and you will get tired of it too, Eliot. You will miss one day, and another, and then she will have to drag herself onto a bus just to get herself a bag of lozenges.'

At the fish shop the ice beds were nearly empty, as were the lobster tanks, where rust-colored stains were visible through the water. A sign said the shop would be closing for winter at the end of the month. There was only one person working behind the counter, a young boy who did not recognize Mrs Sen as he handed her a bag reserved under her name.

'Has it been cleaned and scaled?' Mrs Sen asked.

The boy shrugged. 'My boss left early. He just said to give you this bag.'

In the parking lot Mrs Sen consulted the bus schedule. They would have to wait forty-five minutes for the next one, and so they crossed the street and bought clam cakes at the take-out window they had been to before. There was no place to sit. The picnic tables were no longer in use, their benches chained upside down on top of them.

On the way home an old woman on the bus kept watching them, her eyes shifting from Mrs Sen to Eliot to the blood-lined bag between their feet. She wore a black overcoat, and in her lap she held, with gnarled, colorless hands, a crisp white bag from the drugstore. The only other passengers were two college students, boyfriend and girlfriend, wearing matching sweatshirts, their fingers linked, slouched in the back seat. In silence Eliot and Mrs Sen ate the last few clam cakes in the bag. Mrs Sen had forgotten napkins, and traces of fried batter dotted the corners of her mouth. When they reached the nursing home the woman in the overcoat stood up, said something to the driver, then stepped off the bus. The driver turned his head and glanced back at Mrs Sen. 'What's in the bag?'

Mrs Sen looked up, startled.

'Speak English?' The bus began to move again, causing the driver to look at Mrs Sen and Eliot in his enormous rearview mirror.

'Yes, I can speak.'

'Then what's in the bag?'

'A fish,' Mrs Sen replied.

'The smell seems to be bothering the other passengers. Kid, maybe you should open her window or something.'

One afternoon a few days later the phone rang. Some very tasty halibut had arrived on the boats. Would Mrs Sen like to pick one up? She called Mr Sen, but he was not at his desk. A second time she tried calling, then a third. Eventually she went to the kitchen and returned to the living room with the blade, an eggplant, and some newspapers. Without having to be told Eliot took his place on the sofa and watched as she sliced the stems off the eggplant. She divided it into long, slender strips, then into small squares, smaller and smaller, as small as sugar cubes.

'I am going to put these in a very tasty stew with fish and green bananas,' she announced. 'Only I will have to do without the green bananas.'

'Are we going to get the fish?'

'We are going to get the fish.'

'Is Mr Sen going to take us?'

'Put on your shoes.'

They left the apartment without cleaning up. Outside it was so cold that Eliot could feel the chill on his teeth. They got in the car, and Mrs Sen drove around the asphalt loop several times. Each time she paused by the grove of pine trees to observe the traffic on the main road. Eliot thought she was just practicing while they waited for Mr Sen. But then she gave a signal and turned.

The accident occurred quickly. After about a mile Mrs Sen took a left before she should have, and though the oncoming car managed to swerve out of her way, she was so startled by the horn that she lost control of the wheel and hit a telephone pole on the opposite corner. A policeman arrived and asked to see her license, but she did not have one to show him. 'Mr Sen teaches mathematics at the university' was all she said by way of explanation.

The damage was slight. Mrs Sen cut her lip, Eliot complained briefly of a pain in his ribs, and the car's fender would have to be straightened. The policeman thought Mrs Sen had also cut her scalp, but it was only the vermilion. When Mr Sen arrived, driven by one of his colleagues, he spoke at length with the policeman as he filled out some forms, but he said nothing to Mrs Sen as he drove them back to the apartment. When they got out of the car, Mr Sen patted Eliot's head. 'The policeman said you were lucky. Very lucky to come out without a scratch.'

After taking off her slippers and putting them on the bookcase, Mrs Sen put away the blade that was still on the living room floor and threw the eggplant pieces and the newspapers into the garbage pail. She prepared a plate of crackers with peanut butter, placed them on the coffee table, and turned on the television for Eliot's benefit. 'If he is still hungry give him a Popsicle from the box in the freezer,' she said to Mr Sen, who sat at the Formica table sorting through the mail. Then she went into her bedroom and shut the door. When Eliot's mother arrived at quarter to six, Mr Sen told her the details of the accident and offered a check reimbursing November's payment. As he wrote out the check he apologized on behalf of Mrs Sen. He said she was resting, though when Eliot had gone to the bathroom he'd heard her crying. His mother was satisfied with the arrangement, and in a sense, she confessed to Eliot as they drove home, she was relieved. It was the last afternoon Eliot spent with Mrs Sen, or with any baby-sitter. From then on his mother gave him a key, which he wore on a string around his neck. He was to call the neighbors in case of an emergency, and to let himself into the beach house after school. The first day, just as he was taking off his coat, the phone rang. It was his mother calling from her office. 'You're a big boy now, Eliot,' she told him. 'You okay?' Eliot looked out the kitchen window, at gray waves receding from the shore, and said that he was fine.

V.S. NAIPAUL

Mr Biswas Rebels

In the long room Mr Biswas gathered his painting equipment and
sang over and over:

> *In the snowy and the blowy,*
> *In the blowy and the snowy.*

Words and tune were based, remotely, on *Roaming in the Gloaming*,
which the choir at Lal's school had once sung to entertain important
visitors from the Canadian Mission.

Yet almost as soon as he had left Hanuman House through the
side gate, Mr Biswas's high spirits vanished, and a depression fell
upon him and lasted all day. He worked badly. He had to paint
a large sign on a corrugated iron paling. Doing letters on a
corrugated surface was bad enough; to paint a cow and gate, as he
had to, was maddening. His cow looked stiff, deformed and
sorrowful, and undid the gaiety of the rest of the advertisement.

He was strained and irritable when he went back to Hanuman
House. The aggrieved and aggressive stares he received in the hall
reminded him of his morning triumph. All his joy at that had
turned into disgust at his condition. The campaign against the

This extract is taken from *A House for Mr Biswas*, published by Penguin
Books India, New Delhi, 1992.

Tulsis, which he had been conducting with such pleasure, now seemed pointless and degrading. Suppose, Mr Biswas thought in the long room, suppose that at one word I could just disappear from this room, what would remain to speak of me? A few clothes, a few books. The shouts and thumps in the hall would continue; the *puja* would be done; in the morning the Tulsi Store would open its doors.

He had lived in many houses. And how easy it was to think of those houses without him! At this moment Pundit Jairam would be at a meeting or he would be eating at home, looking forward to an evening with his books. Soanie stood in the doorway, darkening the room, waiting for the least gesture of command. In Tara's back verandah Ajodha sat relaxed in his rocking-chair, his eyes close, listening perhaps to *That Body of Yours* being read by Rabidat, who sat at an awkward angle, trying to hide the smell of drink and tobacco on his breath. Tara was about, harrying the cowman (it was milking-time) or harrying the yard boy or the servant girl, harrying somebody. In none of these places he was being missed because in none of these places had he ever been more than a visitor, an upsetter of routine. Was Bipti thinking of him in the back trace? But she herself was a derelict. And, even more remote, that house of mud and grass in the swamplands: probably pulled down now and ploughed up. Beyond that, a void. There was nothing to speak of him.

He heard footsteps and Shama came into the room with a brass plate loaded with rice, curried potatoes, lentils and coconut chutney.

'How often you want me to tell you that I hate those blasted brass plates?'

She put the plate on the floor.

He walked round it. 'Nobody ever teach you hygiene at school? Rice, potatoes. All that damn starch.' He tapped his belly. 'You want to blow me up?' At the sight of Shama his depression had turned to anger, but he spoke jocularly.

'I always say,' Shama said, 'that you must complain only when you start providing your own food.'

He went to the window, washed his hands, gargled and spat. Someone shouted from below, 'Up there! Look what you doing!'

'I know, I know,' Shama said, running to the window. 'I know this was bound to happen one day. You spit on somebody.'

He looked out with interest. 'Who it is? The old she-fox, or one of the gods?'

'You spit on Owad.'

They heard him complaining.

Mr Biswas took another mouthful of water and gargled. Then, with cheeks puffed out, he leaned as far out of the window as he could.

'Don't think I not seeing you,' the god shouted. 'I marking what you doing, Mr Biswas. But I standing up right here and if you spit on me again I going to tell Ma.'

'Tell, you little son of a bitch,' Mr Biswas muttered, spitting.

'Man!'

'O God!' the god exclaimed.

'You lucky little monkey,' Mr Biswas said. He had missed.

'Man!' Shama cried, and dragged him from the window.

He walked slowly around the brass plate.

'Walk,' Shama said. 'You walk until you tired. But wait until you provide your own food before you start criticizing the food other people give you.'

'Who give you that message to give me? Your mother?' He pulled his top teeth behind his lower teeth, but his long flour-sack pants prevented him from looking menacing.

'Nobody didn't give me any message to give you. It is just something I think of myself.'

'You think of it yourself, eh?'

He had seized the brass plate, spilling rice on the floor, and was rushing to the Demerara window. Going to throw the whole damned thing out, he had decided. But his violence calmed him,

and at the window he had another thought: throw the plate out
and you could kill somebody. He arrested his hurling gesture, and
merely tilted the plate. The food slipped off easily, leaving a few
grains of rice sticking to streaks of lentils and oily, bubble-ridden
trails of curry.

'O God! Oo-Go-o-od!'

It began as a gentle cry and rose rapidly to a sustained bawling
which aroused sympathetic shrieks from babies all over the house.
All at once the bawling was cut off, and seconds later—it seemed
much later—Mr Biswas heard a deep, grating, withdrawing snuffle.
'I going to tell Ma,' the god cried. 'Ma, come and see what your
son-in-law do to me. He cover me down with his dirty food.'
After a sirenlike intake of breath the bawling continued.

Shama looked martyred.

There was considerable commotion below. Several people were
shouting at once, babies screamed, there was much subsidiary
bawling and chatter, and the hall resounded with agitated
movements.

Heavy footsteps made the stairs shake, rattled the glass panes
on doors, drummed across the Book Room, and Govind was in
Mr Biswas's chamber.

'Is you!' Govind shouted, breathing hard, his handsome face
contorted. 'Is you who spit on Owad.'

Mr Biswas was frightened.

He heard more footsteps on the stairs. The bawling drew
nearer.

'Spit?' Mr Biswas said. 'I ain't spit on anybody. I just gargle out
of the window and throw away some bad food.'

Shama screamed.

Govind threw himself on Mr Biswas.

Caught by surprise, stupefied by fear, Mr Biswas neither
shouted nor hit back at Govind, and allowed himself to be
pummelled. He was struck hard and often on the jaw, and with
every blow Govind said, 'Is you.' Vaguely Mr Biswas was aware

of women massing in the room, screaming, sobbing , falling upon Govind and himself. He was acutely aware of the god bawling, right in his ear, it seemed: a dry, deliberate, scraping noise. Abruptly the bawling ceased. 'Yes, is he!' the god said. 'Is he. He asking for this a long time now.' And at every cuff and kick Govind gave, the god grunted, as though he himself had given the blow. The women were above Mr Biswas and Govind, their hair and veils falling loose. One veil tickled Mr Biswas's nose.

'Stop him!' Chinta cried. 'Govind will kill Biswas if you don't stop him. He is a terrible man, I tell you, when his temper is up.' She burst into a short, sharp wail. 'Stop it, stop it. They will send Govind to the gallows if you don't stop it. Stop it before they make me a widow.'

Punched on his hollow chest, short-jabbed on his soft, rising belly, Mr Biswas found, to his surprise, that his mind remained quite clear. What the hell is that woman crying for? he thought. She is going to be a widow all right, but what about me? He was trying to encircle Govind with his arms, but was unable to do more than tap him on the back. Govind didn't appear to notice the taps. Mr Biswas would have been surprised if he had. He wanted to scratch and pinch Govind, but reflected that it would be unmanly to do so.

'Kill him!' the god shouted. 'Kill him, Uncle Govind.'

'Owad, Owad,' Chinta said. 'How can you say a thing like that?' She pulled the god to her and pressed his head against her bosom. 'You too? Do you *want* to make me a widow?'

The god allowed himself to be embraced, but twisted his head to see the struggle and kept on shouting, 'Kill him, Uncle Govind. Kill him.'

The women were having little effect on Govind. They had succeeded only in lessening the swing of his arms, but his short jabs were powerful. Mr Biswas felt them all. They no longer caused pain.

'Kill him, Uncle Govind!'

He doesn't want any encouragement, Mr Biswas thought.

Neighbours were shouting.

'What happening, Mai? Mai! Mrs Tulsi! Mr Seth! What happening?'

Their urgent, frightened voices frightened Mr Biswas. Suddenly he heard himself bawling, 'O God! I dead. I dead. He will kill me.'

His terror silenced the house.

It stilled Govind's arms. It stilled the god, and gave him a fleeting vision of black policemen, courthouses, gallows, graves, coffins.

The women lifted themselves off Govind and Mr Biswas. Govind, breathing heavily, lifted himself of Mr Biswas.

How I hate people who breathe like that, Mr Biswas thought. And how that Govind smells! It wasn't a smell of sweat, but of oil, body oil, associated in Mr Biswas's mind with the pimples on Govind's face. How unpleasant it must be, to be married to a man like that!

'Has he killed him?' Chinta asked. She was calmer; her voice held pride and genuine concern. 'Talk, brother. Talk. Talk to your sister. Get him to say something, somebody.'

Now that Govind was of his chest Mr Biswas's only concern was to make sure that he was properly dressed. He hoped nothing had happened to his pants. He moved a hand down to investigate.

'He is all right,' Sushila said.

Someone bent over him. That smell of oil, Vick's Vaporub, garlic and raw vegetables told him it was Padma. 'Are you all right?' she asked, and shook him.

He turned over on his side, his face to the wall.

'He is all right,' Govind said, and added in English, 'Is a good thing all you people did come, otherwise I would be swinging on the gallows for this man.'

Chinta gave a sob.

Shama had maintained her martyr's attitude throughout, sitting on the low bench, her skirt draped over her knees, one hand supporting her chin, her staring eyes misting over with tears.

'Spitting on me, eh?' the god said. 'Go ahead. Why you don't spit now? Coming and laughing at our religion. Laughing at me when I do *puja*. *I* know the good I doing myself when I do *puja*, you hear.'

'It's all right, son,' Govind said. 'Nobody can insult you and Mai when I am around.'

'Leave him alone, Govind,' Padma said. 'Leave him, Owad.'

The incident was over. The room emptied.

Left alone, Shama and Mr Biswas remained as they were, Shama staring through the doorway, Mr Biswas considering the lotuses on the pale green wall.

They heard the hall return to life. The evening meal, delayed, was being laid out with unusual zest. Babies were consoled with songs, clapping, chuckles and baby-talk. Children were scolded with exceptional good humour. Between everyone downstairs there was for the moment a new bond, and Mr Biswas recognized this bond as himself.

'Go and get me a tin of red salmon,' he said to Shama, without turning from the wall. 'And some hops bread.'

Her throat was tickling. She coughed and tried to hide the swallow by sighing.

This wearied him further. He got up, his pants hanging loose, and looked at her. She was still staring through the doorway into the Book Room. His face felt heavy. He put a hand to one cheek and worked his jaw. It moved stiffly.

Tears spilled over from Shama's big eyes and ran down her cheeks.

'What happen? Somebody beat you too?'

She shook her tears away, without removing her hand from her chin.

'Go and get me a tin of salmon. Canadian. And get some bread and peppersauce.'

'What happen? You have a craving? You making baby?'

He would have liked to hit her. But that would have been ridiculous after what had just happened.

'You making baby?' Shama repeated. She rose, shook down her skirt and straightened it. Loudly, as though trying to catch the attention of the people downstairs, she said, 'Go and get it yourself. You not going to start ordering *me* around, you hear.' She blew her nose, wiped it, and left.

He was alone. He gave a kick at a lotus on the wall. The noise startled him, his toe hurt, and he aimed another kick at his pile of books. He sent them toppling and marvelled at the endurance and uncomplainingness of inanimate objects. The bent corner of the cover of *Bell's Standard Elocutionist* was like a wound silently, accusingly borne. He stooped to pick the books up, then decided it would be a sign of self contempt to do so. Better for them to lie like that for Shama to see and even rearrange. He passed a hand over his face. It felt heavy and dead. Squinting downwards, he could see the rise of cheek. His jaw ached. He was beginning to ache all over. It was odd that the blows had made so little impression at the time. Surprise was a good neutralizer. Perhaps it was the same with animals. Jungle life could be bearable, then; it was part of God's plan. He went over to the cheap mirror hanging at the side of the window. He had never been able to see properly in it. It was an idiotic place to put a mirror, and he was mad enough to pull it down. He didn't. He stepped to one side and looked over his shoulder at his reflection. He knew his face felt heavy; he had no idea it looked so absurd. But he had to go out, leave the house for the time being, get his salmon, bread and peppersauce—bad for him, but the suffering would come later. He put on his trousers, and the rattle of the belt buckle was such a precise, masculine sound that he silenced it at once. He put on his shirt and opened the second button to reveal his hollow chest. But his shoulders were fairly broad. He wished he could devote himself to developing his body. How could he, though, with all that bad food from that murky kitchen? They had salmon only on Good Friday: the influence, doubtless, of the orthodox Roman Catholic Hindu Mrs Tulsi. He pulled his hat low over his forehead and thought that in the dark he might just get away with his face.

As he went down the stairs the chatter became a babel. Past the landing, he waited for the silence, the reanimation.

It happened as he feared.

Shama didn't look at him. Among gay sisters she was the gayest. Padma said, 'You better feed Mohun, Shama.'

Govind didn't look up. He was smiling, at nothing, it seemed, and was eating in his savage, noisy way, rice and curry spilled all over his hairy hand and trickling down to his wrist. Soon, Mr Biswas knew, he would clean his hand with a swift, rasping lick.

Mr Biswas, his back to everyone in the hall, said, 'I not eating any of the bad food from this house.'

'Well, nobody not going to beg you, you hear,' Shama said.

He curled the brim of his hat over his eye and went down into the courtyard, lit only by the light from the hall.

The god said, 'Anyone see a spy pass through here?'

Mr Biswas heard the laughter.

Under the eaves of a bicycle shop across the High Street an oyster stall was yellowly, smokily lit by a flambeau with a thick spongy wick. Oysters lay in a shining heap, many-faceted, grey and black and yellow. Two bottles stopped with twists of brown paper, contained red peppersauce.

Postponing the salmon, Mr Biswas crossed the road and asked the man, 'How the oysters going?'

'Two for a cent.'

'Start opening.'

The man shouted, released into happy activity. From somewhere in the darkness a woman came running up. 'Come on,' the man said. 'Help open them.' They put a bucket of water on the stall, washed the oysters, opened them with short blunt knives, and washed them again. Mr Biswas poured peppersauce into the shell, swallowed, held out his hand for another. The peppersauce scalded his lips.

The oyster man was talking drunkenly, in a mixture of Hindi and English. 'My son is a helluva man. I feel that something is seriously wrong with him. One day he put a tin can on the fence and come running inside the house. "The gun, Pa," he said. "Quick, give me the gun." I give him the gun. He run to the window and shoot. The tin can fall. "Pa," he say. "Look. I shoot work. I shoot ambition. They dead."' The flambeau dramatized the oyster man's features, filling hollows with shadow, putting a shine on his temples above his eyebrows, along his nose, along his cheekbones. Suddenly he flung down his knife and pulled out a stick from below his stall. He waved the stick in front of Mr Biswas. 'Anybody!' he said. 'Tell anybody to come!'

The woman didn't notice. She went on opening oysters, laying them in her scratched, red palms, prising the ugly shells open, cutting the living oysters from their moorings to the pure, just-exposed inside shell.

'Tell anybody,' the man said. 'Anybody at all.'

'Stop!' Mr Biswas said.

The woman took her hand out of the bucket and replaced a dripping oyster on the heap.

The man put away his stick. 'Stop?' He looked saddened, and ceased to be frightening. He began to count the empty shells.

The woman disappeared into the darkness.

'Twenty-six,' the man said. 'Thirteen cents.'

Mr Biswas paid. The raw, fresh smell of oysters was now upsetting him. His stomach was full and heavy, but unsatisfied. The peppersauce had blistered his lips. Then the pains began. Nevertheless he went on to Mrs Seeung's. The high, cavernous café was feebly lit. Flies were asleep everywhere, and Mr Seeung was half-asleep behind the counter, his porcupinish head bent over a Chinese newspaper.

Mr Biswas bought a tin of salmon and two loaves of bread. The bread looked and smelled stale. He knew that in his present state bread would only bring on nausea, but it gave him some satisfaction that he was breaking one of the Tulsi taboos by eating shop bread, a habit they considered feckless, negroid and unclean. The salmon repelled him; he thought it tasted of tin; but he felt compelled to eat to the end. And as he ate, his distress increased. Secret eating never did him any good.

ANITA DESAI

Shopping for More

Mrs Patton, with her hand on the cart that Arun is rolling as rapidly as he can along the aisles of tinned soup, pasta and rice, tries to slow him down. 'We haven't enough yet, Ahroon,' she protests. 'You should have seen the way I'd load a shopping cart when the children were small. I'd have Melanie sitting up here on the shelf, and there'd be such a heap of groceries under her, she'd have to stick her feet right up on top.'

Arun has seen mothers of young children do precisely that— lift their babies onto the collapsible shelf where they sit above hills of cereal and cat food and diapers, usually sucking the candy they have been given in return for allowing their mothers to get on with the shopping. He tries to picture baby Melanie in the cart, queen of the groceries, but what he visualises is a baby monster with elephantine legs.

'And do you know, that load wouldn't last us even a week. Three days and I'd be back for more,' she chuckles, hurrying to keep up with him. The wheels of the cart squeal, the rubber-soled shoes squeak, Arun swivels to avoid another loaded cart trundling past.

'Do they eat less now?' he asks. There is scarcely room in the

This extract is taken from *Fasting, Feasting*, published by Vintage, London, 2000.

cart for another package. He feels revulsion rising in his throat as if from too gigantic a meal.

'My no, they eat all the time,' she laughs, a little out of breath. 'But—but it's different now. We don't sit down to meals like we used to. Everyone eats at different times and wants different meals. We just don't get to eating together much now that they're grown. So I just fill the freezer and let them take down what they like, when they like. Keeping the freezer full—that's my job, Ahroon,' she declares, and grasps the handle to stop him so she can study the labels on the soup cans. Although he hardly felt that mealtimes at home had been models of social and familial gathering—Papa chewing each mouthful like an examiner on duty, Mama's eyes like bright beads, watching, his sisters perched in preparation to flap and fly, the only conversation permitted to do with the grim duty at hand: eating—there seems something troubling about the Pattons' system, too.

'Mushroom,' says Mrs Patton. 'You'd eat that, wouldn't you, Ahroon?'

He wants to point out that he is not her family. He considers saying something about Melanie's needs, the way she had flung them before him on the landing, making it impossible for him to ignore them. But he does not know how to bring up her name without leading Mrs Patton to think he was taking an undue interest in her. At last he says, 'But what about the rest of the family—do *they* eat it?'

'Oh,' she replies, tossing it into the cart and moving on, 'I told you, they take down what they like. Out of the freezer, you know. Or,' she adds vaguely because she is examining the cookies now, 'they make a sandwich. You see,' she goes on, with the faintest frown, 'what I cook, they don't like. And they don't like sitting at a table either—like you and I do,' she smiles at Arun with unmistakable significance, making him look away and redden.

'Counter number six looks free,' he mumbles, and trundles wildly away.

Arun is jogging. With great deliberation he has folded and put away his spectacles, pulled on and laced up his newly bought sneakers, and now he is jogging. With the same deliberation and caution he jogs up Bayberry Lane, down Potwine Lane, along Laurel Way into Pomeroy Road. Amazed at his own daring, he jogs past lawns abandoned to the morning sun and past porches where old men sit, their baseball caps lowered over their noses, allowing the passing traffic to lull them into dusty sleep. He jogs past driveways where families sit expectantly around tablefuls of used clothes and shoes, carpet rolls and picture frames, table lamps and electrical gadgets, all surmounted by a sign saying *Yard Sale*, and other driveways where old ladies in straw hats prod with small trowels at beds of zinnias.

Still driven by resolve, he turns into Elm Street and jogs on past silent houses with rhododendrons screening their picture windows, under dense trees where wind chimes and hammocks dangle in the still air, and out onto Oak Street. His toes stub into his shoes, his ankles ache with the weight thrown on them, pain shoots up his leg muscles. He clenches his fists, and his teeth, and jogs on, hoping the barking dog will not break free of his chain to the dog-house, and that cars that roar their warning into his ears will swerve in time.

Sweat pours from under his hair onto his cheeks and runs down his chin. The heat of the still morning has a sullenness about it, the sparkle it had had earlier has dulled. He is slowing down. He is much slower now, tiring. But he will jog and jog— like Rod, like all those others; he has seen their contorted faces, their closed eyes, their shut expressions as they struggle to leave behind the town, the suburbs, the shopping malls, the parking lots, struggle to free themselves and find, through endeavour most primitive, through strain and suffering, that open space, that unfettered vacuum where the undiscovered America still lies—

Opening his eyes, Arun looks around wildly to see if he has arrived. Just in time, for he is about to run into the low-dipping branches of forest trees that crowd the road along its upward slope, casting shadows like nets in the way of the unwary. It is not where Arun has meant to end. Lifting his feet heavily out of the dust, he plods on, and his shoulders are hunched now, his head is sinking lower. He must go further, further, and leave the trees behind, the smoothing wilderness of them.

Cars are flashing by, dangerously close, forbiddingly silent and fast. He observes them with a kind of desperate appeal, willing one to stop and give him a ride, convey him quickly and efficiently to a given destination. Not one so much as slows done, the drivers clearly assured by his jogger's outfit that he has none.

Arun is dizzied by their passage; he gives his head a shake that sends beads of perspiration flying, and looks down at his feet pounding along the strip of dirt beside the road. Feet: he has never been so aware of their plodding inefficiency, their crippling shortcomings of design. He watches them come down in the dirt, lift up and boringly repeat their rudimentary action from which they seem unable to proceed or improvise, all the while aware of the chromium-centred wheels that flash past with mocking ease and smoothness, blowing insolent fumes back into his face.

The cars speed away like metal darts aimed into space by missile launchers in the towns they leave behind. Up at the top of the road, where it meets the interstate highway, they pause, then part as each makes its decisive movement towards its chosen destination. All along the highway there will be signs, shelter, food, gas stations, motorists' aid call boxes, Howard Johnson motels—everything for the convenience of motorists, the owners of the dream machines. Their passage will be easy, their destinations infinite. It is they, not the earthbound joggers, who are descended directly from the covered wagons and the trusty horses, who are the inheritors of the pioneer's dream of the endlessly postponed and endlessly golden West. They alone can challenge the space and the desolation, pit their steel against the wilderness and the vacuum, and triumph by rolling over it and laying it in the dust—contemptuously. In their sealed chambers, the drivers display their identities, their histories and their faiths in their windows for everyone to see and, with sacred charms dangling all about them, laugh as they plunge on, reckless.

The jogger only pretends. The jogger cannot even begin to compete. The jogger is overtaken and obsolete.

Arun stumbles to a halt at the top of the road, and sinks down on a dusty bank. A driver comes down on his horn in alarm, lets out a toot of warning, then whirls away. He is left sitting blinded by the dust and his own perspiration, nursing his knees and groaning at the thought of making his way back.

When he limps into the Pattons' driveway, he finds Mr Patton has just returned from work. He is getting out of his car, heaving himself out clumsily, holding a briefcase in one hand and a paper bag from the Foodmart in the other. 'Hi, Red,' he says to Arun. 'Here, will you hold this while I lock up?'

Arun puts out his hand and dumbly receives the bag damp from the seeping blood of whatever carcass Mr Patton has chosen to bring home tonight for the fire that will soon crackle its flames on the patio and send its smoke spiraling in at the open windows of the rooms where Melanie hides, where Mrs Patton bustles, where Arun will seek shelter.

Mr Patton locks up the car, emerges from the garage. They walk round the house to the kitchen door together. He asks, 'Where's everybody? Sitting on their butts in front of the TV? Doesn't anyone in this house do any work? That lawn could do with some cutting. Where's Rod?

'He must be out jogging, Mr Patton,' Arun tells him, uncertain if this is an activity that Mr Patton approves of or not.

'Jogging, huh? Jogging. That boy spends so much time getting into shape he hasn't time left over to do anything with it.'

Mr Patton sounds tired, irate. Arun is wary and follows him into the kitchen where he puts the bag down on the table so he can leave quickly.

Mrs Patton, who has indeed been sunk deep into the cushions of the sofa, watching *Dallas* on television, struggles to her feet and appears, blinking. 'Oh dear,' she says, 'the freezer is full to the *top* with chops. I don't know that I want any more.'

Mr Patton ignores her. He is getting a can of beer out of the refrigerator. Opening it with a sharp jerk of his thumb, he demands, 'Where are the kids? Are they going to be in for dinner tonight? What have they been doing all day? Are they doing any work around here?'

Mrs Patton begins hurriedly to put away the chops. As she busies herself, she says, 'You know Rod's in training for the football team, Chuck. It's what you wanted him to do yourself—'

Arun knows when to leave a family scene: it is a skill he has polished and perfected since his childhood. He sidles out of the room and has his foot on the stairs when he hears them starting on Melanie.

'And Melanie? What's she up to? What's she in training for, huh?'

Arun needs a wash but Melanie has taken the cassette player into the bathroom with her and shut the door. The sounds of the saxophone and trumpets and a lead singer in distress are pounding upon the door, hammering it with all its fists. But the door stays shut, a slit of light beneath it. In between songs, Arun can hear, through his open door, water furiously rushing.

When she comes out stumbling across the landing blindly, he looks up to see her passing the door, perspiration beading her clammy face. She can scarcely drag the cassette player along. Going into her room, she slams the door. He thinks he hears her crying but it could be the singer, in agony.

Rod is lying on his bed, amongst toy animals, music albums,

comic books and dirty socks. He is bicycling his legs vigorously around in a giddily whirling motion that is however perfectly steady and rhythmic. His hands support his back and his face is contorted and inflamed.

Arun stands at the door, waiting till Rod's legs slow down and come to a halt. Then he says, with a slight cough, 'Uh, Melanie is sick, I think.'

Rod lowers his legs onto the bed. He lies there waiting for the blood to recede from his head, breathing heavily and evenly. 'That kid,' he grunts at last, 'just poisons herself. All that candy she eats. Won't eat a thing but candy. Anybody'd be sick.' He gives a snort that is both derisive and amused. 'Wants to turn herself into a slim chick. Ha!'

'By—eating candy?' Arun ventures, unconvinced.

'Yeah, and sicking it up!' Rod sits up abruptly, swinging his great legs onto the floor and planting his feet squarely on the boards. He bends down to pick at a nail. 'Man, she's nuts, that kid, she's nuts,' he mutters. 'That's all these girls are good for, y'know. Not like guys. Too lazy to get off their butts and go jogging or play a good hard ball game. So they've got to sick it up.' He straightens himself and sticks a finger into his mouth and wiggles it graphically. 'Can you beat that? Who'd want to be sick?' He gives his head a shake, then rises to his feet, straddles his legs and begins to swing his arms as rapidly as he had done with his legs.

Arun gets out of the way, quickly: one can't tell what is more dangerous in this country, the pursuit of health or of sickness.

CHITRITA BANERJI

A Barisal Winter

The pleasantest surprise I had with eggs was in Bangladesh, during
my first experience of the great Muslim festival of Shab-e-Barat,
night of destiny. On this night, all devout Muslims are supposed
to visit the cemeteries where their family members are buried, to
light incense sticks and say special prayers. These observances are
important because on this night the fate of every believer is
determined in heaven for the coming year. For an outsider like
myself the most memorable aspect of Shab-e-Barat was the quaint
custom of eating bread (mostly made with rice flour) with different
kinds of *halua* on the following day. Most households will make
huge quantities of bread (flat discs like chapatis) and distribute
them to beggars who come in droves. This obligatory sharing of
food on festive days with those who possess nothing is one of the
most beautiful aspects of Islam. It was only on that occasion that
I realized what infinite variety and skill goes into the making of
halua. It could be made out of flour, arrowroot, ground yellow
split peas, eggs, carrots, gourds and even meat. Some of this
bewildering array was on display in the houses I visited on that
day, and the taste of them, eaten in succession, was like an ascending

This extract is taken from *Life and Food in Bengal*, published by Weidenfeld
and Nicolson, London, 1991.

scale of notes. But to my mind the tastiest and one of the easiest *haluas* was that made with eggs.

My sister-in-law would sometimes make a variant of this which was firmer in consistency and could be shaped into diamonds or squares. It tasted divine on a wintry morning with *parota*. It is also an ideal tit-bit to serve the occasional guest, for it keeps better than the *halua*.

Such memories of rich food in winter also take me back to the Bangladeshi village during this season. Going to Dapdapia, my husband's home village in Barisal, was a whole different pleasure during the astringent crispness of the Bengali winter. None of the magical lushness of the monsoon was in evidence. No river in full spate, nor ponds brimful of water and water weeds. The *kutcha* roads were dusty beneath our feet as we walked from the landing place to the family home. This of course was not a traditional thatched cottage but a concrete structure built by one of my brothers-in-law for occasional visits to the village. The ancestral home stood close by, though it was in very poor condition. Next to it was an overgrown plot of land where my father-in-law lay buried. But no ghostly presence marred my pleasure in that wintry landscape where the large trees had lost some of their leaves, the earth looked dry and brown and yet burgeoned with various crops, and the *khejur* trees stood in rows with earthen pots tied to their trunks to catch the *ras* or sap as it trickled from the tapping cuts.

The morning after our arrival in Dapdapia I woke up to find the shutters raised from without and several pairs of curious eyes looking at us. When I came out, the group of giggling girls scattered in haste but not before one of them had invited me to our cousins' house for breakfast. It was a short walk across the garden, but that was the first time my bare feet sank into soft grass wet with the tender dew of a winter morning. As often happens, it had been misty earlier, and I saw the moisture gleaming in glassy beads on the shrubs and branches. That breakfast was the first time I tasted the pure, undiluted sap of the date-palm, naturally chilled in its earthen pot from exposure to the night air. It is the most natural and uncloying sweetness that I have ever encountered.

As a child I had heard my father talk about drinking this *khejur ras* straight from the tree. In fact village boys often incur the wrath of farmers who have tied their pots to the trees by climbing and drinking the *ras*, quietly replacing the pot and disappearing. Though the date-palm tree looks the same round the year—a shorter, less attractive cousin of the tall coconut—the best sap is generated only during the winter. The first tapping takes place in late autumn and successive tappings go on throughout the short winter. Some parts of Bengal provide better habitats for the date-palm and the coconut tree than others. The districts of Barisal, Faridpur and Khulna are particularly well-known and a popular adage in Bangladesh says that the district of Faridpur is noted for its thieves, swindlers and *khejur gur*! But though the trunk provides such a delightful sweetener, the actual dates from the date-palm tree are nowhere near as tasty as those from desert climates.

The date-palm sap is made into three types of *gur*: liquid, grainy and the solid chunks of *patali*. The sap is heated in huge *karais* over wood or coal stoves and it is only an expert who can gauge the different degrees of cooking to achieve the right textures. The arrival of *gur* in the market is the signal for the professional sweet-makers to start preparing one of their most popular products, *sandesh* flavoured with the new *gur*. This *nalen gurer sandesh* has a browny-pink tinge and is very dear to the plump Bengali's heart. At the beginning of the season, *gur* is sold in its liquid form, *jhola gur*. This comes in earthen pots and disappears fast enough. In our home it would be used like maple syrup in America, poured over hot *luchis* or chapatis and as a sweetener in the milk. It ferments easily and so has to be eaten quickly. In rural areas the fermented *gur* is made into a kind of cheap liquor which tribals and poor villagers drink. It was this same *jhola gur* which inspired committed following from exceptional Bengalis like Sukumar Ray, our version of Edward Lear or Lewis Carroll. In one of his delightful poems he spun out an absurdly contradictory list of the good things of life, and the very best of the best was bread with *jhola gur*. The solid *patali gur* can be stored and used for quite a few months after winter is over, and refrigeration gives it even longer life. The most notable application for it is its use in *payesh*, in place of sugar. The pure nutty sweetness of the *gur* makes this winter *payesh* a Bengali gourmet's dream.

The house in the village where I had breakfast belonged to distant relatives, my in-laws, but the shyness between town and country limited our conversation mostly to smiles and nods. As I sat looking at all the activity in the large kitchen, a young girl came in with a bunch of greens and sat down in front of a *bonti* to chop them. The leaves and stems lost all character and fell in a pile of minute green fragments on the plate placed to catch them. Some of the others noticed my amazement and explained that skill at cutting this *koloi shak* was one of the factors that went in a girl's favour when the prospective bridegroom's family was appraising her. The greens were fried with chopped garlic and just before serving, some dry red chillies were roasted and crumbled over them. I have never forgotten the taste nor the magic speed of the hands that went into the cutting.

Along with *koloi shak* there were many items cooked for our lunch that day. But for me the most wonderful experience was seeing the huge *rui* that was caught from the pond to be made into a *jhol*. It was a beautiful specimen, weighing at least 5 kg (11 lbs), its pinkish scales gleaming in the sun as it lay gasping on the beaten earth of the courtyard. The taste of a fresh and mature fish caught immediately before being cooked was ambrosial.

Evening in the village was mystery and heightened awareness. We walked out to some fields in the late afternoon to admire the vegetables and *dals* growing there against the infinite distance of a horizon unencumbered by buildings. The green and maroon of the low-lying leafy greens were harmoniously countered by the white of the cauliflowers and the higher plants of the *dals,* the tomatoes and the aubergines. Soon the darkness came hurtling down on batwings and we hurried back to the house to pick up our shawls, for it was much colder in the village than in the city. Then, with one of my husband's cousins to guide us, we set out along the beaten mud tracks and raised embankments dividing the fields, to eat dinner with a friend of the family at the other end of the village. The darkness was impenetrable, our only visual aid being the lantern carried by our guide. And above was a most unfamiliar sky, cold, moonless and starry with no intervening veil of industrial smog. Halfway down, we came upon a cluster of houses. As we stepped into the courtyard-like space in the centre, doors opened on all sides and people came out with lanterns. Our guide laughed and chatted with them and one by one, the women, impelled by curiosity, came up to me and raised their lanterns to my face in a strange but unconscious parody of a priest holding up his lamp to the face of his divinity.

Another plunge into the darkness of the fields, and a little later we came upon the extended homestead where Kadam Bhai lived with his family. Instead of being taken indoors, we were taken around to the back where our dinner was being cooked in the open. Two pits had been dug in the ground and a wood fire built inside each, a technique which is an old tradition in many villages. Much store is set by the flavour of food cooked over a wood fire and it is generally believed to be good for one's digestion.

Huge *handis* had been placed over the flames to cook the *khichuri* and duck meat, standard combination in Barisal and a common favourite in the winter because that is when the birds are most plump and healthy. In the old days when feudal landlords with huge properties could indulge in all kinds of gustatory refinements, the wretched birds were 'prepared' for eating to produce the extra pleasure similar to that of milk-fed veal. Several ducks, their wings clipped, would be chained to little stakes attached to a large wooden platform, and kept locked up in a pitch-dark outhouse. Once a day a bowlful of rice and yoghurt would be set in front of each bird and every morning the entire platform, together with ducks, would be taken to the pond for bathing and cleaning. But the rest of the time the birds remained cooped up in the dark, unable to move or see. After two or three weeks of such treatment, the birds were considered fit for the plate, their flesh having become exquisitely soft and tender.

The Man Who Couldn't Stop Eating

A Roux-en-Y gastric-bypass operation is a radical procedure and the most drastic means available to lose weight. It is also the strangest operation I have ever participated in in surgery. It removes no disease, repairs no defect or injury. It is an operation that is intended to control a person's will—to manipulate a person's innards so that he will not overeat again. And it is soaring in popularity. Some 45,000 obesity patients had gastric-bypass surgery in the United States in 1999, and this number is on its way to doubling by 2003. Vincent Caselli was about to join them.

At 7.30 a.m. on 13 September 1999, an anaesthesiologist and two orderlies brought Caselli (whose name has been changed) into the operating room where I and his attending surgeon awaited him. Caselli was fifty-four years old, a heavy-machine operator and road construction contractor (he and his men had paved a rotary in my own neighbourhood), the son of Italian immigrants, a husband of thirty-five years, and a father to three girls, all grown now with children of their own. He also weighed 428 pounds, though he stood just five feet seven inches tall, and he was miserable. Housebound, his health failing, he no longer had

This essay is taken from *Complications*, published by Penguin Books India, New Delhi, 2000.

anything resembling a normal life.

For the very obese, general anaesthesia alone is a dangerous undertaking; major abdominal surgery can easily become a disaster. Obesity substantially increases the risk of respiratory failure, heart attacks, wound infections, hernias—almost every complication possible, including death. Nevertheless, Dr Sheldon Randall, the attending surgeon, was relaxed—chatting with the nurses about their weekends, reassuring Caselli that things would go fine—having done more than a thousand of these operations. I, the assisting resident, remained anxious. Watching Caselli struggle to shift himself from the stretcher onto the operating table and then stop halfway to catch his breath, I was afraid that he would fall in between. Once he was on the table, his haunches rolled off the sides, and I double-checked the padding that protected him from the table's sharp edges. He was naked except for his 'universal'-size johnny, which covered him like a napkin, and a nurse put a blanket over his lower body for the sake of modesty. When we tried to lay him down, he lost his breath and started to turn blue, and the anaesthesiologist had to put him to sleep sitting up. Only with the breathing tube in place and a mechanical ventilator regulating his breathing were we able to lay him flat.

He was a mountain on the table. I am six feet two, but even with the table as low as it goes I had to stand on a step stool to operate; Dr Randall stood on two stools stacked together. He nodded to me, and I cut down the middle of our patient's belly, through skin and then dense inches of glistening yellow fat. Inside his abdomen, his liver was streaked with fat, too, and his bowel was covered by a thick apron of it, but his stomach looked ordinary—a smooth, greyish-pink bag the size of two fists. We put metal retractors in place to hold the wound open and keep the liver and the slithering loops of bowel out of the way. Working elbow deep, we stapled his stomach down to the size of an ounce. Before the operation, it could accommodate a quart of food and drink; now it would hold not more than a shot glass. We then sewed the opening of this little pouch to a portion of bowel two feet past his duodenum—past the initial portion of the small bowel, where bile and pancreatic juices break food down. This was the bypass part of the operation, and it meant that what food the stomach could accommodate would be less readily absorbed.

The operation took us a little over two hours. Caselli was stable throughout, but his recovery was difficult. Patients are usually ready to go home three days after surgery; it was two days before Caselli even knew where he was. For twenty-four hours, his kidneys stopped working, and fluid built up in his lungs. He became delirious, seeing things on the walls, pulling off his oxygen mask, his chest leads for the monitors, even yanking out the IV in his arm. We were worried, and his wife and daughters were terrified. But gradually he pulled through.

By the third day after surgery, he was well enough to take sips of clear liquids (water, apple juice, ginger ale), up to one ounce every four hours. On my afternoon rounds, I asked him how the sips had gone down. 'OK,' he said. We began giving him four-ounce servings of Carnation Instant Breakfast for protein and modest calories. He could finish only half, and that took him an hour. It filled him up and, when it did, he felt a sharp, unpleasant pain. This was to be expected, Dr Randall told him. It would be a few days before he was ready for solid food. But he was doing well. He no longer needed IV fluids. The pain from his wound was under control. And, after he'd had a short stay in a rehabilitation facility, we sent him home.

A couple of weeks later, I asked Dr Randall how Caselli was getting on. 'Just fine,' the surgeon said. Although I had done a few of these cases with him, I had not seen how the patients progressed afterwards. Would he really lose all that weight? I asked. And how much could he eat? Randall suggested that I see Caselli for myself. So one day that October, I gave him a call. He seemed happy to hear from me. 'Come on by,' he said. And after work that day, I did.

Vincent Caselli and his wife live in an unassuming saltbox house not far outside Boston. To get there, I took Route 1, past four Dunkin' Donuts, four pizzerias, three steak houses, two McDonald's, two Ground Rounds, a Taco Bell, a Friendly's, and an International House of Pancakes. (A familiar roadside vista, but that day it seemed a sad tour of our self-destructiveness.) I rang the doorbell, and a long minute passed. I heard a slow footfall coming towards the door, and Caselli, visibly winded, opened it. But he smiled broadly when he saw me, and gave my hand a warm squeeze. He led me—his hand on table, wall, doorjamb for support—to a seat at a breakfast table in his flowered-wallpaper kitchen.

I asked him how things were going. 'Real good,' he said. He had no more pain from the operation, the incision had healed, and, though it had been only three weeks, he'd already lost forty pounds. But, at 390, and still stretching his 64 slacks and size XXXXXXL T-shirts (the largest he could find at the local big-and-tall store), he did not yet feel different. Sitting, he had to keep his legs apart to let his abdomen sag between them, and the weight of his body on the wooden chair forced him to shift every minute or two because his buttocks would fall asleep. Sweat rimmed the folds of his forehead and made his thin salt-and-pepper hair stick to his pate. His brown eyes were rheumy and had dark bags beneath them. He breathed with a disconcerting wheeze.

We talked about his arrival home from the hospital. The first solid food he had tried was a spoonful of scrambled eggs. Just that much made him so full it hurt, he said, really hurt, 'like something was ripping', and he threw it back up. He was afraid that nothing solid would ever go down. But he gradually found that he could tolerate small amounts of soft foods—mashed potatoes, macaroni, even chicken if it was finely chopped and moist. Breads and dry meats, he found, got 'stuck', and he'd have to put a finger down his throat and make himself vomit.

It troubled Caselli that things had come to this, but he had made peace with the need for it. 'Last year or two, I'm in hell,' he said. The battle had begun in his late twenties. 'I always had some weight on me,' he said. He was 200 pounds at nineteen, when he married Teresa (as I'll call her), and a decade later he reached 300. He would diet and lose seventy-five pounds, then put a hundred back on. By 1985, he weighed 400 pounds. On one diet, he got all the way down to 190 pounds. Then he shot back up again. 'I must have gained and lost 1000 pounds,' he told me. He developed high blood pressure, high cholesterol and diabetes. His knees and his back ached all the time. He had only limited mobility. He used to get season tickets to Boston Bruins games, and go out regularly to the track at Seekonk every summer to see the auto racing. Years ago, he drove in races himself. Now he could barely walk to his pickup truck. He hadn't been on an airplane since 1983, and it had been two years since he had been to the second floor of his own house, because he couldn't negotiate the stairs. 'Teresa bought a computer a year ago for her office upstairs, and I've never seen it,' he told me. He had to move out of their bedroom, upstairs to a small room off the kitchen. Unable to lie down, he had slept in a recliner ever since. Even so, he could doze only in snatches, because of sleep apnea, which is a common syndrome among the obese, thought to be related to excessive fat in the tongue and in the soft tissues of the upper airway. Every thirty minutes, his breathing would stop, and he'd wake up asphyxiating. He was perpetually exhausted.

There were other troubles, too, the kind that few people speak about. Good hygiene, he said, was nearly impossible. He could no longer stand up to urinate, and after moving his bowels he often had to shower in order to get clean. Skin folds would become chafed and red, and sometimes develop boils and infections. 'Has it been a strain on your marriage?' I asked. 'Sure,' he said. 'Sex life is non-existent. I have real hopes for it.' For him, though, the worst part was his diminishing ability to earn a livelihood.

Vincent Caselli's father had come to Boston from Italy in 1914 to work in construction. Before long, he had acquired five steam shovels and established his own firm. In the 1960s, Vince and his brother took over the business, and in 1979 Vince went into business for himself. He was skilled at operating heavy equipment—his speciality was running a Gradall, a thirty-ton, $300,000 hydraulic excavator—and he employed a team of men year-round to build roads and sidewalks. Eventually, he owned his own Gradall, a ten-wheel Mack dump truck, a backhoe, and a fleet of pickup trucks. But in the past three years he had become too big to operate the Gradall or keep up with the daily maintenance of the equipment. He had to run the business from his house, and pay others to do the heavy work; he enlisted a nephew to help manage the men and the contracts. Expense rose, and because he could no longer make the rounds of city halls himself, he found contracts harder and harder to get. If it hadn't been for Teressa's job—she is the business manager for an assisted-living facility in Boston—they would have gone bankrupt.

Teresa, a pretty, freckled redhead (of, as it happens, fairly normal weight) had been pushing him for a long time to diet and exercise. He, too, wanted desperately to lose weight, but the task of controlling himself, day to day, meal to meal, seemed beyond him. 'I'm a man of habits,' he told me. 'I'm very prone to habits.' And eating, he said, was his worst habit. But, then, eating is everyone's habit. What was different about *his* habit? I asked. Well, the portions he took were too big, and he could never leave a crumb on his plate. If there was pasta left in the pot, he'd eat that, too. But why, I wanted to know. Was it just that he loved food? He pondered this question for a moment. It wasn't love, he decided. 'Eating felt good instantaneously,' he said, 'but it only felt good instantaneously.' Was it excessive hunger that drove him? 'I was never hungry,' he said.

As far as I could tell, Caselli ate for the same reasons that everyone eats: because food tasted good, because it was seven o'clock and time for dinner, because a nice meal had been set out on the table. And he stopped eating for the same reason everyone stops: because he was full and eating was no longer pleasurable. The main difference seemed to be that it took an unusual quantity of food to make him full. (He could eat a large pizza without blinking.) To lose weight, he faced the same difficult task that every dieter faces—to stop eating before he felt full, while the food still tasted good, and to exercise. These were things that he could do for a little while, and, with some reminding and coaching, for perhaps a bit longer, but they were not, he had found, things that he could do for long. 'I am not strong,' he said.

In early 1998, Caselli's internist sternly told him, 'If you cannot take off this weight, we are going to have to do something drastic.' And by this she meant surgery. She described the gastric-bypass operation to him and gave him Dr Randall's number. To Caselli, it was out of the question. The idea of the procedure was trouble enough. No way could he put his business on hold for that. A year later, however, in the spring of 1999, he developed bad infections in both legs: as his weight increased, and varicosities appeared, the skin thinned and broke down, producing open, purulent ulcers. Despite fevers and searing pain, it was only after persistent coaxing from his wife that he finally agreed to see his doctor. The doctor diagnosed a serious case of cellulitis, and he spent a week in the hospital receiving intravenous antibiotics.

At the hospital, he was also given an ultrasound scan to check for blood clots in his legs. Afterwards, a radiologist came to give him the result. 'He says, "You're a real lucky guy."' Caselli recounted. 'I say, "Did I win the lottery? Wha'd I do?" He says, "You don't have blood clots, and I'm really surprised." He says, "I don't mean to break your bubble, but a guy like you, in the situation you're in, the odds are you're gonna have blood clots. That tells me you're a pretty healthy guy"'—but only, he went on, if Caselli did something about his weight.

A little later, the infectious-disease specialist came to see him. The specialist removed his bandages, examined his wounds, and wrapped them back up again. His legs were getting better, he said. But then he added one more thing. "'I'm going to tell you something,'" Caselli recalls the man saying. "'I've been reading your whole file—where you were, what you were, how you were. Now you're here and this is what's going on. You take that weight off—and I'm not telling you this to bust your ass, I'm *telling* you— you take that weight off and you're a very healthy guy. Your heart is good. Your lungs are good. You're strong.'"

'I took that seriously,' Caselli said. 'You know, there are two different doctors telling me this. They don't know me other than what they're reading from their records. They had no reason to tell me this. But they knew the weight was a problem. And if I could get it down . . .'

When he got home, he remained sick in bed for another two weeks. Meanwhile, his business collapsed. Contracts stopped coming in entirely, and he knew that when his men finished the existing jobs he would have to let them go. Teresa made an appointment for him to see Dr Randall, and he went. Randall described the gastric-bypass operation and spoke with him frankly about the risks involved. There was a one-in-two-hundred chance of death and a one-in-ten chance of an untoward outcome, such as bleeding, infection, gastric ulceration, blood clots, or leakage into the abdomen. The doctor also told him that it would change how he ate forever. Unable to work, humiliated, ill, and in pain, Vincent Caselli decided that surgery was his only hope.

It is hard to contemplate the human appetite without wondering if we have any say over our lives at all. We believe in will—in the notion that we have a choice over such simple matters as whether to sit still or stand up, to talk or not talk, to have a slice of pie or not. Yet very few people, whether heavy or slim, can voluntarily reduce their weight for long. The history of weight-loss treatment is one of nearly unremitting failure. Whatever the regime—liquid diets, high-protein diets, or grapefruit diets, the Zone, Atkins, or Dean Ornish diet—people lose weight quite readily, but they do not keep it off. A 1993 National Institutes of Health expert panel reviewed decades of diet studies and found that between 90 and 95 per cent of people regained one-third to two-thirds of any weight lost within a year—and all of it within five years. Doctors have wired patients' jaws closed, inflated plastic balloons inside their stomachs, performed massive excisions of body fat, prescribed amphetamines and large amounts of thyroid hormone, even performed neurosurgery to destroy the hunger centres in the brain's hypothalamus—and still people do not keep the weight off. Jaw wiring, for example, can produce substantial weight loss, and patients who ask for the procedure are as motivated as they come; yet some still end up taking in enough liquid calories through their closed jaws to gain weight, and the others regain it once the wires are removed. We are a species that has evolved to survive starvation, not to resist abundance.

The one group of human beings that stands in exception to this doleful history of failure is, surprisingly, children. Nobody would argue that children have more self-control than adults; yet in four randomized studies of obese children between the ages of six and twelve, those who received simple behavioural teaching (weekly lessons for eight to twelve weeks, followed by monthly meetings for up to a year) ended up markedly less overweight ten years later than those who didn't; 30 per cent were no longer obese. Apparently, children's appetites are malleable. Those of adults are not.

The revealing moment is the meal. There are at least two ways that humans can eat more than they ought to at a sitting. One is by eating slowly but steadily for far too long. This is what people with Prader-Willi syndrome do. Afflicted with a rare inherited dysfunction of the hypothalamus, they are incapable of experiencing satiety. And though they eat only half as quickly as most people, they do not stop. Unless their access to food is strictly controlled (some will eat garbage or pet food if they find nothing else), they become mortally obese.

The more common pattern, however, relies on rapid intake. Human beings are subject to what scientists call a 'fat paradox'. When food enters your stomach and duodenum (the upper portion of the small intestine), it triggers stretch receptors, protein receptors, and fat receptors that signal the hypothalamus to induce satiety. Nothing stimulates the reaction more quickly than fat. Even a small amount, once it reaches the duodenum, will cause the person to stop eating. Still we eat too much fat. How can this be? The reason is speed. It turns out that foods can trigger receptors in the mouth which get the hypothalamus to *accelerate* our intake—and, again, the most potent stimulant is fat. A little bit on the tongue, and the receptors push us to eat fast, before the gut signals shut us down. The tastier the food, the faster we eat—a phenomenon called 'the appetizer effect'. (This is accomplished, in case you were wondering, not by chewing faster but by chewing less. French researchers have discovered that, in order to eat more and eat it faster, people shorten their 'chewing time'—they take fewer 'chews per standard food unit' before swallowing. In other words, we gulp.)

Apparently, how heavy one becomes is determined, in part, by how the hypothalamus and the brain stem adjudicate the conflicting signals from the mouth and the gut. Some people feel full quite early in a meal; others, like Vincent Caselli, experience the appetizer effect for much longer. In the past several years, much has been discovered about the mechanisms of this control. We now know, for instance, that hormones, like leptin and neuropeptide Y, rise and fall with fat levels and adjust the appetite accordingly. But our knowledge of these mechanisms is still crude at best.

Consider a 1998 report concerning two men, 'BR' and 'RH', who suffered from profound amnesia. Like the protagonist in the movie *Memento,* they could carry on a coherent conversation with you, but, once they had been distracted, they recalled nothing from as recently as a minute before, not even that they were talking to you. (BR had had a bout of viral encephalitis; RH had had a severe seizure disorder for twenty years.) Paul Rozin, a professor of psychology at the University of Pennsylvania, thought of using them in an experiment that would explore the relationship between memory and eating. On three consecutive days, he and his team brought each subject his typical lunch (BR got meat loaf, barley soup, tomatoes, potatoes, beans, bread, butter, peaches, and tea; RH got veal parmigiana with pasta, string beans, juice, and apple crumb cake). Each day, BR ate all his lunch, and RH could not quite finish. Their plates were then taken away. Ten to thirty minutes later, the researchers would reappear with the same meal. 'Here's lunch,' they would announce. The men ate just as much as before. Another ten to thirty minutes later, the researchers again appeared with the same meal. 'Here's lunch,' they would say, and again the men would eat. On a couple of occasions, the researchers even offered RH a fourth lunch. Only then did he decline, saying that his 'stomach was a little tight'. Stomach stretch receptors were completely ineffectual. Yet, in the absence of a memory of having eaten, social context alone—someone walking in with lunch—was enough to recreate appetite.

You can imagine forces in the brain vying to make you feel hungry or full. You have mouth receptors, smell receptors, visions of tiramisu pushing one way and gut receptors another. You have leptons and neuropeptides saying you have either too much fat stored or too little. And you have your own social and personal sense of whether eating more is a good idea. If one mechanism is thrown out of whack, there's trouble.

Given the complexity of appetite and our imperfect understanding of it, we shouldn't be surprised that appetite-altering drugs have had only meagre success in making people eat less. (The drug combination of fenfluramine and phentermine, or 'fen-phen', had the most success, but it was linked to heart valve abnormalities and was withdrawn from the market.) University researchers and pharmaceutical companies are searching intensively for a drug that will effectively treat serious obesity. So far, no such drug exists. Nonetheless, one treatment has been found to be effective, and, oddly enough, it turns out to be an operation.

At my hospital, there is a recovery room nurse who is forty-eight years old and just over five feet tall, with boyish sandy hair and an almost athletic physique. Over coffee one day at the hospital café, not long after my visit with Vincent Caselli, she revealed that she once weighed more than 250 pounds. Carla (as I'll call her) explained that she had had gastric-bypass surgery some fifteen years ago.

She had been obese since she was five years old. She started going on diets and taking diet pills—laxatives, diuretics, amphetamines—in junior high school. 'It was never a problem losing weight,' she said. 'It was a problem keeping it off.' She remembers how upset she was when, on a trip with friends to Disneyland, she found that she couldn't fit through the entrance turnstile. At the age of thirty-three, she reached 265 pounds. One day, accompanying her partner, a physician, to a New Orleans medical convention, she found that she was too short of breath to walk down Bourbon Street. For the first time, she said, 'I became fearful for my life—not just the quality of it but the longevity of it.'

That was 1985. Doctors were experimenting with radical obesity surgery, but there was dwindling enthusiasm for it. Two operations had held considerable promise. One, known as jejuno-ileal bypass—in which nearly all the small intestine was bypassed, so that only a minimum amount of food could be absorbed—turned out to be killing people. The other, stomach stapling, was proving to lose its effectiveness over time; people tended to adapt to the tiny stomach, eating densely caloric foods more and more frequently.

Working in the hospital, however, Carla heard encouraging reports about the gastric-bypass operation—stomach stapling plus a rerouting of the intestine so that food bypassed only the first metre of small intestine. She knew that the data about its success was still sketchy and that other options had failed, and she took a year to decide. But the more she gained, the more convinced she became that she had to take the chance. In May of 1986, she went ahead and had the surgery.

'For the first time in my life, I experienced fullness,' she told me. Six months after the operation, she was down to a 185 pounds. Six months after that, she weighed a 130 pounds. She lost so much weight that she had to have surgery to remove the aprons of skin that hung from her belly and thighs down to her knees. She was unrecognizable to anyone who had known her before, and even to herself. 'I went to bars to see if I could get picked up—and I did,' she said. 'I always said no,' she quickly added, laughing. 'But I did it anyway.'

The changes weren't just physical, though. She had slowly found herself to have a profound and unfamiliar sense of willpower over food. She no longer *had* to eat anything: 'Whenever I eat, somewhere in the course of that time I end up asking myself, "Is this good for you? Are you going to put on weight if you eat too much of this?" And I can just stop.' The feeling baffled her. She knew intellectually, that the surgery was why she no longer ate as much as she used to. Yet she felt as if she were choosing not to do it.

Studies report this to be a typical experience of successful gastric-bypass patients. 'I do get hungry, but I tend to think about it more,' another woman who had had the operation told me, and she described an internal dialogue very much like Carla's: 'I ask myself, "Do I really need this?" I watch myself.' For many, this feeling of control extends beyond eating. They become more confident, even assertive—sometimes to the point of conflict. Divorce rates, for example, have been found to increase significantly after the surgery. Indeed, a few months after her operation, Carla and her partner broke up.

Carla's dramatic weight loss has proved to be no aberration. Published case series now show that most patients undergoing gastric bypass lose at least two-thirds of their excess weight (generally more than a hundred pounds) within a year. They keep it off, too: ten-year follow-up studies find an average regain of only ten to twenty pounds. And the health benefits are striking: patients are less likely to have heart failure, asthma, or arthritis; most remarkable of all, 80 per cent of those with diabetes are completely cured of it.

I stopped in to see Vincent Caselli one morning in January of 2000, about four months after his operation. He didn't quite spring to the door, but he wasn't winded this time. The bags under his eyes had shrunk. His face was more defined. Although his midriff was vast, it seemed smaller, less of a sack.

He told me that he weighed 348 pounds—still far too much for a man who was only five feet seven inches tall, but ninety pounds less than he weighed on the operating table. And it had already made a difference in his life. Back in October, he told me, he missed his youngest daughter's wedding because he couldn't manage the walking required to get to the church. But by December he had lost enough weight to resume going to his East Dedham garage every morning. 'Yesterday, I unloaded three tyres off the truck,' he said. 'For me to do that three months ago? There's no way.' He had climbed the stairs of his house for the first time since 1997. 'One day around Christmastime, I say to myself, "Let

me try this. I gotta try this." I went very slow, one foot at a time.'
The second floor was nearly unrecognizable to him. The bathroom
had been renovated since he last saw it, and Teresa had, naturally,
taken over the bedroom, including the closets. He would move
back up eventually, he said, though it might be a while. He still
had to sleep sitting up in a recliner, but he was sleeping in four-
hour stretches now—'Thank God,' he said. His diabetes was gone.
And although he was still unable to stand up longer than twenty
minutes, his leg ulcers were gone, too. He lifted his pants legs to
show me. I noticed that he was wearing regular Red Wing work
boots—in the past, he had to cut slits along the sides of his shoes
in order to fit into them.

'I've got to lose at least another hundred pounds,' he said. He
wanted to be able to work, pick up his grandchildren, buy clothes
off the rack at Filene's, go places without having to ask himself,
'Are there stairs? Will I fit in the seats? Will I run out of breath?'
He was still eating like a bird. The previous day, he'd had nothing
all morning, a morsel of chicken with some cooked carrots and
a small roast potato for lunch, and for dinner one fried shrimp,
one teriyaki chicken strip, and two forkfuls of chicken-and-
vegetable lo mein from a Chinese restaurant. He was starting up
the business again, and, he told me, he'd gone out for a business
lunch one day recently. It was at a new restaurant in Hyde Park—
'beautiful,' he said—and he couldn't help ordering a giant burger
and a plate of fries. Just two bites into the burger, though, he had
to stop. 'One of the fellas says to me, "Is that all you're going to
eat?" And I say, "I can't eat anymore." "Really?" I say, "Yeah, I can't
eat any more. That's the truth."'

I noticed, however, that the way he spoke about eating was not
the way Carla had spoken. He did not speak of stopping because
he wanted to. He spoke of stopping because he had to. You want
to eat more, he explained, but 'you start to get that feeling in your
insides that one more bite is going to push you over the top'. Still,
he often took that bite. Overcome by waves of nausea, pain and

bloating—the so-called dumping syndrome—he'd have to vomit. If there was a way to eat more, he would. That scared him, he admitted. 'It's not right,' he said.

Three months later, in April, Vince invited me and my son to stop by his garage in East Dedham. Walker was four years old then and, as Vince remembered my once saying, fascinated with all things mechanical. So on my Saturday off, we went. As we pulled into the gravel lot, Walker was fairly zizzing with excitement. The garage was cavernous, barnlike, with a two-storey garage door and metal walls painted yellow. Outside, it was an unusually warm spring morning, but inside the air was cool. Our footsteps echoed on the concrete floor. Vince and a buddy of his, a fellow heavy-equipment contractor I'll call Danny, were sitting on metal folding chairs in a sliver of sunlight, puffing fat Honduran cigars, silently enjoying the day. Both rose to greet us. Vince introduced me as 'one of the doctors who did my stomach operation', and I introduced Walker, who shook hands all around but saw only the big trucks. Vince lifted him up into the driver's seat of a front-end loader backhoe in one corner of the garage and let him play with the knobs and controls. Then we went over to Vince's beloved Gradall, a handsome tank of a machine, wide as a country road, painted yield-sign yellow, with shiny black tyres that came up to my chest and the name of his company emblazoned in curlicue script along its flanks. On the chassis, six feet off the ground, was a glass-enclosed cab and thirty-foot telescoping boom on a 360 degree swivel. We hoisted Walker up into the cab and he stood there awhile, high above us, pulling levers and pressing pedals, giddy and scared all at once.

I asked Vince how his business was going. Not well, he said. Except for a few jobs in late winter plowing snow for the city in his pickup truck, he had brought in no income since the previous August. He'd had to sell two of his three pickups, his Mack dump truck, and most of the small equipment for road building. Danny came to his defence. 'Well, he's been out of action,' he said. 'And you see we're just coming into the summer season. It's a seasonal business.' But we all knew that wasn't the issue.

Vince told me that he weighed about 320 pounds. This was about thirty pounds less than when I had last seen him, and he was proud of that. 'He don't eat,' Danny said. 'He eats half of what I eat.' But Vince was unable to climb up into the Gradall and operate it. And he was beginning to wonder whether that would ever change. The rate of weight loss was slowing down, and he noticed that he was able to eat more. Before, he could eat only a couple of bites of a burger, but now he could sometimes eat half of one. And he still found himself eating more than he could handle. 'Last week, Danny and this other fellow, we had to do some business,' he said. 'We had Chinese food. Lots of days, I don't eat the right stuff—I try to do what I can do, but I ate a little bit too much. I had to bring Danny back to Boston College, and before I left the parking lot there I just couldn't take it anymore. I had to vomit.

'I'm finding that I'm getting back into that pattern where I've always got to eat,' he went on. His gut still stopped him, but he was worried. What if one day it didn't? He had heard about people whose staples gave way, returning their stomach to its original size, or who managed to put the weight back on in some other way.

I tried to reassure him. I told him what I knew Dr Randall had already told him during a recent appointment: that small increase in the capacity of his stomach pouch was to be expected, and that what he was experiencing seemed normal. But could something worse happen? I didn't want to say.

Among the gastric-bypass patients I had talked with was a man whose story remains a warning and a mystery to me. He was forty-two years old, married, and had two daughters, both of whom were single mothers with babies and still lived at home, and he had been the senior computer-systems manager for a large local company. At the age of thirty-eight, he had had to retire and go on disability because his weight—which had been above 300 pounds since high school—had increased to more than 450 pounds and was causing unmanageable back pain. He was soon confined to his home. He could not walk half a block. He could stand for only brief periods. He went out, on average, once a week, usually for medical appointments. In December 1998, he had a gastric bypass. By June of the following year, he had lost a hundred pounds.

Then, as he put it, 'I started eating again.' Pizzas. Boxes of sugar cookies. Packages of doughnuts. He found it hard to say how, exactly. His stomach was still tiny and admitted only a small amount of food at a time, and he experienced the severe nausea and pain that gastric-bypass patients get whenever they eat sweet or rich things. Yet his drive was stronger than ever. 'I'd eat right through pain—even to the point of throwing up,' he told me. 'If I threw up, it was just room for more. I would eat straight through the day.' He did not pass a waking hour without eating something. 'I'd just shut the bedroom door. The kids would be screaming. The babes would be crying. My wife would be at work. And I would be eating.' His weight returned to 450 pounds, and then more. The surgery had failed. And life had been shrunk to the needs of pure appetite.

He is among the 5 to 20 per cent of patients—the published reports conflict on the exact number—who regain weight despite gastric-bypass surgery. (When we spoke, he recently submitted to another, more radical gastric bypass, in the desperate hope that something would work.) In these failures, one begins to grasp the depth of the power that one is up against. An operation that makes overeating both extremely difficult and extremely unpleasant—which, for more than 80 per cent of patients, is finally sufficient to cause appetite to surrender and be transformed—can sometimes be defeated after all. Studies have yet to uncover a single consistent risk factor for this outcome. It could, apparently, happen to anyone.

Several months passed before I saw Vince Caselli again. Winter came, and I called him to see how he was doing. He said he was well, and I did not press for details. When we talked about getting together, though, he mentioned that it might be fun to go see a Boston Bruins game together, and my ears pricked up. Perhaps he was doing well.

A few days later, he picked me up at the hospital in his rumbling six-wheel Dodge Ram. For the first time since I'd met him, he looked almost small in that outsize truck. He was down to about 250 pounds. 'I'm still no Gregory Peck,' he said, but he was now one of the crowd—chubby, in an ordinary way. The rolls beneath his chin were gone. His face had a shape. His middle no longer rested between his legs. And, almost a year and a half after the surgery, he was still losing weight. At the FleetCenter, where the Bruins play, he walked up the escalator without getting winded. Our tickets were taken at the gate—the Bruins were playing the Pittsburgh Penguins—and we walked through the turnstiles. Suddenly, he stopped. 'Look at that,' he exclaimed. 'I went right through, no problem. I never would have made it through there before.' It was the first time he'd gone to an event like this in years.

We took our seats about two dozen rows up from the ice, and he laughed a little about how easily he fit. The seats were as tight as coach class, but he was quite comfortable. (I, with my long legs, was the one who had trouble finding room.) Vince was right at home there. He had been a hockey fan his whole life, and could supply me with all the details: the Penguins' goalie Garth Snow was a local boy, from Wrentham, and a friend of one of Vince's cousins; Joe Thornton and Jason Allison were the Bruin's best forwards, but neither could hold a candle to the Penguins' Mario Lemieux. There were nearly 20,000 people at the game, but within ten minutes Vince had found a friend from his barbershop sitting just a few rows away.

The Bruins won, and we left cheered and buzzing. Afterwards, we went out to dinner at a grill near the hospital. Vince told me that his business was finally up and running. He could operate the Gradall without difficulty, and he'd had full-time Gradall work for the past three months. He was even thinking of buying a new model. At home, he had moved back upstairs. He and Teresa had taken a vacation in the Adirondacks; they were going out evenings, and visiting their grandchildren.

I asked what had changed since I saw him the previous spring. He could not say precisely, but he gave me an example. 'I used to love Italian cookies, and I still do,' he said. A year ago, he would have eaten to the point of nausea. 'But now they're, I don't know, they're too sweet. I eat one now, and after one or two bites I just don't want it.' It was the same with pasta, which had always been a problem for him. 'Now I can have a taste and I'm satisfied.'

Partly, it appeared that his taste in food had changed. He pointed to the nachos and Buffalo wings and hamburgers on the menu, and said that, to his surprise, he no longer felt like eating any of them. 'It seems like I lean towards protein and vegetables nowadays,' he said, and he ordered a chicken Caesar salad. But he also no longer felt the need to stuff himself. 'I used to be real reluctant to push food away,' he told me. 'Now it's just—it's different.' But when did this happen? And how? He shook his head. 'I wish I could pinpoint it for you,' he said. He paused to consider. 'As a human, you adjust to conditions. You don't think you are. But you are.'

These days, it isn't the failure of obesity surgery that is prompting concerns but its success. For a long time it was something of a

bastard child in respectable surgical circles. Bariatric surgeons—
as obesity surgery specialists are called—faced widespread
scepticism about the wisdom of forging ahead with such a radical
operation when so many previous versions had failed, and there
was sometimes fierce resistance to their even presenting their
results at the top surgical conferences. They sensed the contempt
other surgeons had for their patients (who were regarded as
having an emotional, even moral, problem) and often for them.

This has all changed now. The American College of Surgeons
recently recognized bariatric surgery as an accepted specialty. The
National Institutes of Health issued a consensus statement
endorsing gastric-bypass surgery as the only known effective therapy
for morbid obesity, one able to produce long-term weight loss
and improvement in health. And most insurers have agreed to pay
for it.

Physicians have gone from scorning it to encouraging,
sometimes imploring, their severely overweight patients to
undergo a gastric-bypass operation. And that's not a small number
of patients. More than five million adult Americans meet the
strict definition of obesity. (Their 'body mass index'—that is,
their weight in kilograms divided by the square of their height in
metres—is forty or more, which for an average man is roughly a
hundred pounds or more overweight.) Ten million more weigh
just under the mark but may nevertheless have obesity-related
health problems that are serious enough to warrant the surgery.
There are ten times as many candidates for obesity surgery right
now as there are for heart-bypass surgery in a year. So many
patients are seeking the procedure that established surgeons cannot
keep up with the demand. The American Society of Bariatric
Surgery has only 500 members nationwide who perform gastric-
bypass operations, and their waiting lists are typically months
long. Hence the too familiar troubles associated with new and
lucrative surgical techniques (the fee can be as much as $20,000):
newcomers are stampeding to the field, including many who have

proper training but have not yet mastered the procedure, and others who have no training at all. Complicating matters further, individual surgeons are promoting a slew of variations on the standard operation which haven't been fully researched—the 'duodenal switch', the 'long limb' bypass, the laparoscopic bypass. And a few surgeons are pursuing new populations, such as adolescents and people who are only moderately obese.

Perhaps what's most unsettling about the soaring popularity of gastric-bypass surgery, however, is simply the world that surrounds it. Ours is a culture in which fatness is seen as tantamount to failure, and get-think-quick promises—whatever the risks—can have an irresistible allure. Doctors may recommend the operation out of concern for their patients' health, but the stigma of obesity is clearly what drives many patients to the operating room. 'How can you let yourself look like that?' is often society's sneering, unspoken question, and sometimes it's a spoken one as well. (Caselli told me of strangers coming up to him on the street and asking him precisely this.) Women suffer even more than men from the social sanction, and it's no accident that seven times as many women as men have had the operation. (Women are only an eighth more likely to be obese.)

Indeed, deciding *not* to undergo the surgery, if you qualify, is at risk of being considered the unreasonable thing to do. A 350-pound woman who did not want the operation told me of doctors browbeating her for her choice. And I have learned of at least one patient with heart disease being refused treatment by a doctor unless she had a gastric bypass. If you don't have the surgery, you will die, some doctors tell their patients. But we actually do not know this. Despite the striking improvements in weight and health, studies have not yet proved a corresponding reduction in mortality.

There are legitimate grounds for being wary of the procedure. As Paul Ernsberger, an obesity researcher at Case Western Reserve University, pointed out to me, many patients undergoing gastric bypass are in their twenties and thirties. 'But is this really going to be effective and worthwhile over a forty-year span?' he asked. 'No one can say.' He was concerned about the possible long-term effects of nutritional deficiencies (for which patients are instructed to take a daily multivitamin). And he was concerned about evidence from rats that raises the possibility of an increased risk of bowel cancer.

We want progress in medicine to be clear and unequivocal, but of course it rarely is. Every new treatment has gaping unknowns—for both patients and society—and it can be hard to decide what to do about them. Perhaps a simpler, less radical operation will prove effective for obesity. Perhaps the long-sought satiety pill will be found. Nevertheless, the gastric bypass is the one thing we have now that works. Not all the questions have been answered, but there are more than a decade of studies behind it. And so we forge ahead. Hospitals everywhere are constructing obesity-surgery centres, ordering reinforced operating tables, training surgeons and staff. At the same time, everyone expects that, one day, something new and better will be discovered that will make what we're now doing obsolete.

Across from me, in our booth at the grill, Vince Caselli pushed his chicken Caesar salad aside only half eaten. 'No taste for it,' he said, and he told me he was grateful for that. He had no regrets about the operation. It had given him his life back, he said. But, after one more round of drinks and with the hour growing late, it was clear that he still felt uneasy.

'I had a serious problem and I had to take serious measures,' he said. 'I think I had the best technology that is available at this point. But I do get concerned: is this going to last my whole life? Someday, am I going to be right back to square one—or worse?' He fell silent for a moment, gazing into his glass. Then he looked up, his eyes clear. 'Well, that's the cards that God gave me. I can't worry about stuff that I can't control.'

Notes on Contributors

ABDUL BISMILLAH, a leading Hindi writer, began his academic career teaching first at Benaras University and later at Jamia Millia Islamia, New Delhi. His published works include four novels, one novella, five collections of short stories and two collections of poetry. His writings have been translated into Urdu, Bengali, Marathi, Punjabi and Japanese. In 1987 he received the Soviet Land Nehru Award for his novel *Jhini Jhini Bini Chadariya*.

AMITAV GHOSH has been a journalist and is the author of *The Circle of Reason*, *The Shadow Lines* (Sahitya Akademi Award, 1990), *In an Antique Land*, *The Calcutta Chromosome*, *Dancing in Cambodia*, *At Large in Burma*, *The Glass Palace* and *The Hungry Tide*. A selection of his prose pieces has been published in *The Imam and the Indian*. He currently holds the post of Distinguished Professor in the Department of Comparative Literature, Queens College, City University of New York.

ANITA DESAI has written eight novels, including the internationally acclaimed *Clear Light of Day*, *In Custody* and *Fasting, Feasting*, all three finalists for the Booker Prize, and *Journey to Ithaca*. She won the Winifred Holtby Prize (1978) from the Royal Society of Literature for her novel *Fire on the Mountain* and the 1982 Guardian Award for Children's Fiction for *Village by the Sea*. She currently teaches creative writing at MIT, Boston.

ANJANA APPACHANA was educated at Scindia Kanya Vidyalaya, Delhi University, Jawaharlal Nehru University and Pennsylvania State University. Her first book, *Incantations and Other Stories*, was published in India, England and the US and was translated into German. Her story, 'Sharmaji', was included by Salman Rushdie in the collection *Mirrorwork: 50 Years of Indian Writing*. Appachana is the recipient of an O. Henry Festival Prize and a National Endowment for the Arts Creative Writing Fellowship.

ANURADHA ROY has worked in literary journalism and publishing. After a long stint at Oxford University Press, she and Rukun Advani co-founded a publishing imprint, Permanent Black. Her essay, 'Cooking Women', won the first prize in the 2004 *Outlook*-Picador Non-fiction Contest.

ATUL GAWANDE is a resident in surgery in Boston and a staff writer on medicine and science for the *New Yorker*. He received his MD from Harvard Medical School as well as an MPH from the Harvard School of Public Health. His writing has appeared in *The Best American Science and Nature Writing 2000* and the *New Yorker* essay collection *In Sickness and in Health*.

BEHRAM CONTRACTOR (1930–2001) was born and brought up in Mumbai. His journalistic career spanned over forty-two years. He worked with *Free Press Journal*, the *Times of India* and *Midday*, from where he left as executive editor to launch his own paper, the *Afternoon Despatch & Courier* in 1985. His column 'Round and About', which he wrote under the byline 'Busybee', had a large fan following. He was awarded the Padma Shri in 1990 and the B.D. Goenka Award for Excellence in Journalism in 1996.

BIBHUTIBHUSHAN BANDOPADHYAYA (1894–1950) was born in Muratipur, a small village about hundred miles north of Calcutta, and attended a local village school. In 1914 he was admitted to Ripon College in Calcutta, from where he graduated in 1918. He was a teacher for most of his life. His first publication was a short story which appeared in a Calcutta journal in 1922. He wrote seventeen novels, including *Pather Panchali* and *Aparajito*, which inspired Satyajit Ray's Apu trilogy, and published twenty collections of short stories.

BULBUL SHARMA is a writer and artist based in Delhi. She holds a BA in Russian literature from Jawaharlal Nehru University, New Delhi. She has participated in group shows, held one-person art exhibitions and works as an art teacher for children with special needs. She has published three collections of short stories—*My Sainted Aunts*, *The Perfect Woman* and *The Anger of Aubergines*, one novel, *Banana Flower Dreams*, a non-fiction work, *The Book of Devi* and several books for children, including *Tales of Fabled Beasts, Gods and Demons* and *The Ramayana for Children*.

CHITRA BANERJEE DIVAKARUNI is the best-selling author of the novels *Sister of My Heart* and *The Mistress of Spices*; the story collections *The Unknown Errors of Our Lives* and *Arranged Marriage*, which received several awards, including the 1996 American Book Award; and four collections of prize-winning poetry. Her work has appeared in the *New Yorker, Atlantic Monthly, The Best American Short Stories 1999* and the *New York Times*.

CHITRITA BANERJI has written *Life and Food in Bengal, Bengali Cooking: Seasons and Festivals* and *The Hour of the Goddess: Memories of Women, Food and Ritual in Bengal*. Her articles have been published in *Granta* and *Prospect* among other publications.

DAVID DAVIDAR began his career in journalism and now works in publishing. *The House of Blue Mangoes*, his first novel, was published in 2002 and has been translated in sixteen languages around the world.

DIANE RAINES WARD is a journalist whose work has appeared in the *Smithsonian, Newsweek, Connoisseur* and *International Wildlife*. She is also the author of *Water Wars: Drought, Flood, Folly and the Politics of Thirst*, the outcome of a decade of research on water-related problems and solutions that took her to five continents.

E.M. FORSTER (1871–1970) was a member of the Bloomsbury Group, and a noted author and critic. Forster's early works included *Where Angels Fear to Tread*, *The Longest Journey* and *A Room with a View*, besides short stories and essays. His novels include *Howard's End*, *Maurice* and *A Passage to India*. He travelled extensively in India between 1912 and 1913 and returned in 1921 to work as the private secretary to the Maharaja of Dewas, an experience he recorded in *The Hill of Devi*.

FRANK SIMOES (1934–2002), advertising legend, was born in Mumbai but had a special bond with Goa, where his family came from. His first proper job was as dishwasher and general dogsbody on a cargo ship, but it was as a copywriter that he was to make his name. Frank Simoes Associates was one of the most successful firms of its day; his campaigns for the Taj Group and Reliance are still remembered. He quit advertising in the 1990s and wrote two books, *Uncertain Liaisons* and *Glad Seasons in Goa*. A collection of his columns, essays and other writings, *Frank Unedited*, was published posthumously in 2002.

GEOFFREY C. WARD is a historian and screenwriter. His books include *A First-Class Temperament*, which won the 1989 National Book Critics Circle Award and the 1990 Francis Parkman Prize of the Society of American Historians. He has written or co-written many documentary films, including *The Civil War*, *Baseball*, and *Jazz*.

GITHA HARIHARAN's first novel, *The Thousand Faces of Night*, won the Commonwealth Writers Prize in 1993. Since then, she has published a collection of stories, *The Art of Dying*, and three novels, *The Ghosts of Vasu Master*, *When Dreams Travel* and *In Times of Siege*. She has also edited *A Southern Harvest*, a volume of stories in translation, and co-edited a collection of stories for children, *Sorry, Best Friend!* She lives in New Delhi, where she works as a freelance editor.

GOPA MAJUMDAR has translated several works from Bengali to English, the most notable of these being Ashapurna Debi's *Subarnalata*, Taslima Nasrin's *My Girlhood* and Bibhutibhushan Bandyopadhyaya's *Aparajito*, for which she won the Sahitya Akademi Award in 2002. She has translated several volumes of Satyajit Ray's short stories, all of the Feluda stories as well as Ray's Professor Shonku stories.

I. ALLAN SEALY has written four novels, *The Trotter-Nama*, *Hero*, *The Everest Hotel* and *The Brainfever Bird*, and a travel book, *From Yukon to Yucatan*. *The Everest Hotel* was short-listed for the Booker Prize in 1998 and won the Crossword Book Award in the same year. Sealy lives and works in the foothills of the Himalayas.

IPSITA CHANDA is a translator and scholar of literature. She teaches comparative literature at Jadavpur University, Kolkata.

JHUMPA LAHIRI was born in 1967 in London and grew up in Rhode Island. She graduated in English literature from Barnard College. At Boston University, she earned master's degrees in English, creative writing, comparative literature and the Arts, and a Ph.D in Renaissance studies. Several of her short stories have been published in the *New Yorker*. Her debut collection of short stories, *The Interpreter of Maladies*, won the 1999 PEN/Hemingway Award, and the Pulitzer Prize for Fiction, the New Yorker Best Debut of the Year Award and the American Academy of Arts and Letters Addison Metcalf Award in the year 2000. Her first novel, *The Namesake*, was published in 2003. She lives in New York City.

KHALID HASAN, the Kashmiri-born Pakistani writer, journalist and literary translator, has produced over twenty-five books including eight collections of short pieces on Pakistan's social, political and literary life. Since 1988 he has published three volumes of Saadat Hasan Manto's stories and sketches—*Kingdom's End*, *Partition* and *Mottled Dawn: Fifty Sketches and Stories of Partition*. He has also translated Raja Anwar's *The Tragedy of Afghanistan*, published in London in

1987, and Anwar's 'Al-Zulfikar', *Poisoned Fruit.* Hasan is currently the Washington-based US correspondent of *The Nation*, one of Pakistan's leading independent English language daily newspapers.

M. ASADUDDIN translates Assamese, Bengali, Urdu, Hindi and English. He has edited *For Freedom's Sake: Stories and Sketches of Saadat Hasan Manto, Image and Representation: Stories of Muslim Lives in India* and *Lifting the Veil: Selected Writings of Ismat Chughtai.* A former fellow at the British Centre for Literary Translation, University of East Anglia, UK, he currently teaches English literature and translation studies at Jamia Milla Islamia, New Delhi.

M.K. GANDHI (1869–1948), better known as Mahatma Gandhi, is perhaps the world's most famous peace activist. He found his political awakening in South Africa where he was practising law. He returned to India, joined the Indian National Congress, and was soon seen as the leader of the Indian nationalist movement. He advocated a policy of non-violent non-cooperation to achieve independence from colonial rule. His writings include *An Autobiography, or The Story of My Experiments with Truth*, *Key to Health*, *Hind Swaraj, or Indian Home Rule* and *Satyagraha in South Africa.* He was assassinated in January 1948, four months after India gained Independence.

MAHASWETA DEVI was born in 1926 in Dhaka and educated in Shantiniketan. After earning a master's degree in English literature from Calcutta University, she began working as a teacher and journalist. Her first book, *Jhansir Rani* (*The Queen of Jhansi*), was published in 1956. Since then she has published twenty collections of short stories and close to a hundred novels. Her important literary works include *Aranyer Adhikar, Hazar Churasir Ma, Chetti Munda o Tar Tir.* She has been a regular contributor to many literary magazines such as *Bortika*, a journal dedicated to the cause of oppressed communities in India. One of the most eminent writers of modern India, she is the recipient of many prestigious awards such as the Jnanpith, Sahitya Akademi and Magsaysay awards, as well as the Padma Shri. Her works have been translated into many languages.

MANJULA PADMANABHAN is a writer and artist living in New Delhi. Her books include *Hot Death*, *Cold Soup*, *Getting There*, *This Is Suki!* and *Kleptomania: Ten Stories*. *Harvest*, her fifth play, won the 1997 Onassis Award for Theatre. She has illustrated twenty-two books for children including, most recently, her own first novel for children, *Mouse Attack*. Her comic strips appeared weekly in the *Sunday Observer* (Bombay, 1982–86) and daily in the *Pioneer* (New Delhi, 1991–97).

MUKUL KESAVAN has taught history at Jamia Millia Islamia. He is the author of a novel, *Looking through Glass*, and a non-fiction title, *Secular Commonsense*. He is a frequent contributor to *Outlook* and *Telegraph* and has been one of the editors of *Civil Lines*, a journal of new writing from India.

MULK RAJ ANAND (1905–2004) was a pioneer of Indian writing in English and a founding member of the Progressive Writers Association, an organization that wielded considerable influence during India's freedom struggle and beyond. In England, Anand interacted with the likes of E.M. Forster, Herbert Read, George Orwell and members of the Bloomsbury Group and wrote short reviews in T.S. Eliot's *Criterion* magazine. During the Second World War, he worked for the BBC's films division as a broadcaster and scriptwriter. His works include *Untouchable*, *Coolie*, *The Sword and the Sickle*, *Private Life of an Indian Prince*, *Confessions of a Lover* and *The Bubble*. He was the recipient of the Sahitya Akademi Award in 1972 and the Padma Bhushan in 1974.

P. SAINATH has been the foreign editor of *Daily,* and deputy chief editor of the weekly *Blitz* in Mumbai. His work on rural poverty (which he joined full-time after winning a *Times of India* fellowship), on which he based his best-selling book, *Everybody*

Loves a Good Drought, has won him thirteen awards and fellowships, including the prestigious European Commission's journalism award, the Lorenzo Natali Prize and Amnesty International's Global Human Rights Journalism Prize. Sainath has been a visiting lecturer in journalism, development and politics at universities in India, Canada, the United States, Europe and Australia. A regular contributor to the *Telegraph* in Calcutta, he also writes for the fortnightly *Frontline* and the daily *Business Line* in India.

PURABI BASU was born in Vikrampur, in today's Bangladesh. A scientist, she was educated at Dhaka University and received her Ph.D in the USA. In the 1990s she was director, health and nutrition, of BRAC, one of the largest NGOs of Bangladesh, and is currently working with Wyeth Pharmaceutical, USA. She has published twelve books of short stories and essays and translated feminist short stories into Bengali. She writes mainly on women's issues and on communalism in South Asia.

R.K. NARAYAN (1906–2001) published his first novel, *Swami and Friends*, in 1935. His other novels include *The English Teacher*, *Waiting for the Mahatma*, *The Man-eater of Malgudi*, *The Painter of Signs* and *The World of Nagaraj*. He was awarded the Sahitya Akademi Award in 1958 for *The Guide*. He has also published six collections of short stories including *An Astrologer's Day and Other Stories*, *Malgudi Days* and *Under the Banyan Tree*, two travel books, *My Dateless Diary* and *The Emerald Route*, five collections of essays, and a memoir, *My Days*. His translations of Indian epics and myths (*The Ramayana*, *The Mahabharata* and *Gods, Demons and Others*) are well-known. R.K. Narayan was awarded the A.C. Benson Medal by the Royal Society of Literature in 1980 and was made an honorary member of the American Academy and Institute of Arts and Letters. The Government of India conferred on him the title of Padma Vibhushan in 2000.

RADHIKA JHA is a writer and a dancer. Her first novel, *Smell*, was translated into several languages, and won the Prix Guerlain in

France in 2002. Her book of stories, *The Elephant and the Maruti*, was published in 2003.

RAJ KAMAL JHA was born in 1966 and grew up in Calcutta. After graduating with a degree in mechanical engineering from the Indian Institute of Technology, Kharagpur, he received his master's in journalism from the University of Southern California. He is the author of *The Blue Bedspread*, a novel that has won acclaim around the world, and *If You Are Afraid of Heights*, published in 2004. He lives in New Delhi, where he is executive editor at the *Indian Express*, a national newspaper.

ROHINTON MISTRY is the author of *Swimming Lessons and Other Stories from Firozsha Baag*, *Such a Long Journey* (which won the Commonwealth Writers Prize for Best Book of the Year in 1991) and *A Fine Balance* (winner of the Commonwealth Writers Prize and the Royal Society of Literature's Winifred Holtby Memorial Award in 1996 and a Booker Prize finalist the same year). His most recent novel, *Family Matters*, was short-listed for the Booker Prize in 2002.

RUCHIR JOSHI was born and brought up in Calcutta. A trained and practising film-maker and photographer, he has made several award-winning documentaries, including *Eleven Miles* and *Tales from Planet Kolkata*. His first novel, *The Last Jet-Engine Laugh*, was published in 2001. He is currently writing a novel set in Calcutta during the Second World War.

SAADAT HASAN MANTO (1912–1955) is regarded as one of the greatest twentieth-century Urdu short story writers though his career was tragically brief. He was born in Samrala in the Ludhiana district of Punjab. He worked for All India Radio during the Second World War and was a successful screenwriter in Bombay before moving to Pakistan during Partition. During his controversial two-decade career, Manto published twenty-two collections of stories, seven collections of radio plays, three collections of essays and a novel.

SALMAN RUSHDIE is the author of the novels *Grimus*, *Midnight's Children* (the 'Booker of Bookers'), *Shame*, *The Satanic Verses*, *Haroun and the Sea of Stories*, *East*, *West*, *The Moor's Last Sigh*, *The Ground Beneath Her Feet* and *Fury*. He has also written *The Jaguar Smile: A Nicaraguan Journey* and *Imaginary Homelands*, a collection of his essays and criticism. His most recent collection of essays is titled *Step across This Line*.

SARAT CHANDRA CHATTERJEE (1876–1938) was an immensely popular writer of family dramas and socially relevant novels, written in colloquial everyday language and set in early twentieth-century Bengal. He is the author of several novels still widely read and translated in India, including *Badadidi* (1913), *Palli Samaj* (1916), *Charitraheen* (1917), *Datta* (1918) and *Bipradas* (1935). His famous autobiographical novel *Srikanta* was published in four volumes between 1917 and 1933.

SARMISTHA DUTTA GUPTA is a book-editor, translator and independent researcher. She is the founder and joint secretary of a voluntary organization called *Ebong Alap* which focuses on innovative modes of dissemination in Bengali for widening people's options for action.

SUDHA KOUL got her bachelor's and master's degrees in political science from the University of Jammu & Kashmir and taught political science at Lady Shri Ram College, New Delhi. Koul was the first woman from Jammu & Kashmir to be selected as an officer of the Indian Administrative Service. She has held the post of Manager in The Institute of Semitic Studies in Princeton, New Jersey, and has been a guest lecturer at Princeton University, Bowdon College, and Seton Hall University. In 1983, Koul founded Cashmir, Inc., a publishing company. She is the author of *Curries without Worries: An Introduction to Indian Cuisine*, *Come with me to India on a Wondrous Voyage through Time* and *The Tiger Ladies: A Memoir of Kashmir*.

SUKETU MEHTA is a fiction writer and journalist based in New York. For his fiction writing he has won the Whiting Writers

Award, the O. Henry Prize and a New York Foundation of the Arts fellowship. His work has been published in the *New York Times Magazine*, *Granta*, *Harper's*, *Time*, *Condé Nast Traveler*, *Village Voice*, *Indian Express*, *Man's World* and *India Magazine* and has been featured on National Public Radio's 'All Things Considered'. Mehta co-wrote the script for the movie *Mission Kashmir* and is the author of *Maximum City: Bombay Lost and Found*.

SIR V.S. NAIPAUL is the author of a number of novels including *The Mystic Masseur* (John Llewellyn Rhys Memorial Prize, 1957), *The Suffrage of Elvira*, *Miguel Street* (Somerset Maugham Award, 1959), *A House for Mr Biswas*, *Mr Stone and the Knights Companion* (Hawthornden Prize, 1963), *The Mimic Men* (W.H. Smith Award, 1968), *In a Free State* (Booker Prize, 1971), *The Enigma of Arrival* and *The Magic Seeds* (2004). He has also written *Reading and Writing: A Personal Account*, *Half a Life* and several travel books—*The Return of Eva Peron*, *An Area of Darkness*, *Among the Believers: An Islamic Journey*, *A Turn in the South* and *India: A Million Mutinies Now*. He was awarded the Nobel Prize for Literature in 2001.

VIR SANGHVI is probably the best-known Indian journalist of his generation. In 1978 he became the youngest editor in the history of Indian journalism when he was appointed editor of *Bombay* at the age of twenty-two. He became editor of *Imprint* at twenty-six and of *Sunday* at thirty. From 1999 to 2004 he was editor of the *Hindustan Times*, where he is currently editorial director. He is also one of India's leading television anchors and has hosted several programmes for the Star TV group. *Rude Food*, a selection of his food writings from the popular Sunday column of the same name in *Hindustan Times*, was published in 2004.

Copyright Acknowledgements

The Provost and Scholars of King's College, Cambridge, and The Society of Authors as the Literary Representatives of the Estate of E.M. Forster for the extract from *The Hill of Devi* by E.M. Forster;

I. Allan Sealy for the extracts from *The Trotter-Nama*;

Oxford University Press India for the extracts from *Tiger-wallahs* by Geoffrey C. Ward and Diane R. Ward; and 'Mahesh' by Sarat Chandra Chatterjee and 'Guest is God' by Abdul Bismillah from *Image and Representation: Stories of Muslim Lives in India*, edited by Mushirul Hasan and M. Asaduddin, reproduced by permission of Oxford University Press India, New Delhi;

Ravi Dayal Publisher and Permanent Black for the extract from *The Imam and the Indian* by Amitav Ghosh;

Macmillan, London, UK, for the extracts from *The Blue Bedspread* by Raj Kamal Jha, *Getting There* by Manjula Padmanabhan, and for 'Cooking Women' by Anuradha Roy;

HarperCollins *Publishers* Ltd for the extract from *The Last Jet-Engine Laugh* by Ruchir Joshi, copyright © Ruchir Joshi 2001, reprinted by permission of HarperCollins *Publishers* Ltd;

The author for the extracts from *Untouchable* by Mulk Raj Anand;

The author for the extract from *Maximum City: Bombay Lost and Found* by Suketu Mehta;

Stree for 'French Leave' from *The Stream Within: Short Stories by Contemporary Bengali Women*, translated and edited by Swati Ganguly and Sarmistha Dutta Gupta, copyright © of the original Bengali text, Purabi Basu, copyright © of this particular story's translation, Sarmistha Dutta Gupta, published by Stree, Kolkata, 1999;

Women Unlimited, New Delhi, for 'The Anger of Aubergines' by Bulbul Sharma, first published in *The Anger of Aubergines*, New Delhi by Kali for Women in 1998;

David Godwin Associates, Penguin Books India and the author for the extract from *The House of Blue Mangoes* by David Davidar;

HarperCollins *Publishers* India Limited, New Delhi, for the extract from *Aparajito* by Bibhutibhushan Bandopadhyaya, translated by Gopa Majumdar;

The legal heirs of R.K. Narayan for the extract from *The Guide* by R.K. Narayan;

Roli Books Pvt. Ltd for the extract from *Listening Now* by Anjana Appachana, first published by IndiaInk, an imprint of Roli Books Pvt. Ltd;

Seagull Books, Calcutta, for 'Salt' from *Bitter Soil* by Mahasweta Devi, first published in 1998 by Seagull Books, Calcutta, in an English translation by Ipsita Chanda;

Janklow & Nesbit Associates, New York, HarperCollins Publishers Ltd and the author for 'Mrs Sen's' from The Interpreter of Maladies by Jhumpa Lahiri;

Gillon Aitken Associates and the author for the extract from *A House for Mr Biswas* by V.S. Naipaul, copyright © V.S. Naipaul 1961, copyright renewed 1989 by V.S. Naipaul;

Rogers, Coleridge and White Ltd, 20 Powis Mews, London W11 1JN, for the extract from *Fasting, Feasting* by Anita Desai, copyright © 1999 by Anita Desai, reproduced by permission of the author c/o Rogers, Coleridge and White Ltd, 20 Powis Mews, London W11 1JN;

The author for the extract from *Life and Food in Bengal* by Chitrita Banerji;

Profile Books Ltd, London, for 'The Man Who Couldn't Stop Eating' from *Complications* by Atul Gawande;

Penguin Books India for 'My First Buffet Lunch' and 'Charms of Life' from *Busybee: The Best of Thirty-six Years* by Behram Contractor; 'Past Times: First Tastes That Lasted Forever' and 'Bhelpuri: It's All about Texture' from *Rude Food: The Collected Food Writings of Vir*

Sanghvi by Vir Sanghvi; 'Everything You Ever Wanted to Know about Feni but Were Too Drunk to Ask' from *Glad Seasons in Goa* by Frank Simoes; 'The Remains of the Feast' from *The Art of Dying* by Githa Hariharan; 'Jelly' from *Mottled Dawn: Fifty Sketches and Stories of Partition* by Saadat Hasan Manto; the extract from *Smell* by Radhika Jha; 'Everybody Loves a Good Drought' from *Everybody Loves a Good Drought* by P. Sainath.